THE GHOULS OF HOWLFAIR

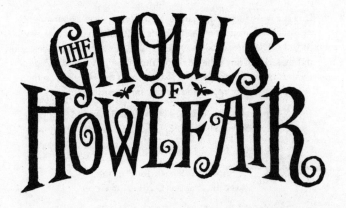

NICK TOMLINSON

WALKER
BOOKS

First published 2019 by Walker Books Ltd
87 Vauxhall Walk, London SE11 5HJ

2 4 6 8 10 9 7 5 3 1

Text © 2019 Nick Tomlinson
Cover illustrations © 2019 Kim Geyer

This book has been typeset in Book Antiqua and Youbee

Printed and bound by CPI Group (UK) Ltd, Croydon CR0 4YY

British Library Cataloguing in Publication Data:
a catalogue record for this book is available from the British Library

ISBN 978-1-4063-8668-4

www.walker.co.uk

MIX
Paper from
responsible sources
FSC® C020471

This is dedicated to
My beautiful Jayne
and to my superb family
and to Peter Camichel
and to Ab, as promised.

Oh, and to all you
unstoppable bookworms.

The (Possibly) Mysterious Excelsior Guesthouse

THE GHOST-TOUR GUIDES HAD GIVEN UP after another day without customers, the awnings were coming down outside the tourist office on Zaleska Street, and gently, cheep by cheep, the summer starlings sang the sun to sleep. The Ethelhael Valley, shadow-dappled, grew drowsy, and the strange town it cradled blinked with lamplight. Here and there a stray car yawned homeward along a street. A heavy gate snored shut. Soon the children of Howlfair, the naughty and the good, were grumbling their nightly ways to bed — all except Molly Thompson, who was climbing the extra flight of stairs to the attic of the Excelsior Guesthouse to catch a vampire bat.

The moon gaped through the window as the small, serious local historian came into view. First the froth of her badly behaved brown curls. Then her face, tense with anticipation. With the long slender nose, the little round mouth, the left eyebrow inquisitively cocked, her face resembled a question mark. Which was appropriate, really, because Molly Thompson was full of questions. Questions like: *Is my Aunt Carol an undead fiend who drinks the blood of the living?*

And: *Is she secretly living in my attic?*

The moonlight made her squint. She halted. There was definitely something moving in the attic. She could hear it scratching around.

Molly was certain she knew what it was. She'd seen it circling above the garden last week.

With a fishing net in one hand, she took another steep step up the staircase. Her foot wobbled. She grimaced as the stair voiced a musical croak beneath her foot.

"Molly!"

There were copper pipes snaking at floor level along the stark white walls of the Excelsior Guesthouse – down the corridors, up the stairs and along the skirting boards in certain rooms, such as the lounge and dining room and lobby – and from these pipes, every few feet, there sprouted an open valve. Through these pipes, Molly's mother could hear what was going on throughout the building. It was through one of the valves that Mum's voice now hissed, and like a gorgon's glare it turned Molly to stone. Her camera swung from her neck on its strap.

"Molly! Where are you? You'd better be getting ready for bed!"

No, Mum, she might have said into the open valve. *I'm just investigating the possibility that Aunt Carol is a shape-shifting vampire who haunts the attic in the form of a winged mammal.*

But she didn't say anything of the sort. Instead she blurted, without thinking:

"Yes, Mum! G'night, Mum!"

Then she winced at her blunder — for now, of course, she had given herself away.

The vampire would have heard her.

The familial fiend in the attic would know that she was halfway up the towering, narrow flight of stairs.

The scratching noises stopped, and with a tingle of terror Molly realized that Aunt Carol was waiting for her.

The Excelsior Guesthouse, impossibly ancient and dizzyingly tall, had always reminded Molly of a haunted galleon, with its low-ceilinged white corridors braced with timber beams, the portholes set in the doors of the cabin-like rooms, the front gable like a ship's prow. The burnt-orange exterior with tar-blackened timbers over which knots of ivy hung like rigging. The square windows just big enough to fire a cannon through. But Molly had never before experienced the odd phenomenon of which so many guests had complained: the sensation of the house pitching and swaying as though lurching into a storm on high seas. She felt it now. Or was it just fear making her stomach flop like a freshly netted fish?

Molly Thompson steadied herself, reached inside her hair, rummaged around in the curls and found a stray bobble. Then, from her pocket, she pulled a small flimsy notepad with MYSTERIES written on the front. Her hands, she noticed, were trembling. The notepad fell open to reveal pages covered with scribblings: recorded bat sightings with times and dates; doodles of ghosts. Underlined red-penned questions about Aunt Carol, about the mysterious symbols on the Howlfair flag, about mad Mr Wetherill who owned the gift shop that sold stakes and silver bullets. Questions about Dad.

Molly folded the notepad over the mouth of the open valve and secured it with the bobble. Then, carefully, she climbed the remaining steps and took hold of the handle of the attic door, her net raised.

She'd always known in her bones that the Excelsior Guesthouse had a sinister secret. And now — at last! — she was going to come face to face with it.

She took a breath and shoved the door open.

Flight of Gabriel

STRAIGHT AWAY MOLLY SAW THAT ONE OF the two attic windows was open.

The curtains were flapping.

Then she spied the fat shadowy shape squatting on the Persian rug with poison in its eyes.

The sight of those eyes made Molly reach for the cross around her neck. But the chain had got entangled with her camera strap, and somehow she whapped herself in the nose with the camera. Like lightning, a camera flash blasted the chamber and revealed to Molly that the vampire bat on the floor had a tail and no wings. In fact, it wasn't a vampire bat at all! O, ye gods, it was a vampire *cat*! No, wait — it was just her pet cat, Gabriel, who, blinded by the flash, gave a startled meow and ran straight towards the open window…

"Gabriel!"

Molly tripped over her fishing net and fell headlong

onto the rug, sprawling. The rug ripped; her mother's beloved grandfather clock, which encroached upon the far end of the rug, wobbled. And now it seemed that her cat had indeed become a bat, for in his mad panic he sailed through the window frame as Molly watched in horror from the floor. The grandfather clock keeled sideways and fell onto a glass table with a crash like the end of the world, but Molly didn't even notice; on hands and knees she scrambled to the window through which Gabriel had flown.

Grabbing the frame, she hauled herself up to see the cat looking back at her from the other side of the window's lip — Gabriel was clinging to the frame by his front claws.

"Gabriel, give me your paw!"

The cat raised a paw — then plummeted.

"No!"

Down the side of the Excelsior Guesthouse her beloved sidekick, her companion through a thousand adventures, dropped!

Gabriel landed (it must have been painful) on the flagpole that jutted out from above Mrs Helastroom's room. The flagpole was already bowing under the weight of three oversized rooks who'd been using it as a perch. The cat's descent bent it further. Gabriel and the rooks exchanged awkward looks. Then all at once the rooks took flight, causing the flagpole to whip upwards and catapult Gabriel wailing into the air. Molly heard the *meow* volleying above the roof as Gabriel soared over her head. Whimpering, she sprinted to the other side of the attic, dodging the fallen clock and the smashed table. Hoisting open the opposite window with a mighty grunt, she thrust her fishing net out –

Meeeaaaooooowwww!

– and then into the net the flying cat plopped. With a sob of relief, Molly hauled him back into the attic and tipped him onto the floor.

"Gabriel, how could you have been so crazy?" she wailed. "How did you even get in here? That *definitely* cost you another one of your lives!"

The cat escaped her as she tried to scoop him into her arms, and he ran for the door, slipping between the legs of the shadow-figure standing there.

It was Molly's mother.

The People Versus
Molly Thompson

ONLY NOW DID MOLLY REALLY NOTICE THE wreckage in the room. The Persian rug: sundered. The grandfather clock like a felled tree. The shattered glass-top table.

"Molly!" Mum screeched. "Snakes alive, what have you done to my attic?"

Molly cowered. She looked around. "The attic?" she coughed, small-voiced. "Oh, I thought I was in the…"

"Don't treat me like a fool, Molly Thompson! I forbade you from coming in here! I forbade you!"

Mum waded into the attic, a gangly creature with hip-length rose-gold hair who looked like someone else's mother entirely. Her moonlit face was all horror. She stepped on a stray shard of glass and cried out as though a zombie had bitten her.

"Sorry, Mum!" said Molly while Mum hopped around clutching her stockinged foot. "I just – I heard

Gabriel in here, and I, um, wanted to play fishing with him, and…"

"Are you sure it wasn't a *vampire bat* you heard?" Mum snapped, whirling round to confront her.

"A vampire?" Molly coughed. "How do you…?"

Mum held up the notepad that Molly had affixed to the listening-pipe. It was open at a page showing a picture of a vampire bat dripping blood. Underneath the doodle was written, in big red letters: Is Aunt Carol a bat in our attic??

"Uh-oh," said Molly under her breath.

"I can't believe my own daughter thinks such things about her family!" Mum pulled flabbergasted faces as she flipped through the notepad's pages. "Why would you think my sister is a vampire bat who lives in our attic?"

"Because she's always really pale, Mum! And she's never at home during the day, and I keep seeing a bat flying over the garden, and I keep hearing scratching in the attic, and…"

"Enough!" cried Mum. "Molly, there's only one mystery in this house — the mystery of why you're so convinced that this house is full of mysteries! Why is it, Molly? Why are you so sure that I'm trying to keep secrets from you?"

Molly coughed. She glanced over at the cupboard on

the other side of the attic, the one with chains wrapped around it and a padlock in the shape of a skull. Then she looked at the small door — no more than elf height — on the far wall of the attic, with the sign saying KEEP OUT. She eyed the cryptic fandangles on the shelves: odd ivory figurines, locked jewellery boxes, a key attached to a necklace hung with dozens of tiny sharp fangs. She squinted at Gabriel, who was curling like fog around Mum's ankles and who knew a secret way to get into the attic, even when the door was shut.

"Um, just a hunch…"

"Well, I have a hunch that you'll be doing your ridiculous investigating somewhere else. This guest-house is our livelihood, Molly. It's all we have, and I can't let you demolish it."

"But I've investigated everything in Howlfair!"

"You've investigated a million local ghost stories that nobody believes in — and you've never found a single ghost. All you ever find is the skeletons in people's cupboards."

"Not just ghost stories, Mum. I've investigated the history of the town and all the families too. I found out that Reginald Pinkside murdered his wife and his two daughters in 1937. I found out that Mrs Henderson was really Mr Farley's daughter …"

"Yes, that caused quite a stir," tutted Mum.

"… and I learned about the plague pit under the new housing development! And I finally translated the motto on the Howlfair flag! And I also learned what Mayor de Ville was doing visiting that woman who grows those prize-winning carrots, and… Mum, why are you looking at me like that?"

Mum stood shaking her head.

"What is it, Mum?"

Mum hesitated. "I wasn't going to tell you."

Molly frowned. "Tell me what?"

"There's been a local petition."

"A *petition*?"

"Some people came to me with a list of signatures. They want me to put a stop to your investigations."

"Who?" Molly staggered as though punched in the gut. "How many people? *Why?*"

"Molly, pretty much every grown-up in Howlfair lives in fear of your next scandal. Almost half the town signed the petition."

"But I'm not *causing* scandals, Mum — I'm just trying to find out the truth!" Molly fought the urge to cry. "What did you tell them?"

"I told them to stop being silly." Mum knelt down and, with a wince, picked up a broken ornament. "Since then business has gone downhill. We hardly have any new bookings for after the end of the month.

People are finding ways to sabotage us." She looked up, eyes narrow. "I stuck up for you, Molly. And now I've found out that you've been disobeying me."

Molly hung her head.

"No more investigations," said Mum coldly. "I want your library books returned tomorrow. And I'll be confiscating your library card until further notice."

Molly gasped. "What for?"

"So you can't spend every waking hour leafing through old almanacs and prying into the history of every family in Howlfair!" Mum gave an awful sigh. "Just get to bed, Molly. I bet you've woken up every guest in the house."

"Doubt it," muttered Molly, staring at her feet. "They're all about a hundred years old."

"What did you say?"

Molly looked up. "Can I sleep in a normal room tonight?"

"We've been through this," Mum said. "Mrs Fullsway is an important guest, and when she stays, she likes to sleep in your bedroom; and the only other free rooms are the *themed* rooms, with lots of very valuable antiques, and I can't trust you not to break anything while you're pacing around solving mysteries in your head. So I need you to sleep in … the *spare* room."

"Why does she like my room so much? She's got a

huge house of her own down the road!"

"Because it overlooks the graveyard where her husband is buried."

"But, Mum, that's so weird! Why would anyone want to look at someone's grave?"

"Not everyone thinks like you," snapped Mum. "Now please, Molly — go to bed and leave me to clear up your devastation in peace."

Molly muttered apologies as she headed past Mum, out of the attic, Gabriel following. She tiptoed down the stairs while Mum knelt despondently amidst the debris, and paused for a second by the stair window. She glanced out at hill-hemmed Howlfair — a town with more scary legends than any other town on earth, a town that tourists, for some reason, hardly ever came to, no matter how hard the tourist board worked to attract them. A town positively crammed with creepy old mysteries that the townsfolk thought were very amusing and very quaint, but which almost nobody other than Molly seemed the slightest bit interested in actually solving.

She didn't spot the stark skeletal face glaring out from a hedge on the other side of her street. And Molly turned away too soon to see the skull-faced creature crawl out of the hedge and begin creeping through the shadows towards the Excelsior Guesthouse.

Mrs Fullsway

CLICK-CLICK-CLICK!

You could hear it from two floors away: the sound of Hectoria Fullsway's ancient typewriter. By the time Molly reached the bedroom door, the machine-gun clacks were making her blink. The curtain was drawn across the silver-rimmed porthole in the door. Molly paused before the oval wooden sign with *Molly's Room* written in red calligraphy, then knocked.

"Mrs Fullsway?"

The clacking ceased.

A fear-wobbled voice within the room warbled something incoherent.

Molly knocked again. "Mrs Fullsway, it's Molly."

With superb drama Mrs Fullsway flung open the door and stood looming. Her colossal face glowed with terror and night cream. Her tasselled violet robe swayed. She grabbed one end of her opulent emerald shawl and flung it over her shoulder. "Oh! Yug Mommy!"

"Yug Mommy?"

Mrs Fullsway pirouetted, flowed to her bedside table, plucked her teeth from a glass of water and slotted them into her mouth. She grabbed a sheaf of papers from the desk with its window view of Howlfair New Cemetery, and beckoned Molly into the room.

"Young Molly!" she said again. Mrs Fullsway had a voice like a very heavy tomato sauce. "My favourite amateur folklorist! What a relief to see you. Couldn't sleep, eh?"

"Sorry, Mrs Fullsway, I was just wondering…"

"Wondering if I'd made progress with the new novel?" Hectoria boomed. "Ah, Molly, this one's literally killing me. Usually a couple of days in the *peace* and *quiet*" — she emphasized the words *peace* and *quiet* by shouting them — "of the Excelsior Guesthouse, overlooking the spot where my dear George lies buried, gets my creative juices bubbling. But I've barely finished the first chapter! As usual I would like your opinion — and if you could do that thing with the spelling and grammar, I would appreciate it very much. Highly creative persons like myself rarely have time to bother with spelling or grammar, and I have a very tight deadline to meet." She thrust the pages into Molly's hands. "Of course, you will be rewarded handsomely for your efforts."

Molly surreptitiously sniffed the pages. They were perfumed. "Rewarded?"

"Yes — you'll get a break from this poky bedroom! Your mother tells me that she makes up one of the honeymoon suites for you whenever I am in residence. It must be a wonderful adventure."

"The honeymoon suites?"

"Molly, you are becoming an echo. What's wrong with you this evening? Ah — I imagine you're excited to get stuck into my book's opening chapter. I'm going with the title *Petals in the Stream of Love's Longing*. What do you think? Dear Molly, you've gone a little green."

Molly put a hand to her stomach as she scanned the first page. "Sorry, Mrs Fullsway. I think I ate some bad ... cheese. I'd better hurry back to the, um, honeymoon suite." She scuttled over to a bookcase. Already Mrs Fullsway had piled her own files and notes on top of Molly's library books. "I just need to find something first..."

"You appear to have half of Howlfair Library taking up my shelf space, dear."

"Yeah..." *And by tomorrow,* she thought, *Mum will*

have made me take back every last book. "I think I left my toothbrush here somewhere…"

Molly moved a potted cactus aside and her heart jolted as she saw, pencilled on the wall, a doodle of a cat. Beside it were nine vertical lines, some struck through with horizontal slashes. Miserably she took a pencil from her top pocket and crossed out another line.

"What are you doing?" Hectoria hissed. "Please don't touch my things!"

"I won't be a second, Mrs Fullsway."

She grabbed a few leather notebooks and some loose leaves covered in diagrams and some important books on Egyptology, Demonology, Thanatology. She tucked them under Mrs Fullsway's perfumed pages, then returned the cactus so that it hid her wall scribblings.

"A honeymoon suite and the first chapter of Hectoria Fullsway's latest blockbuster — at least *you* shall have a pleasant time while I am toiling away, dear!" Mrs Fullsway sighed as Molly pulled tomorrow's school clothes from her wardrobe and headed for the door. The novelist clasped her hands, spun to face Howlfair New Cemetery, and warbled at the window: "Oh, George, do you remember our bridal suite in Budapest?"

Molly bid the vast woman good night, but Mrs

Fullsway was no longer aware of her. She was clutching the edge of the desk and staring at her own fearful expression reflected in the window. It was an odd, desolate sort of fear that Molly saw on Hectoria's face; Molly had the feeling that she'd seen that exact same expression before, on someone else. But she couldn't remember who.

Molly took the opportunity to hurry from the bedroom and head to her own sleeping quarters, wondering what on earth was spooking the lavender-laced mind of Hectoria Fullsway.

Skeleton Visitor

No, IT WASN'T A BRIDAL SUITE TO WHICH Molly dashed with her salvaged stash. It wasn't even a bedroom. It was a giant disused bathroom with black and white tiles and golden fittings. Unfortunately, to get into the bathroom, you had to feel your way through the *real* bridal suite — a large unlit chamber that had long since been converted into a storage room for cleaning equipment and laundry, its pretty window shutters locked. The chances of getting your foot stuck in a bucket while navigating your way through the darkness were high—

"Flipping Nora!"

Molly cursed and hopped and kicked a bucket from her foot, sending a slipper flying.

The bathroom twitched with the flickery lights of a chandelier. The vast white bathtub was lavishly padded with bed linen. After draping her school

25

uniform over the linen basket, Molly stepped into the bath, her arms full of books and papers — and at that moment she saw a face leering through the small window on the other side of the room...

A skull face!

Molly yelped and thrashed in the bathtub, throwing the papers overboard. The skeleton raised a hand and tapped on the glass.

"It's OK!" said a muffled voice from the other side of the window. "It's me!"

Annoyed, Molly scrambled from the bath and opened the window. The skeleton was swaying amidst the branches of the monumental crooked oak tree that idled against the north side of the house. "What are you doing in that stupid mask?"

"It's a disguise," said the skeleton, squeezing like toothpaste through the window frame. "So I could get across town without being recognized."

"Lowry, only seven people in town can get their hands on the tourist board's costumes, and only one of them has a daughter who's a clothes thief. How'd you know I'd be in here?"

"I saw Madame Fullfat at your window, so I knew you'd been evicted," said Lowry Evans, removing her skull mask. Under the mask was a charming innocent-eyed face and a bob of very golden hair. "She looked dead frightened. I think there was someone in the room with her. Maybe it was a phantom?"

Molly rolled her eyes. "It was me."

"Well, obviously *you're* not a phantom," Lowry said. She frowned. "You've never even *seen* a phantom. You just sit in the library all the time *researching* phantoms."

"Not any more," said Molly. "People have been complaining to Mum about me. They're saying I'm causing mischief. She's banned me from investigating anything. Tomorrow she's taking my library books and my library card."

"Nightmare!" said Lowry. "But this summer you were supposed to be finding out if my gran is the legendary Kroglin Werewolf!"

"Can't you find out yourself?" grumbled Molly. "Just tell her what big teeth she has and see what she says."

"I can't. She's in Switzerland, desperately scouring the mountain villages for a werewolf cure."

Molly tutted. "She's on *holiday*, drinking schnapps with your great-aunt Pam and flirting with waiters."

Lowry wasn't listening. "Your nose is bleeding."

Molly checked the mirror. She was prone to nosebleeds; Mum used to say it was because she was always sticking her nose where it didn't belong. She grabbed some toilet roll and dabbed.

"No more investigations!" Lowry sighed, scooping

up fallen papers and getting into the bath while Molly leaned against the sink with the wad of toilet roll pressed to her nostril. "Hey, if it makes you feel better, you'll probably be dead by the summer holidays anyway."

"What? The summer holidays start the day after tomorrow."

"My sister heard Felicity Quick saying she's going to kill you tomorrow." Lowry pulled the bed linen over herself. "Killed on the last day of school! That's got to be the worst timing ever."

"What does she want to kill me for?"

"Since when has Felicity Quick needed a reason to want to kill anyone? But if you really want to know, it's because you're a meddling snoop who tries to investigate folk-tales but always ends up digging up local dirt instead."

"Fair enough... But why *now*?"

"Something to do with the site of the new housing development. You found out that there are plague victims buried there."

"So?"

"So her grandfather is the one who was going to build houses on it."

"Oh, rats."

"Apparently he's desperate for money, but now

everyone's heard about the plague victims and the houses might not get built, and it's all your fault."

"It's not my fault! If I was a housing developer I would definitely check for medieval plague victims before I planned to build any houses."

"Don't worry about Felicity Quick," said Lowry, settling back in the bath as if it were a four-poster bed. "I guarantee I'll think of a way to deal with her by tomorrow. I'll need some excitement now that we're banned from having any adventures this summer." She flapped through one of Molly's notepads. "Hey, did you manage to figure out that thing you were figuring out? The thing with the words on the Howlfair coat of arms?"

"The town motto?" said Molly. "I think so. It's only a short motto, but it's in code, and to crack the code you need to understand five different ancient mythologies. I had to read about fifty books."

"So what does it mean?"

"It means *If Howlfair falls, the whole world falls.*"

"That's a stupid motto," said Lowry, deflating. "How can Howlfair fall? It's in a valley."

Molly rolled her eyes.

"I think your mother is downright cruel for saying you can't investigate mysteries," Lowry went on. "You wouldn't even *have* all this mad meddling curiosity if she wasn't so obviously keeping secrets from you." She flipped through another notepad. "Woah — Aunt Carol's living in your attic as a vampire bat?"

"No," grumbled Molly. "It was just Gabriel."

"Gabriel's a vampire bat?" She dropped the notepad and picked up Mrs Fullsway's chapter. "Gabriel, you disappoint me. Oh, hey, this must be Mrs Fullfat's new book. It smells like a posh toilet."

Molly discarded the wad of toilet roll and looked at herself in the mirror. "Maybe I *should* take a break from investigating local legends," she said, more to herself than to Lowry. "I'm sick of getting into trouble all the time. And my mum's right — I've never seen a real ghost or vampire or zombie or egrimus or... What's wrong?"

Lowry Evans, frowning, looked up. "Molly, there's something here that I don't think Mrs Fullsway meant for you to see."

The Gulls! The Ghouls!

MOLLY SAW THAT LOWRY WAS HOLDING A small piece of paper. An unfolded letter.

"What is it?"

"It was stuck to one of your maps," Lowry said. "It's addressed to Mrs Fullsway. Looks like it was written by her housekeeper."

"What does it say?"

Lowry read the letter out loud:

Dear Mrs Fullsway,

It is with much regret that I must give notice, and although I will of course keep to the terms of our contract if necessary, I would prefer to quit immediately.

I have found these last fifteen years of service extremely character-building, but recent events have left me scared witless and I am afraid that you are in mortal danger. With great respect I must confess that I do not think you are telling me the whole truth. I do not think you were shouting about "gulls" in your sleep during your nap-time last Wednesday. Even though I was downstairs, I most definitely heard you shout, four or five times, "The ghouls are coming for me!"

I saw that gravedigger boy hanging around again and I think he knows something too, but when I tried to question him he ran away like a rat.

Please do everything you can to get out of whatever trouble you are in, Mrs Fullsway. I can tell that you are frightened. If you would only confide in me I might be able to help you, but as things stand I feel I must get away from whatever nightmare is coming before I get engulfed too.

Yours sincerely,

Eleanor Quincy (Mrs)

A haunted hush fell when Lowry finished reading.

"What does it mean?" Molly whispered.

Lowry shook her head. "I don't know. We should start looking into it straight away."

Molly tutted. "If Mrs Quincy is anything like Mrs Fullsway, she's probably just got an overactive imagination…"

"That's what everyone says about *you*," observed Lowry, arching an eyebrow.

"My mum's serious this time, Lowry. If she catches me investigating a letter by a mad housekeeper…"

"Molly Thompson, didn't you hear what I just read?" Lowry sat up in the tub. "There's danger afoot! Peril! Here in our town! Mrs Quincy said that a *nightmare* is coming!"

"But my mum…"

"Leave your mum to me," said Lowry. "We've just got to make sure you survive the last day of school — and after that, I promise you I'll come up with a plan to deal with your mother." She checked her watch. "I have to get back."

Lowry climbed out of the bath tub, put her mask back on, and headed for the window. She was startled by Gabriel, who had ascended the oak tree with the intention of joining Molly in the bathroom.

"Naughty little vampire," Lowry said to Gabriel,

lifting him from the windowsill and handing him to Molly. "Tell Thompson here to stop being such a scaredy-cat."

The skeleton climbed through the window and into the tree. She saluted Molly and was gone.

Gabriel looked at Molly and licked his paw.

"Stop giving me that You-need-to-investigate-Mrs-Fullsway look," said Molly, and she got back into the bath-bed. "That weird scared look on her face, though ... I wish I could remember where else I've seen it."

With Gabriel settled on her knees, she read and re-read the mysterious letter until she knew it by heart.

While Lowry Evans was sneaking back home through the silent town, Hectoria Fullsway was sitting at her desk hammering honeyed words onto sheets of vellum, ripping the pages from her typewriter, scrunching them up, and chucking them on the floor.

She babbled desperately as she typed. Occasionally she rose from her chair and wiped the sweat from her face with a corner of her shawl and glared out at the graveyard. It was during one such vertical moment, while she was cursing her departed husband for the ghastly mess he'd left her to deal with alone, that Mrs Fullsway noticed somebody walking among the tombstones.

She squinted. She gasped. She swayed like the mast of a storm-struck ship, her eyes fixed on the man who was heading towards the Excelsior Guesthouse.

It was George. Her late husband, dead for the past six years.

Dead — but now sauntering towards the Excelsior Guesthouse, dressed in his funeral suit, thick-haired, tanned as though back from an Italian jaunt, weaving between the graves through the night mist.

The dead man looked up. His eyes met Hectoria's and he smiled. But there was something loveless about his smile. And one eye was glowing.

Hectoria clutched at her breathless gullet as her impossible visitor made his way to the ivy-wracked wall of the Excelsior. Now he was directly underneath Hectoria's window, far below — though she could no longer see him.

By the time he had floated into view — floated right up the side of the guesthouse like a helium balloon — he had already started to transform. His clothes had turned white and become a shroud. Things glinted on his torso. Mrs Fullsway realized that George was weighed down with *jewellery*. And his face —

It was not George's face.

It was bony and pallid. The forehead had shrunk away to almost nothing; the hair on top of it had turned to jaundice-yellow fluff, a stark mockery of George's superb silver curls. One of the eyes, enlarged, glowed bright blue. There were no lower teeth, only upper fangs. The thing lifted its waxy face and grinned at Hectoria through the window. And when it stretched out a claw-like hand, its long index finger pointing towards the moon, poor Hectoria Fullsway's heart stopped.

The moon ran into an ambush of clouds as Mrs Fullsway fell. The sky went black. By the time the moon had struggled free, the thing in the window had flown and Hectoria lay frozen-eyed on the carpet.

Across town, the awnings were down outside the tourist office. The silly cardboard ghoul and the silly cardboard phantom that flanked the office's doorway had been stored indoors. The Ethelhael Valley, night-sodden, slept, and the strange town pulsed with mysteries unsolved. The children of the town, whether naughty or good, were dreaming of summer holidays – all except Molly Thompson, who was woken in the small hours by a sudden nightmare. A nightmare in which she was falling, and the haunted town of Howlfair was falling too, and the whole world was falling with it.

She woke with a gasp, jolting upright. Gabriel,

annoyed, meowed. Molly sat frowning in the dark for some minutes, her head singing with unnamed fear. She thought of the look she'd seen on Hectoria's face, so unnervingly familiar. And of Mrs Quincy's ominous words about a horror that was on its way. Then she climbed from the bath, turned the flickery light on, took a pencil and her investigator's notepad, and wrote on a clean page:

The Strange Case of Mrs Fullsway

"Sorry, Mum," she muttered. "Just one more investigation."

Dead to the World

WORDS, WORDS, WORDS.

Brightly lit words glowing before her eyes. Molly woke in the bath the next morning with Mrs Quincy's letter stuck to her cheek, sunlight pulsing through it. She prised it off and noticed a hairy face gazing at her.

"Agh!"

It was Gabriel.

"Stop giving me that You-need-to-sneak-Mrs-Fullsway's-letter-back-where-you-found-it look," she said.

But she knew that Gabriel was right. The letter should not be in her possession.

She got ready for school and tucked the missive underneath the appalling first chapter of *Petals in the Stream of Love's Longing*. Then she put her library books and notepads in a stripy laundry bag and headed off to return the chapter and the letter to their owner, who could always be counted on to be up early, writing noisily.

But Mrs Fullsway, Molly discovered when she reached her room, was not typing this morning. The chamber was silent. A few gentle raps on the door did not rouse the writer.

"Mrs Fullsway!" Molly stage-whispered. "Mrs Fullsway, I've got your chapter!" She paused and set down the laundry bag full of books. "And I need to get my satchel for school..."

Not a peep.

"Mrs Fullsway?"

She knocked again.

Nope.

"Hey, Mrs Fullsway, how about we swap places for the day?" Molly muttered. "*You* can get savaged by Felicity Quick, and *I'll* finish writing about the adventures of swooning Letitia and dashing Glenn."

She knocked one last time. No response. Mrs Fullsway, Molly reasoned, had clearly been up late last night.

Molly slipped the papers back into the laundry bag — which for today would have to serve as a school bag — and headed downstairs to see if she was still in Mum's bad books.

"Don't touch any food!"

It looked like the whole world was in Mum's bad books this morning.

The big L-shaped kitchen was as messy now as the attic had been last night. The freezers had stopped working, the floor was flooded and the surfaces were covered with thawed foodstuffs. It appeared that the shelves of one of the fridges had collapsed too; the door hung open and the food the fridge had housed was now in bin-bags, mingled with broken glass from the shelves.

"Flipping Nora, what happened here?" Molly asked.

"These stupid ancient contraptions!" Mum spat, gesturing at the freezer and kicking a nearby cupboard with a long lanky leg. The cupboard door fell off and a tin of lentil and bacon soup rolled out. Molly scurried over to help, but Mum held her hands up to ward her off, as though Molly were a spectre floating at her through a wall.

"Just go to school, Molly — get there early for a change," Mum sighed. "Take some money from the jar for lunch. I've got to find something edible to feed all those zombies."

"Zombies?" said Molly, shocked. "Oh, the *guests*..."

She let out a giggle. Despite herself, Mum smirked. She did a brief but accurate impression of a zombie. Molly remembered that she and Mum used to have lots of fun together. She headed for the door. The money jar was empty but Molly decided not to say anything. "Good luck with the zombies, Mum."

But already Mum was slipping back into the grey sadness that had overpowered her since Dad had died. They'd made such a great double act, Mum and Dad, and Molly had loved getting caught up in their jokes and made-up songs and mad debates. Without him, Mum seemed lost, adrift. "Enjoy your last day," she mumbled, scooping salad leaves off the floor. And although Molly knew that Mum meant her last day of *school*, not her last day *full stop*, there was something ominous about Mum's choice of words. Because if the thoroughly nasty Felicity Quick had her way, today could well be Molly's last day.

Full stop.

Little Valley Drive

THERE IS A PARTICULAR SENSE OF DOOM YOU
feel when you are a small-ish person carrying
a laundry bag to a school where a bully named Felicity
is planning to murder you. Molly felt it that morning
as she walked along, trying to read her battered copy
of *The Castle of Otranto* without bumping into any
lampposts. She felt like she had a belly full of wasps.
But even the threat of Felicity Quick could not prevent
Molly's spirits from lifting a little when she lowered
her novel and stepped through the fringe of trees that
curtained off Little Valley Drive.

This is where Lowry lived, in one of eight quaint,
bashfully bow-roofed bungalows. Here was a
forgotten part of town, enclosed by a ring of ancient
trees of a sort only found here in the Ethelhael Valley.
Old-timers nicknamed the species *darksbane*, as its
wood was exceptionally slow-burning. Howlfair

Astronomy Tower was on one side of the tree-circle, and its shadow sheared daily across Little Valley Drive like a scythe. Nearby was the Circuit, a triangle of bustling roads along which fine townhouses and posh shops stood straight-backed and snooty. But Lowry's cul-de-sac was shabby and peaceful, set around a shy circular green that dipped in the middle as though it were a small-scale model of the Ethelhael Valley. In good summer weather, Little Valley Drive turned into a perfect bowl of light. And in the autumn it filled gloriously with gold leaves from the darksbane trees, like a gold panner's pan crammed with nuggets.

Summer was Lowry's favourite season, and autumn was Molly's. As Molly knocked on the bungalow door that morning, autumn seemed an awfully long way off, but for a moment she imagined she could smell its lovely approach.

Lowry's sister, Frances, answered the door.

"Hi, Molly," she said. "Come in and listen to my dad ranting."

In the living room, Lowry's mother was feeding bits of breakfast sausage to four-year-old Felix. Lowry was finishing her toast and watching Mr Evans as he strode up and down the room shaking a newspaper, followed comically by the family puppy, a black and white English bull terrier named Sheila.

Mrs Evans waved at Molly. Lowry winked and motioned for Molly to sit down.

"You'll never believe what this columnist wrote about our tourist board!" Mr Evans cried. "Listen to this: 'Howlfair's overactive tourist board fails to see that the silly outfits, cardboard cut-outs of werewolves, endless ghost tours and silver-bullet-peddling gift shops do not leave you with the impression that Howlfair is spookier and more haunted than any other town on earth. They leave you with the impression that Howlfair is more desperate to attract tourists than any other town on earth.'" He gestured at Molly with the newspaper. "Molly Thompson, haven't I been saying exactly the same thing for years?"

"For years, Mr Evans," said Molly, squirming at being put on the spot. "But nobody…"

"But nobody listens to me because they think I'm mad! I'm a lone voice in the wilderness! Meanwhile Benton Furlock is buying all the tourist board's property! And now my boss is accusing me of stealing costumes from work!"

"But, Dad, you *do* steal costumes from work," Lowry observed. "Felix is wearing one now."

Felix looked up ghoulishly.

"That's because the costumes are unbelievably stupid and we need to get them off our streets! Why are we paying schoolkids to stand around dressed in pantomime zombie outfits? We hardly get any tourists anyway!"

"What's a pantomime zombie?" Lowry asked.

"And listen to this!" Mr Evans shouted at Sheila, who was delirious with excitement. He flapped the newspaper and cleared his throat. "'The grand irony of Howlfair is that for all its corny tourist-baiting nonsense, the place is genuinely terrifying. After an hour in Howlfair, I was ready to believe that the old stories were true — that the town really *was* built over the gateway to Hell. If the fools on the tourist board ever came to their senses and banished the funny outfits, they might find to their delight that Howlfair, stripped of its silliness, is almost too scary for words.'" He lowered the paper, his eyes bulging with frustration under his sandy fringe. "That's *me* he's calling a fool!"

"Not *just* you," said Mrs Evans.

"Mum, stop trying to be reasonable with Dad when he's enjoying a good outburst," said Lowry, rising to take her empty plate to the kitchen. "It's like poking a Doberman in the eye — you'll just get bitten."

"Less of your lip, young lady!" said Mr Evans, flinging the newspaper after Lowry as she slipped past him into the kitchen. But the pages flew in different directions and settled across the living room carpet. Sheila attacked them valiantly, which Felix found entertaining.

"Time for school," sighed Lowry, returning from the kitchen with her satchel. "Molly, are you coming?"

Molly followed while Mr Evans tried to wrestle the bits of newspaper from Sheila.

"What's with the laundry bag?" Lowry asked in the hallway. "A new fashion?"

"Not exactly," said Molly. "Lowry, is it OK if I hide some stuff in your room? I couldn't get into my bedroom this morning because Mrs Fullsway was dead to the world, and I've got nowhere to hide all my notepads and library books."

"Molly, my room is overflowing with your stuff. Actually overflowing."

"Please, Lowry, if my mum finds it…"

For a moment Lowry's face darkened with annoyance. Then she switched on a breezy smile. Lowry never got angry, not really. That's one of the things Molly liked about her. "Of course," Lowry said. "Give me everything you want me to hide."

"Thanks, Lowry." Molly opened the laundry bag and handed over the notepads, library books, Mrs Fullsway's chapter and Mrs Quincy's troubling letter, dawdling in the hallway while Lowry took them to her room.

"If we don't start attracting tourists soon," she heard Mr Evans saying to his audience in the living room, "Howlfair will end up being a ghost town in more ways than one, mark my words."

Moments later Lowry bounded back down the corridor. "Last day of school!" she said, holding up a fist. "Let's get it over with."

Haunted Grandma

THERE WERE NO OTHER SCHOOL CHILDREN on the streets. It was too early. The girls dawdled, took a long-cut through Tangletree Park, new-mown and summer-scented. Overhead the clouds were separating, and bursts of fresh white sun were blasting the grass. Molly trailed Lowry past Howlfair Museum, festooned with twitching flags and guarded by gargoyles, its three spires rising skyward. Down dozing lanes, posters advertised candidates for the upcoming mayoral elections, known locally as the Blue Moon Elections. Mayoral elections in Howlfair were rare, only ever taking place on or around the time of what astronomers call a *blue moon*, the second of two full moons in the same month. Some candidates didn't stand a chance:

There were posters featuring the current mayor, Lawrence de Ville, posing in the pictures with his wife, Doris, who happened to be Molly's form tutor:

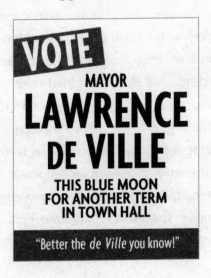

But most posters looked downright shabby alongside the glossy billboard displays urging passers-by to:

VOTE
BENTON
FURLOCK
LOCAL PHILANTHROPIST AND FORMER MAYORAL RUNNER-UP

LET'S MAKE HOWLFAIR **SCARY** AGAIN

Thanks to a lavish advertising campaign, Benton Furlock's giant displays were all over town, his intense white face glaring from scores of posters: the abysmal scooped-out caverns of his eye sockets; the astonishing moustache whose slick ends hung heavy and hornlike, stretching below his chin; the thin lips drawn back in what might have been intended as a smile. One hand was stuffed into his shiny-buttoned overcoat. Behind him, the huge disc of a full moon glowed sapphire, the blue moonlight glinting off his bald patch.

"His campaign must be costing a fortune," said Molly as the girls passed a huge poster. "He's got adverts on the radio and telly every two minutes. And have you seen the World War One biplanes flying over the valley with the *Make Howlfair Scary Again* banners?"

"I can't believe you like him," said Lowry. "Dad's hated him ever since he persuaded the council to let him use Loonchance Manor for his ghoul tour."

"Howlfair has more scary legends than any town on earth," said Molly. "Our town could be *world famous* if it had a really creepy mayor who knew how to attract tourists."

"Well, Furlock's definitely creepy," said Lowry. "He's got a face like a short cut through a graveyard."

The girls had some time to spare before they were expected at registration. So Molly asked Lowry if they could pop into Howlfair Infirmary to visit Grandma Thompson, who was recovering from what the doctors had described, not very helpfully, as "something like pneumonia".

"But visiting hours don't start for ages," Lowry said, steadying Molly, who'd tripped over a cobblestone and nearly ended up on her face. "Unless you're planning to break your neck falling over, in which case they'll let you in any time you want."

"Larry on reception lets me in," said Molly. "Gran threatened to run him over in a wheelchair if he ever stops me from visiting."

"This is because of Felicity Quick, isn't it?" said Lowry. "You always go to your gran for a pep talk when you're stressed."

Molly blushed. "Put a sock in it, Lowry."

"Your gran is so fantastic," Lowry sighed as they took a detour past the Old Dark Movie House, turning right onto Poorhouse Lane and past the offices, now derelict, of F&H Property Surveyors. "She's not like a gran at all."

She wasn't. She was like a prize-fighter. But since she'd been committed to the plain-brick Genevieve Wakely wing of Howlfair Infirmary, in a ward with nine other patients, she seemed to Molly to have lost some of her gusto. She spent most of her time in the ward sleeping.

Larry, the receptionist, authorized Molly's visit without protest. But Ben, a young nurse, stopped the girls as they headed down the corridor to the ward.

"Your gran's awake," Ben told Molly, "but she's been acting a bit strange."

"Are you sure she's not just teasing you?" asked Molly, worried. "Like when she hid her arm up her sleeve and pretended it had fallen off?"

"She says someone visited her last night."

"Who?" Lowry asked. "A nurse?"

"She said a woman in a green shawl came into the ward and told her that something horrible was on its way to Howlfair. And she said something about a sandwich."

"So, basically, she was dreaming," Lowry said.

"She was *definitely* dreaming," said Ben. "No green-shawled women wandered in here last night. Which is just as well, because all of our beds are taken up."

"So what's the problem?" Molly asked.

"Well, your gran swears blind that she was awake. I tried to convince her otherwise and she got argumentative and put me in a headlock."

Molly said, "I'll talk to her."

In her hospital bed Gran lay scowling like an imp. But she broke into a gaping grin when she saw Molly and Lowry. Her candy-floss hair looked as frantic as ever. The girls tiptoed across the snore-filled ward and hugged her.

"What are you doing, visiting at this time?" Gran whispered.

Lowry said, "Molly needs a Grandma Thompson pep talk."

Gran narrowed her eyes at Molly. "Is someone picking on you?"

Molly did not have to answer. Gran could tell.

"Whoever it is, tell them I'll strangle the life out of them!" Gran rasped, miming wringing a goose's neck. "Ah, but I won't need to strangle them, will I? 'Cause your granddad's looking out for you, and he doesn't stand for anyone picking on his Molly! And your dad will be with you, too. He was always a bit of a wimp, of course…"

"He was *not*!"

"Molly, when he was your age, your dad's way of dealing with bullies was to fall over and pretend to be dead. Except he'd always sneeze or start giggling."

"Yeah — and that's how he learned to make people laugh," said Molly indignantly. "Just 'cause he was friendly to everyone, it didn't make him a wimp."

"Well, I'm sure he'll be sticking up for you in his own watery way, unless he's upset at you for not visiting him."

"Gran…"

"You really should visit him, Molly. It's been three years."

"Two years and eleven months," Molly mumbled.

"And it's lovely up there, at the foot of the hills."

"It's not really *him* up there Gran. It's just a gravestone. I don't want to see it."

Gran shrugged. "Well, I'm sure he'll help you out anyway. And I wouldn't be surprised if that cat of yours turns up too — he can sense when you're in trouble. Tell me, who's the brat who's giving you grief?"

"Oh, it's no one, Gran…"

Lowry said, "It's Felicity Quick, Mrs Thompson."

Gran's brows levitated. "Hmph! Nice family, the

Quicks. Locksmiths. Weren't you and Felicity friends once, Molly? Never understood why she turned into such a grotty scab of a girl."

"Me neither!" said Lowry. "She used to be a proper teacher's pet, didn't she?"

"Ben said you were upset about something in the night," Molly said to Gran, keen to change the subject.

"Molly, it was the strangest thing! I had a visit from Hectoria!"

The girls looked at each other.

"She walked right in here. Lord knows why they let her in. A jade shawl wrapped around her gigantic shoulders and her chins dancing in the moonlight..."

"That's definitely Mrs Fullsway," murmured Lowry. "Mrs Thompson, are you sure you didn't dream it?"

"I know the difference between being awake and having a dream, Lowry Evans! I may be barmy, but I'm not mad."

"Did she say anything?" Molly asked.

"Ah!" Gran's eyes glimmered. From under her duvet she drew a huge flour-topped ham bap, wrapped in clingfilm. "She said to give you this!" Gran handed it to Molly.

"A ham bap?"

"Exactly. Have you brought any lunch today?"

"Um, our kitchen flooded this morning and all our food got spoiled…"

"Well, Hectoria must've known about it, 'cause she told me to give you some lunch if I saw you. So as soon as she'd gone, I sneaked over and stole a bap from Bert's cupboard." She gestured towards Bert, who was snoring apocalyptically on the other side of the ward. "He stole my pudding off the trolley last week. I'm prepared to forgive him and not smother him to death with a pillow — but only if you take that bap."

Molly dropped it guiltily into her laundry bag. "Did Mrs Fullsway, uh, say anything else?"

"I think she wanted to tell me about the plot of her latest awful novel," sniffed Gran. "Actually, it's a bit better than the usual romantic puke. Something about a dreadful horror coming to Howlfair…"

Molly and Lowry exchanged looks.

"Doesn't sound like one of Mrs Fullsway's books," said Lowry. "I read her last one for a bet, and the worst thing that happened in it was that Lady Agatha got her foot stuck in a Ming vase. By the end of the book even the hero's and heroine's *horses* had got married. I nearly heaved up my lunch."

"I think Hectoria's gone soft in the head, truth be told," said Gran, tapping her cranium. "She was building up to telling me who the villain of the story was — as if I'd care — but then suddenly she got all flustered and said that her transportation had arrived, or something, and she scarpered."

"I'll have a word with her," said Molly. "She's staying at the guesthouse."

"Oh, how lovely that must be for you," Gran cackled, but then her laughter dissolved into coughs.

"Gran, are you OK?"

"Frog in my throat," wheezed Gran. "You don't need to worry about me, Molly — Hectoria said she was convinced I wouldn't be in here much longer..." She squinted up at the clock on the opposite wall. "You'd better get to school, young ladies. Molly, stop looking so sombre — I can't remember the last time I saw you smile. And come over later and tell me how the three of you got on today."

"Three?" said Molly.

"You, Dad and Granddad," said Gran.

"And me," Lowry added. "I'm not leaving Molly's side."

Gran nodded. "Then Miss Quick doesn't stand a chance."

Mr Ham Sandwich

ST FELL'S SCHOOL WAS NEAR THE CIDER orchards in the oldest part of Howlfair, in the direction of Sibyl Hill and Howlfair Old Cemetery. Treacherous cobbled streets with names like Sprain Lane led you there. As the girls walked, they talked about Gran's strange visitation.

"So you definitely think she was dreaming?" Lowry said.

"Of course she was dreaming," said Molly. "Why would Mrs Fullsway wander across town and talk to my gran about horror and sandwiches?"

"Stranger things have happened," said Lowry. "Oh, wait, no they haven't. Anyway, it's a bit funny that your gran had a vision of Mrs Fullsway talking about a horror coming to Howlfair on the same night that we found that letter from Mrs Quincy talking about a horror coming to Howlfair…"

"I suppose. But then again, I read the beginning of Mrs Fullsway's book, and it wasn't about horror coming to Howlfair. It was about a woman called Letitia who can talk to flowers."

"Bleurgh," said Lowry, holding her stomach. "But listen, Hectoria *was* wearing a green shawl last night. I saw her in the window."

"She's always wearing that shawl," said Molly.

Ahead, school loomed. The sight of its weathered bell-tower silhouetted against the sky triggered in Molly a sick surge of dread.

"Hey, looks like our school's been given the T.T.T.," said Lowry as they joined the stream of morning-faced pupils trudging grudgingly through the gates of the cold, grey-stone school.

Molly said, "Huh?"

"The Tourist Trap Treatment." Lowry pointed to the painted plywood sign on the front playground:

ST FELL'S SCHOOL

for children aged 4-13

VAMPIRE TOUR
OPEN ALL SUMMER

**Come in and see the school
whose brave pupils, according
to legend, survived a vampire
siege in 1611 — and gave the
undead fiends a LESSON
in monster-slaying!!!**

There were pictures of the vampire siege below the wording, apparently painted by some of the school's less artistically able pupils. Molly made a face.

"They weren't *vampires* — they were *booncranks*," she said. "And the children only survived three weeks."

"And what's with the pink-spotted vampire capes?" Lowry snorted as the school bell clanged pompously. "Those are some deeply untrendy bum-cracks."

"Booncranks."

"Whatever."

At registration, with the children seated at their old-fashioned individual desks with lids and inkwells, Molly was relieved to notice that Felicity Quick wasn't paying her any attention. Although, to be fair, it was hard for Felicity to pay *anyone* any attention, what with the jagged purple-highlighted fringe that sliced diagonally across her eyes.

Molly relaxed a little and turned her focus to her form tutor, Mrs de Ville, a short, round-cheeked Caribbean woman with dainty feet and a glare that could halt a glacier. Her husband, Lawrence de Ville, was the Mayor of Howlfair.

"Thank you to our volunteers," Mrs de Ville was saying to the form group. "The inside of the bell-tower looks stupendous — just like in the days when the children rang the bell to warn of the invasion of vampires."

"They were *bum-cramps*," muttered Lowry, imitating Molly's indignation. Molly gave her a glare.

"Thank you to those who've offered to play the parts of vampires and seventeenth-century pupils in our re-enactments. Thank you also to those who've volunteered to join Doris de Ville's Street Cleaning Crew over the summer to make our town tidy. As for those of you who haven't volunteered for any activities: you will never amount to anything in life, because you are lazy and you don't care. But you can at least do me the favour of staying away from our wonderful bell-tower display, so you don't ruin it. Understand? Now let's get to assembly."

Felicity did not look at Molly once all morning. She didn't throw anything at Molly during assembly. She didn't pass threatening notes during lessons. She spent morning break playing rounders in the playground. She was nowhere to be seen at lunchtime in the echoey canteen. And when Molly realized that she'd left her bag in the classroom at lunch and ran back to get her ham bap, she peeked through the window and was relieved to see that Felicity wasn't there.

But when Molly was scooping up the bag from under her desk, Felicity suddenly appeared behind her. It was as though she'd popped up through a secret trap door — with her fiend-like, block-jawed friend Belinda in accompaniment.

Molly didn't see Felicity until she'd been tugged backwards, off-balance, and dumped on her rump.

"Ow!"

She sprawled across the scratchy green carpet, her laundry bag coughing its contents onto the floor. Molly's exercise books lay open, revealing spidery handwriting and illustrated stories. Her ham roll rolled across the room.

"My granddad finds out in four days' time," spat Felicity Quick. She blew aside her long fringe. "If he's not allowed to build his houses, you're going to wish that *you* were one of the corpses in that stupid plague pit."

Molly lay on the floor and stared at Felicity's feet. She wondered if Lowry, or the ghost of her granddad, would turn up to rescue her. She noticed that Felicity was wearing cheerful socks that clashed with her personality. She kept her eyes down; the last thing Molly wanted was to look at Felicity's wide, vicious face.

"Tell her what you're going to do," said Belinda in her lifeless, creepy drawl.

Felicity squatted next to Molly. "Remember that story you read out in class, about your cat's nine lives and how he keeps losing them?" Felicity moved her face close to Molly's. "If my granddad doesn't get permission to build houses on that land, I swear your stupid cat's going to lose the rest of his lives in one go."

Molly gasped. "But, Felicity, what if the plague pit is cursed or something, and your granddad builds houses on it and—"

"Just shut up, Thompson!" Felicity snapped. "My granddad needs the money. Are you listening to me?"

"She's not listening," said Belinda, rolling up her sleeves. "I'll make her listen."

Now Belinda was stomping over with mean intent. Molly knew it was time to face facts: nobody was coming to rescue her. She'd have to rescue herself.

She thought of the stories her dad used to tell her, about how he'd learned to outwit school bullies, back when he was a small boy. He'd play dead and make the bullies laugh, or he'd tell jokes, or he'd cause a zany

63

distraction so he could escape. Molly didn't think she'd be able to play dead, and she wasn't good with jokes. But she was pretty sure she could cause a distraction.

"Wait!" she yelped, looking around for anything that might help her.

"Hold her," said Belinda. And now Molly felt Felicity's talons digging into her shoulders.

"But — but... How can you attack me when he's being rude to you?" Molly babbled.

Belinda frowned. "Who?"

Molly pointed at the floury bap, from which a pink semicircle of ham was poking.

"Him! Mr Ham Sandwich! He's sticking his tongue out at you!"

Belinda looked. Felicity shifted to look. For a second the grip on Molly's shoulders loosened — and Molly seized her opportunity. Pushing Felicity away as hard as she could, she scrambled to her feet, and she ran.

She nearly fell on her face as she veered around Belinda, pedalling wildly towards the door. The corridor beyond was empty — the teachers would all be up in the staff room by now — so there was nobody to help her.

"Get her!" Felicity yelped.

Whimpering, Molly tripped along, the clopping footfalls of her cursing pursuers sounding so much more assured in her ears than her own rhythmless patter. The corridor seemed endless; Molly realized that Felicity — a tall, fit girl, captain of the school rounders team — would catch her long before she could make it to the canteen or playground.

Swerving suddenly, she blundered through a doorway into upper middle school.

Now she was running through a classroom, bouncing off desks, knocking over an ink-pot. Felicity and Belinda had almost caught up with her as she crashed through the far door into a dark, arch-ceilinged corridor; they spat insults and threats as the classroom door swung back into their faces. Molly lurched leftwards down the corridor, wondering where she was, and headed through an archway that led to a spiral staircase.

The staff room, she thought. *Upstairs.*

But Molly realized too late that she wasn't heading towards the staff room. She was heading up to the bell-tower. Once there, unless she flung herself from the tower and managed to learn how to fly on the way down, she'd have nowhere to go.

Bell-tower Blunderings

MOLLY'S SPIRITS BUCKLED. BUT STILL SHE mounted the steps, the muscles in her legs liquefying as she ascended.

Her pursuers were close now and snorting with laughter. There was no need to hurry any more. No need to grab Molly on the stairs. They knew that she was trapped.

At the top of the stairs was a circular lookout, stone-floored, with the Bell of St Fell's dangling from the eaves. Usually the room would have been empty except for the rows of stakes fixed to the walls; according to the old stories, some pupils had, in 1611, staged a last stand here against booncranks – bloodsuckers that looked like, and preyed on, children. Now, though, the room was full of life-sized cardboard cut-outs of pupils holding stakes. One was reaching up to ring the bell.

From the corner of an eye, Molly noticed a real

human standing amidst the cardboard ones as she tripped into the room. Wait — *two* humans. One was a studious pupil named Kiran, who'd helped make the display. The other was Molly's form tutor, Mrs de Ville.

Molly had time to register a smidgen of relief at the sight of the teacher before she waded slap-bang into the cardboard cut-outs.

And Felicity and Belinda arrived just in time to trample the fallen display pieces.

Kiran screamed. Molly stumbled and fell, her nose bumping on the stone floor. Belinda tumbled over Molly with the gawky grace of a circus clown. Felicity ran into a wall, trying to stop herself from ploughing into her form tutor.

Molly looked up to see that Mrs de Ville was very angry indeed.

The telling-off went on for a long time, and concluded with a grisly punishment.

"Felicity Quick, I used to be able to count on you! But this year you haven't volunteered to help with a single thing, and now you've helped destroy Kiran's work! Belinda Penhall, I'm tired of seeing your sneery face on the scene every time there's trouble! And, Molly Thompson — no girl as accident-prone as you should be running around a school." Molly lowered her head and felt blood trickle from a nostril where she'd bumped her nose. Mrs de Ville narrowed her eyes at the shamefaced trio. "As of now, the three of you have volunteered to spend the summer holidays as members of Doris de Ville's Street Cleaning Crew."

"What!" choked Belinda. "All summer?"

"We'll be cleaning every street, starting Sunday. And we've been asked to clean the museum before the opening of a new exhibition called *The Silver Forest*. And don't look so sour-faced. Some people – like Kiran here – *volunteered* to help."

"Will they get tee-shirts too?" said Kiran, sulking.

"Yes, they will get *Doris de Ville's Street Cleaning Crew* tee-shirts, Kiran."

"Not fair," Kiran muttered.

Felicity said, "Honestly, I don't need a tee-shirt."

"Nor me," said Belinda.

"You will all wear *Doris de Ville's Street Cleaning Crew* tee-shirts, and you will wear them with pride," snapped Mrs de Ville. "We're meeting by the bandstand at the dance square at two o'clock on Sunday. Felicity and Belinda – stay here and help me get these cardboard people back on their feet. Molly – you've got a nosebleed. Go and see the nurse. And all three of you – I hope you enjoy each other's company, because you'll be spending the holidays together."

Definitely a Serious Mystery

MOLLY DIDN'T GO TO THE NURSE. SHE WENT to the toilets to dab the blood away, then headed off in search of Lowry.

She found her friend strolling across the playground, just as the other children, having concluded their lunches, were coming out to play.

"Hey, where did you get to?" Lowry asked her. "Are you OK? You're all red in the face."

"I was getting beaten up by Felicity Quick and Belinda Penhall," said Molly, her hands and knees still shaking with shock.

"What!"

"They chased me into the bell-tower and we ruined Mrs de Ville's display, and now she's forced us to join her street cleaning crew, so I'll be stuck with Felicity and Belinda for the whole summer."

"That's an outrage!" cried Lowry. "Hey, can you get me a tee-shirt?"

"Volunteer and you can have your own."

"Can't. The first clean-up session is on Sunday. My sister's having an all-day garden party for her birthday."

"Where did you go? Why didn't you come looking for me when I disappeared? Wasn't it obvious that I was being murdered?"

"I was talking to Carl Grobman."

Felicity and Belinda stormed outside and joined their friends for a spirited game of rounders. Soon Felicity was pitching the ball angrily at her friends' heads while glaring in Molly's direction and mouthing threats. Lowry steered Molly towards the cluster of willow trees at the far end of the playing field. "Carl Grobman?" said Molly.

"You know, works in scary Mr Wetherill's shop. I think he lives in the orphanage. Writes horror comics. Does that silly gravedigger act for the tourists..."

"I know who Carl Grobman is," tutted Molly, trudging across the field. "But why were you chatting to him while I was in peril?"

"Well, that letter addressed to Mrs Fullsway mentions a *gravedigger boy* who Mrs Quincy kept seeing hanging around Mrs Fullsway's house, doesn't it? And Carl Grobman is the only gravedigger boy in town, isn't he? So if we're going to investigate Mrs Quincy's letter, we should start by interviewing him. I mean, we can't just go straight to Mrs Quincy and tell her we stole her note, and it didn't sound like she knew anything anyway."

They sat down under one of the willow trees.

"So what did you find out from Carl?" said Molly.

Lowry, stretching out on the grass, yawned. "He wouldn't answer any questions. Actually, he looked scared out of his tiny mind."

"So, basically, it was a waste of time."

Lowry propped herself up on her elbows. "No, actually! Because I had a brainwave. I told Grobman that Molly Thompson, local historian and solver of mysteries, is on his case, and I said that it's only a matter of time before you uncover the truth about Mrs Fullsway and Mrs Quincy, so he'd better tell us everything he knows before you find it out for yourself!"

"Flipping Nora, Lowry. What did you say that for?"

"Molly, weren't you listening?" tutted Lowry, exasperated. "Carl looked *scared*. Which means he's definitely *hiding* something. He knows why Mrs Quincy wrote that weird letter about some nightmarish evil that's about to happen! He knows why Mrs Fullsway thinks ghouls are after her! Which means there's definitely a serious mystery to be solved!" Collapsing back on the grass, Lowry stared up at the willow branches. "For the best investigator in town, you aren't half thick sometimes."

Lowry insisted on walking Molly all the way home after school, in case she got ambushed by Felicity and Belinda. But Felicity Quick and her sidekick did not bother them again.

The girls arrived at the Genevieve Wakely Wing just as Grandma Thompson had woken up expecting dinner, and Molly (skipping some of the details) reported that she'd made it through the last day of term unscathed. Even if she had been drafted into her form tutor's street-cleaning gang, it was still a relief to have six weeks off school ahead of her.

But an awful surprise was waiting for Molly back at the Excelsior Guesthouse.

Gravedigger Boy

OUTSIDE THE GUESTHOUSE STOOD A SMALL tense crowd of elderly guests, some nosy neighbours — and an ambulance. As Molly and Lowry neared, Mrs Thompson dashed over with a stricken face.

"Molly, it's Mrs Fullsway! Mrs Gill kept knocking and there was no answer, so I had to use the master key, and —"

"What happened?" blurted Molly, aghast.

Mum put a hand on Molly's shoulder. "She died, Molly. Heart attack. I'll be sitting up with Mrs Gill tonight. She's inconsolable. Lowry, can Molly stay with you?"

For once it took Lowry a few moments to find any words. She looked helplessly at her friend. " 'Course, Mrs Thompson."

Molly too was in shock. "This morning…" she said. "Gran… We…"

Lowry mastered her emotions and grabbed Molly's hand. "Come on, Molly — let's get your overnight bag. Don't worry, Mrs Thompson, I'll look after her."

Molly thought that Lowry was going to rip her arm off, so vigorously did her friend haul her across the guesthouse forecourt.

"Lowry, stop dismembering me!"

"I had to stop you from saying anything," Lowry hissed. "Don't you see — that was Mrs Fullsway's *ghost* who visited your gran last night!"

"What?"

"She arranged for you to have a sandwich because she saw that your kitchen was flooded when she floated downstairs! And she said that something horrid is coming to town — just like Mrs Quincy's letter said that a nightmare is on the way. Maybe something horrid *killed* her!"

"Lowry—"

"Think, Thompson! We're the only ones who know about this right now, and if we're going to investigate without your mum suspecting anything, we'll need to keep it to ourselves." She and Molly ducked under the branches of the oak tree on the forecourt. "And also—"

Suddenly both girls cried out — for as they emerged from the tangle of branches, they found their path blocked by a greasy-haired boy in a too-small school uniform. The boy, just as startled as they, gave a small scream.

The boy was in Molly's year at St Fell's, but she knew very little about him, other than that his name was Carl Grobman, he lived in Howlfair Orphanage, and he spent all of his time doodling comic-book illustrations — that is, when he wasn't working at Mr Wetherill's Weaponry Store or playing a gravedigger in ghost tours. Oh, and lately, of course, Molly had learned that Carl had been haunting Hectoria Fullsway, for he was the boy Mrs Quincy had mentioned in her letter.

"Carl!" snapped Lowry. He cowered. "You can't just loom at people like that!"

"Mrs Fullsway's dead, isn't she?" the boy said in a put-on deep voice, his black eyes twitchy and nervous. "We gravediggers know when new business is heading our way."

Lowry punched the boy's arm. "Stop trying to sound creepy, Grobman," she snapped. "It's disrespectful."

"Sorry," mumbled Carl Grobman. "I just heard that she died and I thought I should come over." To Molly, he said: "Is it true that you're investigating the ... stuff that's going on?"

Molly glanced at Lowry. "Um, yes, it is." She straightened her spine and imagined she was someone more confident, like Lowry or Gran or Felicity Quick.

"I know what you've been up to — how you've been hanging around Mrs Fullsway's house," she said. "I'm not going to report you to the police *yet* — as long as you tell me everything you know."

"Yeah!" said Lowry, impressed with Molly's performance. *"Everything."*

Carl Grobman gaped with terror. He looked like he was going to cry. "Are you *mad*?" he blurted. "He'd kill me!"

"Kill you?" frowned Molly.

Carl looked around shiftily like a villain in a silent film. "I've got to go."

"Wait — can we talk to you later?" Molly said. "I could call for you tonight. At seven?"

"No! He's coming over to the orphanage for an inspection at seven-thirty."

"Who is?" asked Lowry.

Carl seemed to realize he'd said too much. He pulled up his blazer collar and turned to go. "Nobody," he said. "Forget it."

"Who's he talking about?" said Lowry as Carl scurried off. "Who's this guy who's going to kill him if he tells us anything?"

"That's what we need to find out," said Molly. She turned back towards the Excelsior Guesthouse. "Follow me — I've got an idea."

Follow the Fear

IN THE COOL, WOOD-PANELLED LOBBY FROM which a huge spiral staircase swept steep and rickety up to the first floor, Molly headed to the pamphlet stand beside the coat racks.

"What are you looking for?" Lowry asked Molly.

"This," Molly said, picking up the Howlfair directory. She flipped through its pages until she found what she was seeking.

HOWLFAIR ORPHANAGE

1 Empty Nest Lane,
Howlfair, Ethelhael Valley

"Burdens Proveth the Meek"

"Carl's afraid of a man who's coming over to inspect the orphanage tonight," said Molly, returning the Howlfair directory. "Before we can push Carl for information about Mrs Fullsway, we need to find out who this mystery guy is." She wandered to the desk and idly turned a few pages of the guest book. "Remember, secrets like to hide underneath fears. What am I always saying to you?"

"Um … stop putting sunglasses on Gabriel?"

"No, the other thing."

"Follow the fear and you'll find the secret."

"Exactly. What are you doing tonight?"

"Helping Mum with the birthday cake for Frances's garden party on Sunday."

"How long will that take?"

"By the time we've thrown away six burnt cakes and had a massive argument and discovered that Sheila has eaten all the icing while we weren't looking, it'll be at least midnight."

"I'll have to go on my own, then." Molly frowned. "While you're baking, do you reckon I could sneak out of your house without anyone noticing?"

"Thompson," Lowry tutted. "What are you planning?"

"I'm going to sit outside Howlfair Orphanage and see who comes over at seven-thirty to inspect the place."

"Sounds a bit risky," said Lowry. "You don't usually do risky things. You're more of a stay-in-the-library kind of gal."

Molly ran her finger over a florid message in the guest book with Mrs Fullsway's lavish signature underneath. She lifted the book and sniffed it — the page still retained the scent of a squirt of perfume. Instantly it called up a memory: the image of Hectoria Fullsway's face reflected in Molly's bedroom window. That oddly familiar expression...

Suddenly she staggered, her blood draining. The guest book fell from her hands and thudded to the table.

"Hey, what's wrong?" Lowry asked.

For some moments Molly was unable to speak. Then she looked at Lowry. "Remember that summer when we all knew my dad was ill but he was refusing to go to the doctor, in the weeks before he died?"

Lowry frowned. " 'Course."

"And remember I told you that he had this weird scared look on his face all the time? Not normal fear — something bigger."

"Yeah, I remember."

"The last time I saw Mrs Fullsway, she had the same expression on her face," said Molly. "The *exact* same expression." She moved the guest book back to its place. "Maybe my dad knew that something scary was going on in this town. Maybe whatever was frightening Mrs Fullsway has been frightening people in the past."

Lowry scratched her ear thoughtfully. "Maybe it's up to us to stop it."

The Common Ghoul

WHILE LOWRY AND HER MUM ARGUED loudly in the kitchen over flour measurements that evening, with Sheila occasionally joining in and Felix watching, Molly sat on Lowry's bed frowning into one of the many books of Howlfair legends that she'd stored in her best friend's room.

Footsteps.

Lowry came into her bedroom flustered and dusted in icing sugar. "So you found your books then."

"Sorry, I didn't realize how many boxes of stuff I'd left here."

Lowry shrugged and fell into the gingham armchair.

"Oh, and I found this," said Molly, holding up one of the tomes that lay on the bed, a scrapbook cluttered with notes and photographs.

"That's my research into the Kroglin Werewolf,"

said Lowry. "It proves there's a definite link between my gran and the Kroglins, who were known for dabbling in wolf-magic."

"Lowry, there's no way your gran is the Kroglin Werewolf," said Molly, examining a picture of Lowry's gran in a restaurant, daintily eating a small hamburger. Underneath it, Lowry had written: GRANDMA FEASTING ON CATTLE FLESH. "I know a lot about werewolves and trust me, your gran shows no signs of being one. Though I'm pretty sure that at least one generation of your family was *raised* by wolves, and some wolfy habits might have been passed down through the ages…"

"But, Molly, what if there's a wolf-curse in my family and it's skipped a generation and I'm about to inherit it?" said Lowry. "Promise me you'll look at the evidence."

"OK, I promise," Molly sighed, returning to the book of Howlfair lore. "I'd forgotten how gripped by ghoul legends Howlfair once was," she said. "The whole town used to be scared to death of ghouls, back in the Dark Days. Rich people got buried in special ghoul-proofed graveyards, or they were put in silver coffins, to keep the ghouls from eating their dead bodies. Then there were all these folks who sold special charms and perfumes that people could put on their dead loved ones before they buried them, to repel ghouls."

"Try new *Ghoul-Begone!*" cried Lowry. "The stinky spray that keeps ghouls away."

"Grave robbers used to steal the silver coffins and trinkets and sell them back to the coffin makers and charm sellers. And then there were grave watchers armed with cutlasses who used to guard tombs, but they charged a fortune for their services. Ghouls were big business in Howlfair."

Lowry looked sheepish. "Confession time. I don't actually know what a ghoul is," she said. "I'm guessing some kind of corpse-eating ... zombie?"

Molly switched books. "Layali Mangil, an expert on Arabian folklore, has discovered very early legends describing ghouls as junior demons expelled from Hell as a punishment for annoying senior demons. They're desperate to get back to the underworld, but they have to stay on earth and feed on rotten corpses until they've paid off their debt to Hell. They eat living people too, but only if they're commanded to by a senior demon or a witch who knows how to control them." She showed Lowry a sketch of a ghoul.

"I think my sister went out with him once."

"In their natural state they look pretty disgusting, but they're able to shape-shift," Molly went on. "Often they'll impersonate someone you know very well, and

lure you to a lonely place where they can kill you."
Another book. "According to Elspeth Blinkhorne,
who was a scholar and probably a witch, the common
ghoul is really a type of *egrimus* —"

"Oh, you told me what that means!" said Lowry
excitedly, sitting up straight in her armchair. "It's
a monster made of the putrid flesh of a thousand
murder victims!"

"A *hundred* victims," said Molly, "and no, that's a
putrimus. An egrimus is any spirit or phantom that can
become at least slightly corporeal."

"Slightly what-the-heck-did-you-just-say?"

"Corporeal. Solid." She switched books again.
"There's one thing all the scholars agree on, though.
Ghouls are desecrators."

"Like painting and wallpapering?"

"Not *decorators*, Lowry. *Desecrators.* They get a kick
out of spoiling things that people hold sacred."

Lowry checked her watch. "Speaking of spoiling
things, I'd better get back to the kitchen and help
Mum ruin the cake. And you'd better get out of here if
you're going to catch this mystery guy who's visiting
the orphanage."

"Wait — how am I supposed to sneak out without
your parents seeing me? I think your dad's in the
living room."

"Go through my window, of course!"

"Are you kidding?"

"Why would I be kidding?" Lowry bounded over to the window and with a grunt hoisted up the heavy lower sash. "It's easy — see?" She scrambled through the frame and dropped, letting out a diminishing cry as though she were falling a thousand feet. But of course Lowry's house was a bungalow.

Molly rolled her eyes, dropped her book and went over to the window. Suddenly Lowry popped up. Behind her, Little Valley Drive's circular green was lavishly buttered with evening sunlight. "Hey, look what I found!"

She was holding a cat.

"Gabriel! What are you doing here?"

"I thought cats were supposed to stick to their own territory," said Lowry, putting Gabriel down on the grass and helping Molly through the window.

Molly dropped to the ground. The cat leaned dramatically against her leg.

"Gabriel, go home!" she said. "You don't have enough lives left to be wandering around town."

"Yeah, Gabriel — scram!" commanded Lowry, pointing northwards with great authority. Nonchalantly Gabriel sauntered south. Lowry put her arm down and sighed. "You know why he came here? It's

85

like he's saying, *I'm* Molly's *real* best friend, not *you*, and don't you forget it."

"Lowry, you've gone insane," said Molly, checking her pocket to make sure that she had a notepad and pen. "I'll see you later. Good luck with baking."

"Good luck with your investigations," said Lowry, crawling back into her house. "Give me a full report when you get back. And don't let any ghouls decorate you!"

Hounded!

MOLLY LIKED TO READ AS SHE WALKED. She always kept a slim book in her back pocket or satchel. Tonight she walked with her copy of *The Castle of Otranto* so close to her face that twice she blundered into hedgerows. By the time she'd reached Merrygoe Road, in the tangle of steep narrow streets at the back of the swimming baths, it was getting hard to see the words. The sun, an orange egg yolk in a white of fluffy clouds, was sliding towards the bowl of the neighbouring valley, throwing a heavy shadow over Howlfair.

Dusk always came unnaturally early in the Ethelhael Valley. It was as though the sky over Howlfair became too weak to hold the light. Stars would begin to pinprick the firmament well before nightfall, and an impatient moon would force the setting sun to share the sky.

An old family friend, Mr Cromble, called a greeting to Molly as he walked home. She waved back and headed up Empty Nest Lane, a hilly, deserted-looking road over which hung a stale, secretive hush. The houses were unlit. At the road's end, set in overgrown, untended gardens, was one of the oddest buildings in town: Howlfair Orphanage.

There was nothing unusual about the building's shape; the orphanage was a large, simple, flat-fronted white house with a black slate roof. No — the odd thing about Howlfair Orphanage was that it had no windows. Instead, windows had been *painted on*. Within their phony frames were painted various scenes of happy orphans in bygone attire playing in cosy firelit rooms. But the paint had run and faded, and the children's features were misshapen. The eyes had lost their definition and resembled empty hollows. The hands dangled. The mouths gaped, so that the painted-on orphans looked like screaming phantoms.

Molly felt a sharp pang of pity for Carl Grobman, stuck in this horrible place, waiting for the arrival of someone who terrified him.

Molly wedged *Otranto* into her back pocket and scurried across the tangled front garden to the nearest oak tree. She crouched behind the trunk and waited.

Dusk thickened around her. Dark clouds clotted overhead. Bats squeaked and dashed among the tree tops. And at 7.28 p.m., Molly spotted a tall, grimly thin man making his way up the road with a dog.

The man wore a long grey overcoat with silver buttons. His grey-brown hound, hefty and wolflike, padded at the end of a long, thick chain attached to its collar. The man's left hand was tucked inside his coat. His silver hair was a wavy moat guarding a diamond-shaped bald patch. The twin horns of his heavy-hanging moustache were instantly recognizable. He was Benton Furlock, the man who wanted to be Mayor of Howlfair.

"No way," Molly muttered.

Arriving at the front door of Howlfair Orphanage, Furlock slid a link of the dog's chain over a spike near the porch, and let himself into the building. Inside, he shouted something in a bullying tone, and then the front door swung shut behind him.

Mission complete, thought Molly. *Time to get out of here.*

Cautiously, hoping not to be seen by the dog, she broke cover. Creeping at a crouch through the riotous grass, she moved across the lawn towards the garden's fenceless perimeter.

She was halfway across the front garden when

she heard growling. Then a chain unfurling. And a deep thunderclap *woof* from the creature outside the orphanage.

Molly looked over her shoulder. "OK, I'm going!" she whispered. "Let's just pretend I was never here..."

The unfurling chain clanked as its links locked, and now the dog was straining to get free, whining with frustration, pulling against the metal stake.

Molly's spooked feet filled with frightened energy and she began to run. Behind her were loud barks. Molly prayed that Furlock would not emerge through the front door, roused by the canine commotion, and spot her.

Stars clamoured to watch her tumble down the steep road, her arms windmilling as she struggled not to fall headlong. She spotted an alley on the other side of the road and veered towards it. The moon was a yellow toenail clipping overhead. As she reached the mouth of the alley, she turned and saw that the dog had uprooted the metal stake and got free, and was chasing her, dragging its chain.

"Flipping Nora!"

Molly ran full pelt.

The long shadow-soaked alley climbed steadily upwards, its shady summit obscured by dustbins. It was punctuated with high wooden gates leading to back gardens; Molly bashed them as she ran, hoping that one was open. She crashed into the dustbins and rebounded off the alley walls like a pinball. She could hear her own ragged breathing and the dog barking and the chain scraping as the beast gained ground.

It wasn't until she neared the top of the twilit alley that Molly realized she was heading towards a dead end. It was like the bell-tower fiasco all over again.

If she reached the wall ahead of her, there was a chance she could scale it and then leap into the tree that stood on the other side. But the dog, panting behind her, would have run her down long before then.

With a grunt she shoved an empty metal dustbin over and rolled it towards the dog as it drew near. Barmy with bloodlust, the dog tried to scramble over the dustbin but rolled backwards, sliding off the bin's cylindrical body, paws paddling. It came to its senses and decided to go around the bin instead. Meanwhile Molly had grabbed one of the two dustbins at the alley's end. She ripped the lid off, spun the bin upside down and clambered on top of it so she could scale the wall ahead, her chest burning with fear and strain.

Her foot twisted. She fell sideways with a cry, crunching into the side wall, her right arm going numb. She sobbed, cursing her clumsiness as she fell sprawling to the ground. Now the ripe-smelling dog was descending on her. The moon was a frown above her, and a scream, stuck in her throat, was strangling her. She grabbed the metal dustbin lid by the handle and swung it hard into the dog's snout. Her trapped scream came out as a small warlike roar. The dog snapped its huge jaws around the rim of the lid and pulled it from Molly's grasp. Now, without hope, she heard a screeching *meow* and looked up —

There was a cat standing on top of the garden gate to her left, hissing and threatening, its fur standing vertical, giving it an electrified look.

"Gabriel!"

The dog's huge head swung round, and in a single muscular motion the creature leapt up at the gate, its front paws hammering into the wood, nails digging in. Gabriel was dislodged; he slipped from the top of the gate, towards the dog's teeth. Vertical, clinging to the gate by his claws, the cat kicked furiously with his back legs in an attempt to scramble to safety, but the gate was juddering violently as the dog pounded at it, and Gabriel stood no chance.

Meanwhile Molly was straining to hold the bin aloft.

She brought the bin down over the dog's head, encasing the creature in metal, just before Gabriel fell. The cat landed on the upturned base and leapt down into the alley. With a great groan, Molly toppled the bin sideways. The dog's hind quarters, protruding, thrashed fearsomely. Molly gave the dustbin a kick and watched it roll down the alley, Gabriel skittering out of the way, and it was then that Molly noticed a silhouette at the alley's mouth.

Benton Furlock!

He halted — and then he began to lope up the alley towards Molly with alarming speed.

Molly upended the remaining dustbin, shoved it against the wall and climbed onto it. Gabriel mounted the wall fluidly and meowed encouragement from the top while she hoisted herself up, managing to fling a leg over the wall. She looked over her shoulder and saw Furlock running silently up the alley, his white face shining, left hand still tucked into his flowing coat. Molly flopped into the scratchy embrace of the blue-barked tangletree on the other side of the wall. She fell through the spiky branches, spores filling her nostrils and making her sneeze, and as she slithered to the ground she heard the wolfish dog's growls.

It had got free. Within seconds it had reached the head of the alley and vaulted onto the upturned dustbin. Molly saw its head and paws as it sought to surmount the wall.

She glared left and right.

Where on earth am I?

Thimble Street.

Faces in windows, people were wondering what the hullabaloo was about. They saw the twig-riddled girl and drew their curtains.

Then Molly saw that a light was on in the old chapel halfway down the road. The little wooden door was open. The exterior was covered with posters promoting Mayor de Ville.

As the dog cleared the wall and fought its way down the tree, Molly grabbed Gabriel and ran for both their lives.

Spying and Frying

THE SMALL HALL OF THE OLD CHAPEL WAS warmly lit and plain, with a varnished wooden floor and a low stage at one end; it had spent a couple of years as Howlfair Youth Theatre and was still occasionally used for performances. Standing at one of several trestle tables, arranging neat piles of Mayor de Ville merchandise — posters, badges, bags of sweets, tee-shirts — was Molly's form tutor, the mayor's wife, wearing dungarees and a boating hat. Mrs de Ville spun around, startled, as Molly tripped, wheezing across the threshold of the chapel with Gabriel dangling ungracefully from her arms.

"Mrs de Ville! Help!"

She was halfway across the hall before she remembered that she hadn't shut the door to bar her furry pursuer. She skidded to a halt as Doris de Ville drew a huge breath, her eyes immense with anger, opened her mouth wide, and shouted at a hair-raising volume:

"GET OUT!"

Molly gripped Gabriel and garbled apologies as Mrs de Ville's dainty feet brought her closer — and then Molly realized that the teacher wasn't looking *at* her; she was looking *past* her.

Molly turned to see the dog slavering outside the chapel, swaying and baying. It seemed incapable of passing the boundary of the doorway.

Doris de Ville pushed in front of Molly, getting between the girl and the dog. "What is that wolf doing here?"

Molly didn't have time to answer, for the owner of the beast had now appeared in the doorway.

Though Molly knew his name and fame, and had seen his photo on posters, she had never seen him in the flesh. She was amazed at the dimensions of his weighty, drooping moustache, which terminated in two spikes just below his jawline. He did not remove his left hand from his coat. With his right hand — Molly noticed that it was white and puffy as though it had been soaked in bleach — he took hold of his dog's chain.

"Good evening, Doris," the philanthropist intoned deeply. "I see you've caught the earnest young lady who just attacked my dog with a dustbin."

"Mr Furlock," said Doris de Ville, "I see you've

come to collect the wolf who was trying to eat one of my pupils."

"Hecate is harmless," Furlock said, patting the dog's head. "Your pupil attracted the poor creature's attention by snooping around my orphanage like a … well, like a *spy*." Furlock narrowed his eyes and looked at Molly as a general might look at a map of enemy territory. "Ah, I recognize you now, girl! Your mother runs the Excelsior Guesthouse, yes? Terrible news about poor Mrs Fullsway."

Molly said nothing. Something about Furlock made her feel that it was wise to keep silent. She hugged Gabriel harder.

"A secretive child," Furlock chuckled. "David Thompson's daughter, yes? He was a jolly fellow, if I remember. A *cockney*. Very fond of the smugglers' pubs on Lastmead Lane. How curious that his daughter turned out so *sombre*!"

Molly gasped with outrage.

Furlock's eyes left Molly. He looked at the tables, his gaze grazing the piles of posters and badges and sweets and pens and other merchandise relating to the mayoral elections. "Well, I didn't mean to invade your campaign headquarters while you're so hard at work, Doris," he said. "I hope I won't have any cause to visit again. The mayor is a lucky man to have such a loyal helper." He glanced at Molly. "Or should I say *helpers*?"

Molly's form tutor frowned. "I beg your pardon?"

But now Benton Furlock had turned and was walking briskly with his guard dog into the decomposing evening gloom, leaving Molly with the extremely irate teacher.

"I'm almost lost for words," Mrs de Ville said, shaking her head. "It's one thing to be out sneaking around orphanages, but it's another thing to lead Benton Furlock and his dog to my campaign headquarters!"

"Mrs de Ville, I didn't know that I—"

Doris de Ville held up a hand. "You are aware that my husband is running against that man in the mayoral elections, aren't you, Thompson? You do know that Benton Furlock is after my husband's job? And now he thinks I've been sending a famously nosy twelve-year-old girl to spy on him!"

"But I wasn't spying! I was just, um—"

"Spare me your excuses, Molly. Does your mother know that you and your cat are walking the streets at sundown?"

Molly squirmed. "She knows that I like to, um, investigate things and research local buildings, miss. And I swear I was just on my way home after looking at the artwork on the orphanage when Mr Furlock's dog attacked me. I didn't even know that Mr Furlock had anything to do with the orphanage."

"Benton Furlock is involved in *everything*, Molly." Mrs de Ville sighed, taking off her hat and rubbing her temple. "He runs the orphanage; he runs Loonchance Manor and the ghoul tour; he owns a wing of the museum; he's looking at buying Spittlebrim School and restoring it."

Mrs de Ville turned to the trestle table and pulled a tee-shirt from the pile. She threw it to Molly. Molly tried to catch it, but succeeded only in dropping Gabriel, on whom the tee-shirt settled like an opened parachute. Molly removed it from him. It was grey with white lettering. On the front it said:

DORIS DE VILLE'S STREET CLEANING CREW

"Stop snooping around investigating mysteries and getting into trouble, Molly," said Mrs de Ville. "Do something useful instead, like helping me clean up our streets. You never know — a bit of outdoor work with my litter-picking crew might even put a smile on that stern little face."

Molly turned the tee-shirt over in her hands. On the back, in smaller type, was written:

VOTE
MAYOR
LAWRENCE DE VILLE
FOR ANOTHER TERM
"Better the de Ville you know!"

"Your dad loved this town," Mrs de Ville added. "He'd want you to look after it."

Molly looked up. "Did you know him?"

"Of course — very fond of the smugglers' pubs on Lastmead Lane." Doris smirked. "But Mr Furlock forgot to mention *why* your dad liked to visit the smugglers' pubs on Lastmead Lane. Do you know?"

"A club," said Molly. "A book club…"

Doris nodded. "Your dad loved to read, and he couldn't bear to think that so many people hadn't learned to enjoy a good book. So he decided to start a book club for people who'd never read a book in their lives. One day he asked some grizzly old-timers if they wanted to join his book club, and they laughed and said that they'd rather spend their free time in the pub. And I'm sure you know what happened next."

"Yes," said Molly quietly. "But go on."

"Your dad had an idea. He decided he'd hold the book club meetings in the rough pubs on Lastmead Lane. Everyone thought he was mad — me included."

She frowned at the ceiling. "What was it he used to order at the bar?"

"Limeade with a slice of orange."

"That's it. He'd sit there with his pint of limeade and orange and a pile of books, and little by little, as the weeks went by, he drew people into his reading group. I'll never forget the day when I saw twenty tattooed labourers pour out of the Last Drop Inn with your father, all of them clutching copies of *Wuthering Heights*. Or when a girl at school told me that her parents had started reading her bedtime stories at night — all because of your father."

"Mum used to read lots too," mumbled Molly. "She and dad used to have these big debates about books. But she doesn't read any more."

"Well, right now I imagine she's wondering where her daughter is," said Doris. "What do you think?"

Molly shrugged. She decided not to mention that she had sneaked out of her best friend's house.

"It's time you got home, Molly. Remember, we meet at two o'clock on Sunday afternoon. The dance square." Doris de Ville cracked her knuckles. "Let's make Howlfair nice again."

Outside, the evening had turned deep denim blue. Benton Furlock and his dog were nowhere to be seen, but Molly decided to take the best-lit route back to Little Valley Drive, where Lowry was anxiously waiting for her.

With torn clothing and with a frazzle-furred cat walking beside her, she headed down South Circuit Street, where she spotted Mr Cromble for the second time that day. He was up in the window of one of the Circuit's lovely tall townhouses, frowning into the evening. Mr Cromble and Molly's father had been friends, and the sight of the kind-faced man in the window comforted Molly. But there was something about Mr Cromble's worried frown that troubled her. She watched as he rubbed a tuft of hair and heaved a sigh. Then he turned away from the window and walked out of Molly's view, and she did not see him again.

Stanley Cromble went into his white-tiled, spot-lit kitchen and picked up the instructions for his new king-sized deep-fat fryer. A smiley builder from humble roots who'd made a modest fortune renovating houses across the Ethelhael Valley, Stanley Cromble hadn't lost his taste for life's simple pleasures, and this evening he planned to comfort himself with a chip butty made with thick white bread, salted butter and brown sauce, washed down with a pint of milk.

A nice big sandwich and a tall glass of milk might help him sleep tonight. He'd been finding it difficult to drop off lately.

He put down the instructions pamphlet, poured a litre or two of oil into the monstrous machine, pressed the ON button, then turned to slice the potatoes.

The fat bubbled as the pile of chipped potatoes grew. The day beyond the kitchen window dimmed as evening settled on Howlfair. And then Mr Cromble jumped as his intercom buzzed.

He froze, gripping the knife.

The intercom buzzed again.

Pull yourself together, he told himself, setting down the knife. *The deadline isn't till next week — and in two days' time you'll have left Howlfair for good.*

He crossed the kitchen and pressed the button.

"Hello?"

A crackle. Then a woman's voice: "Stanley?"

Stan frowned. It was a voice he hadn't heard for a long time. He opened his mouth; but before he could speak, the intercom crackled and the visitor said, "It's Lesley." A pause. "Lesley — your sister."

The fat fryer continued to bubble.

"Stan, can you hear me?"

Now this was an unexpected turn of events.

Stan wiped his hands on his trousers. "Of course —

sorry, Lesley — it's, um... It's been a long time. I'll buzz you in."

He pressed the button to unlock the door and stood wringing his hands. What on earth was his sister doing in Howlfair?

He heard footsteps in the corridor outside his apartment and hurried to the front door.

Stanley hadn't heard from his sister since she'd moved abroad almost a decade ago.

As he opened the door, the fat fryer issued a sudden sizzle, like a warning.

Lesley was leaning against the corridor wall opposite Stan's doorway, side-lit by the round wall-set light, half in shadow, wearing a mysterious smile. She looked exactly as she had looked when Stan last saw her. The birdlike frame, the too-big overcoat. The wild hair, looking like she'd put her head out of the window of a speeding train.

"Nice little place you have here," she smirked. "Going to invite me in?"

"Of course!" blustered Stan, stepping back. Lesley squeezed past him. No kiss, no hug. Typical Lesley. She strolled across the lounge and plonked herself on the black leather sofa.

"Um — do you want a cup of tea?" Stan said, heading back through the archway to the kitchen. The fat fryer was bubbling urgently now. Suddenly Stan remembered that Lesley hated tea. She always had. "Sorry, I forgot. You—"

"Yes, please," called Lesley, plucking a magazine from the coffee table.

Stan stopped. He looked over his shoulder. In the long mirror at the far end of the lounge, he could see the reflection of Lesley's profile, and it seemed to him that her left eye was...

Well, sort of *glowing*.

Fighting to control his heartbeat, Stan took a breath and said, "D'you still take your tea the same way, Les? Milk and six sugars?"

Lesley never had sugar in anything. Especially not tea.

"Please," sang Lesley. "Then I'll tell you why I'm here."

Stan's knees buckled. He had a horrible feeling that the person in his living room was not his sister.

Sizzle, warned the fat fryer.

Slowly, shakily, Stan made his way towards the pile of chips. He took the knife from the chopping board. He hoped it was silver. If it was silver, he might be able to—

"You know I'm not Lesley, don't you, Stanley?"

Stan jumped and dropped the knife. He spun

around. The visitor was in the kitchen archway, grinning. Her left eye seemed to bulge. It shone bright blue. Stan staggered backwards, past the surface on which the fat fryer hissed.

"Lesley probably doesn't take sugar in her tea, does she?" the visitor went on.

Stan shook his head. His legs, meanwhile, were shaking of their own accord. "She hates tea," he rasped, terror constricting his windpipe. "You're one of Mr Furlock's … things, aren't you?"

The figure in the archway laughed. Then it began changing. The clothes started turning white. Golden jewellery — necklaces, bracelets, brooches — began to appear over the torso. The thing's face was stretching, turning pale, turning rotten. The bottom jaw receded, then suddenly hinged open revoltingly. A dozen or so teeth fell out of the gaping mouth, clattering on the floor; the upper teeth elongated into fangs.

"I'm going to pay, I swear!" Stan backed away, his throat making a whining noise as the thing rose a couple of inches into the air and began to float over the floor tiles. "Can't you come back in a few more days?"

"I am permitted only to do as my Master commands, Stanley — unless my Mistress tells me otherwise."

"Mr Furlock's letter said I had until the Blue Moon Elections to make the next payment!"

"The Master has checked your finances," the thing said in a gargled spoof of his sister's voice. "You haven't enough money to make your next payment. The Master thinks you might be planning to leave town before the blue moon." The ghoul paused by the oven. Its blue eye was dazzlingly bright. "So the Master has decided it's time for your second warning."

"Thompson!" Lowry hissed. "Thank goodness. I heard an ambulance siren and thought you'd come a cropper. Yikes, you look like you've had a fight with a really ruthless gang of twigs."

Lowry let Molly in through her window.

"I'm fine, thanks to Gabriel." Molly clambered into the bedroom, her cat following. "I heard the siren too."

"Tell me what you learned. Who's our mystery man?"

"Wait for it," said Molly, settling on the bed and rubbing her scratched arms. "It's Benton Furlock."

Lowry put her hands to her mouth. "No way! Mr *Make Howlfair Scary Again*? Your hero?"

"Yeah — Mr Making-Howlfair-so-scary-that-people-die-of-heart-attacks."

"Molly, what exactly did you find out?"

"I found out that he's happy to let giant dogs eat twelve-year-old girls."

"Um … OK, let's back up a bit…"

"And now he thinks I'm a spy working for Mrs de Ville." Molly unfolded the tee-shirt and tossed it onto the bed.

"Slow down, Molly! Tell me what happened!"

"So tomorrow morning we're going to start investigating Benton Furlock, and we're going to find Carl and make him tell us everything."

"Well, good luck with *that*."

"I won't need luck," said Molly. "I'm going to make Carl Grobman more scared of me than he is of Benton Furlock."

Lowry sighed. "Well, you're looking pretty scary right now, I have to admit. Now take a breath, start at the beginning and tell me everything that happened tonight."

Diabolical Cellar of Doom

NOW THAT HER LIBRARY CARD HAD BEEN confiscated, Molly was unable to access the Records Rooms at Howlfair Library the following day. That meant she couldn't look through the back issues of the local newspaper for information about Benton Furlock. So she sent Lowry to the library to make photocopies of any newspaper features concerning the candidates for the last mayoral election, in which Furlock had been a contender. Meanwhile, Molly visited Howlfair Infirmary to find out whether her gran had heard the sad news about Hectoria Fullsway.

"That was Hectoria's *ghost* who visited me?" gasped Gran. She swooned theatrically, her wispy hair splaying.

"It depends when she had her heart attack," said Molly. "You might have just had..."

"A premonition!" said Gran, sitting up. "I've always wanted to be psychic."

"Gran…"

"I went for a job as a psychic once, you know…"

"No you didn't, Gran."

"… but I messed up when they asked me what I saw myself doing in five years' time…"

"Gran! You're not taking this seriously!"

"Of course I am, Molly. Different people have got different ways of taking things seriously. My way is to not take things seriously. Poor Hectoria…"

"Has she been back to see you?"

"Nope. I had the feeling she was on her way somewhere else."

"To the Other Side?"

"To wherever romantic novelists go when they die. Somewhere with lots of windswept cliffs."

"You didn't like her much, did you, Gran?"

Gran frowned quizzically. "I was very fond of her, I'll have you know. We were great friends when we were girls, back when I lived in the Excelsior. She always said she was going to travel the world."

"Really?"

"Yes — but later on she married George and he turned out to be as adventurous as a chewed slipper. So she started to travel in her imagination, and that's

110

how she started writing. Always daydreaming, she was. Once she nearly stepped out in front of a tram. Luckily Fleance had followed us into town, and he stopped her."

"Fleance?"

"The Excelsior cat. But look here — if Mrs Fullsway was trying to warn me about some danger that's heading towards our town, then you have to investigate it!"

"Mum doesn't want me to investigate," Molly said. "She says my investigations cause too much trouble."

Gran made a loud *pffffttt* noise. "Since when have you ever let anyone stop you from investigating a mystery? Didn't I make you promise you wouldn't investigate the Case of the Diabolical Cellar of Doom?"

"I didn't even *want* to investigate that case until you started calling it the Case of the Diabolical Cellar of Doom. And the case turned out to be me clearing out your basement." She looked up at the clock. "I've got to meet Lowry outside the library."

Gran frowned. "What mischief are you up to, Molly?"

"What do you think?" said Molly, kissing Gran's head. "I'm disobeying my mother and solving a mystery."

The Rotten Fate of Daphne Loonchance

"**Y**OU'RE RIGHT – THE NEWSPAPERS WERE full of stuff about Benton Furlock and the other mayoral election candidates," Lowry told Molly as they sat on a bench outside Howlfair Library in the breezy sunshine. "But this is the best one. A whole article about him in the *Ethelhael Panopticon*."

"Bingo!" said Molly, taking the photocopy and wrinkling her nose at the picture of Benton Furlock's younger but still cadaverous face.

"Did you just say *bingo*?"

"Lowry, this is perfect!" She scanned the article. "He and some guy called Preston Halfstar used to have a property-surveying business: Furlock and Halfstar."

"I can't believe you said *bingo*."

"Then Preston Halfstar got ill and died," Molly went on. "Furlock became depressed …"

"That explains his face. Like a goat with stomach ache."

"… and he felt he couldn't carry on with the business, even though it was very successful. Eventually he decided that Preston Halfstar, his lifelong friend and business partner, wouldn't have wanted him to wallow in misery. So he sold the company and spent the money setting up a foundation for good works."

"I bet Furlock killed his business partner so he could get the money, the filthy murderer."

"But why would he kill someone for money, and then spend the money doing good deeds?"

"Maybe he felt guilty."

"Maybe." Molly looked at the other clippings Lowry had provided. "Ooh — here's one from just after the elections." She paused to cast her eye over it. "Apparently Furlock came close to winning. But it looks like the people from the Howlfair Workers' Union decided to vote against him after he said something rude about their leader, and they tipped the vote in Mr de Ville's favour." She checked her watch and slipped the photocopies into her satchel. "Let's get going — I'll finish reading these tonight." She stood up and faced the library grounds' west gate.

"I thought we were going to Wetherill's to find Carl," said Lowry.

"I thought we'd take a scenic route."

"You want to go past Loonchance Manor, don't you?"

"Bingo."

Situated on one of Howlfair's two roundabouts, accessed perilously by an ill-advised zebra crossing, Loonchance Manor was a ghastly wooden ghost-house, tall and crooked, neighboured by a giant yew tree towards which it leaned as though sharing a sinister secret.

BENTON FURLOCK'S
WORLD-FAMOUS
LOONCHANCE MANOR
GHOUL TOUR

CREEPY FUN FOR AGES 13 TO 130

See the blood-splattered
MURDER MANSION
where the Loonchance massacre
of 1736 took place!

Learn how Daphne Loonchance
raised an army of infernal fiends
to do her evil bidding!

Scream your way through the
crypts where the Loonchance family
was ambushed by ghouls and eaten alive —
even CHILDREN and the ELDERLY!

Discounts for children and the elderly

"Dad says it's tacky, but I think it looks super-scary," said Lowry, staring past the roundabout traffic at the looming manor. "Much better than any of the tourist board's attractions. I wish we were old enough to go in. You already know the legend, don't you? Of Loonchance Manor?"

" 'Course I know it," said Molly. "Don't you?"

Lowry shrugged. "Something about a girl called Daphne? And some ... ghouls?"

"The youngest Loonchance girl, Daphne, fell in love with a poor gravedigger called Tom Taffler and they secretly got engaged. When Daphne's family found out about the engagement, they had Tom murdered. But Tom had already told Daphne an old family secret: how to control the ghouls in Howlfair Cemetery. Daphne used the secret to summon the ghouls, and she got revenge on her family."

"Ooh, I do relish a good revenge story."

"Daphne's best friend died around the time of Tom's death. Daphne acted like this was the last straw, and she faked her own suicide. Once her relatives had assembled in the family crypt after the funeral, Daphne jumped out of the coffin. One aunt died of fright on the spot. And then the other funeral guests arrived..."

"The ghouls?"

"Yep. They ate the guests. Daphne ran away through the tunnel up to the house, but the tunnel wall gave way and something fell on her."

"A spider! Yuck."

"It was Tom's corpse."

"Even more yuck!"

"The Loonchance family had buried him in the tunnel wall. The ghouls were mad with blood-lust by this point, and they ate Tom and Daphne on their way up to the house. They ran out onto the streets of Howlfair, causing havoc, and it took a year for the mayor to bring the ghoul problem under control."

"Is it true that you get to see Daphne's diary if you go on the Ghoul Tour?"

"Well, it's just a copy," said Molly. "The real one's in Howlfair Museum. But the most important page is missing."

"The page where she wrote down the secret of controlling ghouls."

"Yeah." She checked her watch. "Enough sightseeing. Let's go to Wetherill's."

They began to walk. "Just so you know, I'm not going inside the shop with you."

"What? Why?"

"Because Mr Wetherill supposedly comes from a long line of werewolf hunters, and I possibly come from a long line of lycanthropes. My kind doesn't associate with his kind, Molly."

Molly tutted. "Oh, stop being a drama queen."

"Drama? Queen? You're the one who told me that Wetherill probably has real weapons hidden in the back of his shop! Pistols loaded with silver bullets!"

"But I don't remember saying he'd use them to shoot twelve-year-old attention-seekers who want to be werewolves."

Lowry stopped, upset. "You think I'm an attention-seeker?"

Molly sighed. "I didn't mean that."

"What *did* you mean, exactly?"

"Nothing, Lowry. I meant that *Mr Wetherill* would probably think you were attention-seeking if he heard you talking about being a werewolf."

"That's not what you meant at all. You meant that *you* think I'm an attention-seeker."

"Lowry, I'm sorry — just forget it. Look, here's the shop." Molly walked on, blushing guiltily. She stopped at the shop window with its rows of sharpened stakes and harpoon guns and silver bullets. "Hurry up, wolf-girl. At least come in and play with the toys while I scare Carl into answering my questions."

Sulky-faced, Lowry followed.

Wetherill's Weaponry Store

INSIDE THE SHOP, MR WETHERILL WAS looming in front of the long mahogany counter, engaged in a tense dispute with an elderly woman. A huge, square-shouldered, long-haired man, Mr Wetherill looked like a scarecrow brought to life by an amateur wizard. He wore big gold-tinted spectacles that resembled sunglasses. He didn't look over when Molly and Lowry, entering the day-defying gloom of the shop, triggered a tiny tinny witch's cackle from the speaker above the door.

"I don't sell real monster-killing weapons, I don't sell real explosives, and I don't sell anything with real magical powers!" Wetherill was informing the woman, his voice backfiring as his patience tank neared empty.

"But, Mr Wetherill, I wasn't—"

"Those things are *illegal*. This is a *gift shop*,

sponsored by the Howlfair tourist board!"

Seeing Molly and Lowry, the woman put her head down and began to back away, towards the door. "I only asked him if he sold mousetraps," the woman mumbled to Molly as she bumbled past her. "That fellow's loopy."

From the kitchen area came the banshee shriek of a boiling kettle. Hearing the kettle, Mr Wetherill — for whom tea was a priority — shuffled around the counter. "Carl! Don't just sit there doodling! See to these customers!"

Molly spotted Carl Grobman sitting at a table in the dark area beyond the mahogany counter, near the door that led to Mr Wetherill's kitchen area. Grobman looked scrawnier than ever in a badly fitting black apron bearing the stark white Wetherill's logo.

Carl raised his head and gave Molly a startled look as Mr Wetherill crashed through the back door into the kitchen. While Lowry stood playing with a toy spiked glove, Molly approached the counter. "Hey, Carl, what're you drawing?" she said, trying to set the boy at ease. "Are you working on your latest comic?"

"You need to get out of here!" hissed Carl, shutting his sketchpad and lurching over to the counter.

"Calm down, Carl — I just came here to do a bit of shopping. There's no law against..."

"That was you last night, at the orphanage, wasn't it?" Carl snapped. "The dog chased you away."

"Yeah — the dog and its owner," said Molly. "Carl, why are you so scared of Benton Furlock?"

"I'm not scared of Mr Furlock," Carl growled. "I'm just not going to blab about him to you, that's all. He's done a lot to help me. He got me this job, and my job as a gravedigger. He runs the orphanage where I live."

Lowry was now using the spiked glove to fight a toy phantom.

"Lovely," Molly said. "Maybe you and Furlock can share a cell in prison."

Lowry, who'd swapped the glove for a replica harpoon gun, looked over.

"Prison?" Carl stammered. "What do you mean?"

"Mrs Fullsway was in danger, and you knew about it. Now Mrs Fullsway is dead, and Benton Furlock had something to do with her death — and you know about it. I'll get to the truth eventually, Carl Grobman, and when I do, you'll wish you'd helped me instead of covering up for Furlock."

"Look, you really should go home, Molly — I mean it. Right now. We can have this conversation another time."

"Actually, Carl..."

He pointed at the door. "Molly, right now!"

"Hey!" called Lowry. "What's wrong with your arm?"

Carl's sleeve had ridden up his forearm as he pointed, revealing a grubby, clumsily wrapped bandage. He lowered his arm, blushing. "Hurry," he said to Molly. His voice had a pleading tone. "I'll come and find you soon. But right now you definitely need to be at home."

He was giving Molly a look that spooked her.

"Come on, Lowry," Molly said, relieving her friend of the replica gun she had been aiming at various mannequins. "Carl, I'll be seeing you."

An unsettling sense of urgency carried her back to the Excelsior Guesthouse.

Mr Let's Make Howlfair
Scary Again

"WHOSE CAR IS THAT?" LOWRY SAID AS they turned the corner from sun-flooded Squint-Eye Lane to Cecily Craven Street, where the Excelsior stood.

A boat-like sports car, grey, bulbous around the wheel hubs and bonnet, was moored on the curb outside the guesthouse. It wasn't the kind of car that would ever come back into fashion (if indeed it had ever *been* in fashion); it had the doomed air of an extinct bird in a taxidermist's window. Molly had an awful idea that she knew who it belonged to.

She crept to the side of the lounge window and peeked through.

The first thing she saw was the bull-horn moustache. Then a stiff-suited man, one arm in his jacket, sitting opposite Molly's mother on one of the high-backed armchairs that had small coffee tables beside them.

Lowry, following, poked Molly in the ribs. "Who is it?"

"It's Benton Furlock — and he's talking to my mum! Probably telling her how he caught me running from the orphanage!"

"Oh, bums."

"Stay outside," said Molly, heading for the front door. "Or go home."

"What? Why would you want me to go home?"

"Furlock's got me in his sights," hissed Molly, dropping her front key and fumbling to pick it up. "I don't want him to get you in his sights too."

"But, Molly..."

"Lowry, trust me. I'll call you as soon as I know what's going on."

Furlock flew to his feet as Molly tripped into the lounge of the Excelsior, which smelled a bit too strongly of lilies and of the contradictory colognes of guests. Curiously, no other residents were present; usually they would be reading newspapers on the sofas at this hour, or gossiping over tea. With one hand stuffed inside his long, vaguely military coat, Furlock looked as though he was about to reach for a pistol. Surprised by his sudden rise, Molly put her hands in the air. She nearly shouted, "Don't shoot!"

"Molly, what are you doing?" said Mum, who had been looking quite relaxed considering the importance of her visitor, blowing on her cup of steaming tea, to cool it.

"Just … stretching," said Molly, embarrassed. She put her hands down. "Um, Mr Furlock…"

The moustachioed philanthropist bowed and sat down. "Molly," he cooed, "our young local historian. Your mother has been telling me all about you."

"Ah," said Molly cautiously.

"Molly, why don't you go upstairs?" said Mum. "Mr Furlock and I are just discussing … local matters."

"Oh, it's fine if Molly stays," Furlock said in his tar-thick tone. He gulped a gulletful of scalding tea and returned the cup to his table. "I just wanted to offer my condolences. I know that Hectoria Fullsway was very close to your family. Isn't that right, Molly?"

Molly cleared her throat. "She stayed here sometimes."

"Your mother says that you and she were good friends. It's comforting to know that Hectoria had someone she could confide in."

"Confide?" Molly spluttered. What was he getting at?

"She talked to you."

"Yeah, 'course," said Molly, fidgeting. She realized she was sounding defensive, cagey, but she couldn't help herself. "She talked to me about her novels," she added, shrugging too energetically. "That's all."

Benton Furlock took another gulp of steaming tea. "She did have quite a remarkable imagination. With people like Hectoria, you often have to take what they say with a pinch of salt."

"Tell me about it!" snorted Mum. "Molly's the same. Always harping on about vampires and ghosts and mysteries."

"*Mum,*" Molly hissed.

"And her best friend Lowry thinks she's a werewolf…"

"Mum, stop!" Molly cried.

Suddenly Benton Furlock gasped. "Oh, what a fool," he hissed, and Molly saw that he'd spilled hot tea over his knees.

Mrs Thompson flew to her feet. "Don't worry, I've got it!" She grabbed a vase, threw the lilies onto the floor, and moved towards Furlock to extinguish his steaming knees with the water.

Furlock showed no sign of pain. "Mrs Thompson, that's not necessary. A towel will suffice."

"Molly, get a towel!" said Mum. "On second thoughts, stay here and don't touch anything!"

She flittered from the room, and now Molly and Furlock were alone. Molly spotted Gabriel blinking on the windowsill outside and wondered if he was signalling to her in Morse code.

"Why didn't you tell my mum?" Molly asked Furlock at last. "About your dog chasing me, and all that?"

He did not speak for several seconds.

"I have plans for this town," he said finally. He stared at his damp knees. "Howlfair has a destiny. But for Howlfair to fulfil its destiny, it must have me as its mayor. So whatever it is that Mrs de Ville is making you do…"

"She's not making me do anything!"

"Whatever it is, it will not work." Still he stared at his knees. His voice vibrated with fury. "I repeat: Howlfair must have me as its mayor. The day — no, the *moment* I become mayor of this town, everything will change. Everything! Howlfair will become scary again. I have sworn to transform this town. I will never give up, and I will not let anything get in my way."

Molly felt a rush of anger. She remembered the look of fear on Hectoria's face. She thought of her dad's face, too, in those horrible final weeks when everything seemed to terrify him and nobody — not Molly, not Mum, not Gran — knew how to help. "Was Mrs Fullsway getting in your way?" she said. "How about my dad? Was he getting in your way?"

Furlock's head snapped upright and his face flushed

an awful pale blue. He ground his teeth briefly before speaking. "I can see why the people of this town despise you, Molly Thompson."

Molly reeled as though slapped. "Pardon me?"

"Such a serious child — and yet you aren't taking *me* seriously," Furlock said, leaning towards Molly, teeth bared. "I will remedy that."

Molly didn't have time to reply, for now Mum was scurrying back with the towel. But Furlock had unfolded himself like a construction crane and was brushing himself down with his free hand.

"I'm sorry I wasn't quicker, Mr Furlock," Mum fussed, holding out the towel. "Can I get you another cup of tea?"

"Not necessary, thank you." He took the towel, dabbed his knees perfunctorily, and handed the towel back to Molly's mother. "I must be off, Mrs Thompson."

He looked down his moustache at Molly. Then, very briefly, he waved his small right hand near her face, the fingers fluttering, swiftly tracing a complex pattern. For a second, Molly thought she saw stars. Then she heard Furlock mutter a few guttural words.

Immediately Molly felt as though the energy had been siphoned from her body. Furlock closed his fist and for a moment Molly had the alarming sensation that part of her personality was now in his palm. She looked desperately towards her mother — but Mum was heading to the door to show Furlock out.

He followed, turning to give Molly one last threatening glare before he left.

"Molly, what got into you?" Mum snapped after she'd shut the door. "Shouting at me like that in front of Mr Furlock!"

"I didn't want that man knowing anything about Lowry," Molly croaked, her stomach still churning. She stumbled to the door at the far end of the lounge, heading for the back staircase, suddenly desperate to rest. "He's a horrible, horrible man."

Her limbs felt fantastically heavy and weak, and her head was buzzing as though a fly had found its way into her skull.

"That man does a huge amount of good work in our community, I'll have you know," Mum called after her. "He's probably going to be our next mayor."

"Not if I have anything to do with it."

"What's that? What did you say?"

"I said I'm going to lie down," Molly wheezed, and she lumbered down the corridor, wondering what kind of hex Benton Furlock had just put on her.

From Beyond the Graves

CRUSHED BY FATIGUE, MOLLY SETTLED ON HER bed. But Gabriel, for some reason, decided that it was a good time to sit next to her head and sniff her hair.

"Gabriel, stop being a weirdo!"

Eventually, with her last reserves of strength, she rose and put him out of the room.

"I'm sorry, Gabriel, but you're going to have to stay out here. That's an order."

He paced up and down the corridor outside her room, mewling, but didn't defy her command.

Molly lay on top of her Dracula duvet, unable to fall asleep. A clammy terror fluttered in her abdomen. She kept hearing noises inside her skull, as though a creepy recording were playing: a clock ticking; dragging footsteps; raspy breathing.

Whispered words.

At some point she heard bells, and then she realized that the telephone was ringing in the scarlet snug down the corridor. Moments later she heard Gabriel hiss, and old Mr Banderfrith banged on the door and shouted: "A call for you! Someone named Lorry!"

"It's *Lowry*, Mr Banderfrith," Molly croaked. "Tell her I'm ill. Tell her I'm dead."

Banderfrith huffed and plodded away.

Hours passed. After tripping over Gabriel in the corridor, Mum shouted to ask if Molly wanted any dinner, but Molly dismissed her with a few groans.

Outside the window, the day dimmed, diminished, darkened.

And at some strange hour, Gabriel began to wail and scratch at the door, and Molly suddenly found that she had her strength back. Her head felt foggy but her limbs felt vigorous.

Then she heard Lowry's voice calling to her from the night beyond her windowpane.

She sprang off the bed and crossed the room. Leaning over her desk, she hoisted up the sash and frowned into the grainy darkness. She fumbled in her desk drawer and pulled out her torch. Pointed the beam. It picked out a shape standing beside one of the yew trees in Howlfair New Cemetery.

"Lowry?" Molly hissed.

"Molly, stop blinding me!" Lowry squinted and shielded her eyes from the torch's light. "Turn that off and get down here now! I've been—"

A tidal surge of wind took the rest of her words away, washing them into the foaming treetops. The tree trunks creaked abysmally.

"Lowry, I can't come down!" Molly rasped into the rustling dark, pocketing her torch. She became aware of scratching at her door. She realized it was Gabriel, frantic to get in. From further down the corridor came a shout — grumpy Mr Banderfrith was barking at Gabriel to shut up. Outside, the winds looped around and came back towards the guesthouse, rattling Molly's window frame.

She blinked, and as her eyes closed she suddenly saw, floating in the black theatre of her cranium, Benton Furlock's insipid hand, the fingers fluttering...

The fingers closed in a fist.

Molly gasped. She opened her eyes, forced them to un-blink — and she found to her astonishment that she was sitting on her desk, one leg out of the window.

"Flipping Nora!"

Then, from outside the window, came a call: "Molly, come on! Down the drainpipe!"

Down the drainpipe? What fresh madness was this? How had she got onto the desk? Did Lowry honestly

131

expect her to climb out of her window on a windy night and shimmy down a hundred feet of copper drainpipe to get to a graveyard and —

She blinked again, involuntarily, and again her eyes locked shut; again she found herself trapped inside her cranium with the puffy white hand fluttering, reaching, clenching, pulling at her. And once again Molly wrested open her eyes to find that she had been *relocated* — for now she was outside the Excelsior Guesthouse, facing the umber wall.

Clinging to a copper pipe!

What the heck was going on?

"That's it, Molly! Come on!" Lowry sang from the graveyard. "You can do it!"

Am I dreaming? Molly thought frantically. But the cold pipe she was hugging seemed perfectly real against her palms and forehead. Her feet wobbled. *Am I being remote-controlled?*

Whatever was going on, the only way was down; there was no way she'd be able to hoist herself back through the window.

Get to Lowry. Find out what's going on. Don't look down!

Utterly petrified, her feet seeking out the metal braces which held the pipe to the wall, cold winds chopping at her, Molly descended.

First Warning, Last Warning

"**O**VER HERE, MOLLY! IT'S *IMPORTANT.*"

Down at ground level, it was hard for Molly to see. A thick milky mist had rolled through the trees into Howlfair New Cemetery. She stepped over the fence, pulled out her torch, and guided the beam across the higgledy graves, which protruded from the sea of mist like the bows of wrecked ships.

The torch beam caught the side of Lowry's face, illuminating one of her eyes, which glowed unnaturally blue. Then Lowry disappeared behind a tall grave.

"Lowry, what are you doing here?" she warbled. "What's going on?"

Molly knew that something was very wrong. But she felt compelled to venture deeper into the cemetery. She couldn't stop herself.

She drew closer to the gravestone.

"Molly, you need to see this!" came her best friend's voice.

Unable to resist, her feet moving almost of their own accord, Molly wobbled her way through the mist to the tall, mossy tombstone, her torch beam bobbing.

"Here — look!" came Lowry's voice from the other side of the stone. Molly poked her head around the gravestone, gripping its cold shoulder, and she gasped.

There was nobody there.

She moved around the gravestone, the torchlight making spectral shadows spring and sprawl. She circled to the other side of the gravestone — nothing. Then she heard a giggle.

She looked up.

Lowry was floating above her.

She was wearing a tattered white dress. No, a *shroud*. Jewellery hung from her, and her skeleton-hands were reaching down towards Molly. Although the dangling wisps of bobbed golden hair were Lowry's, the desiccated white face with the dislocated jaw and the row of brown fangs and the bulbous blue eye glowing in the dark — these were not. And neither was the parch-throated laughter that spilled from the black gullet.

Molly fell to the ground and sprawled in the whorling fog, lock-jawed with terror, her arms flailing to bat away the floating thing that was now descending on her. She struggled to breathe, her heart careening like a dodgem car in her chest. Then she heard the screeching wildcat mewl of Gabriel as he sprinted over, skittling around the side of the Excelsior — somehow he'd found a way out — and bounding through the fog.

A window opened on the side of the towering guesthouse, and the voice of Mr Banderfrith bellowed into the windy night.

"Will someone shut that cat up!"

Lights went on across the black-beamed building. The creature that had impersonated Lowry flew away. As Gabriel found Molly and leapt protectively upon her, Molly squinted up at the gravestone in front of her and saw, scrawled in what appeared to be blood, these words:

THAT WAS YOUR FIRST AND LAST WARNING

She lay there staring, panting. Her face was wet. Those few minutes of fear had forced out all the tears Molly hadn't known she'd contained, and now she felt wrung out. Graveyard soil had made stripes of mud on her face. Her chest rose and fell. Her cat stepped onto her stomach and sniffed her hair meaningfully.

"I was right," Molly said. "They're real. Monsters are real."

Thank goodness she was still wearing her day clothes, and so had a key to the guesthouse in her pocket. Molly took Gabriel back into the Excelsior, and in her bedroom she lay curled on her Dracula duvet, trembling with rage and shock, gripping her cat like a talisman, wondering what to do.

She had felt for so long that there was a mystery to be solved in her life and in her town. She'd felt that there was a secret behind the old legends, a truth too terrible for the town to face. And she had been right.

"This changes everything," Molly said to Gabriel. She wiped her eyes, sat up and lifted him so that they were face-to-face. "Gabriel, I know I'm not exactly strong or brave. But I'm the best investigator in this town. I'm Molly Thompson, and I can find anything out. I'll find out what happened to Mrs Fullsway, and I'll find out how to deal with ghouls, and I'll make sure that Benton Furlock will never, ever be the mayor of this town."

Gabriel sneezed approvingly.

Molly waited for the dawn. She'd made a decision. There was something she'd wanted to do for a long time, and when morning came, she was going to do it.

Pistols and Fudge

MORNING.

First came breakfast, a hurried breakfast with Mum in the kitchen. Molly managed to hide the nervous shaking that had afflicted her since last night's ghoul visitation. Mum was too preoccupied to notice Molly's quivering; she sat sorting through a pile of receipts and old bank statements while spooning cornflakes into her mouth.

"Oh, I forgot to tell you — I'm volunteering for Mrs de Ville's street-cleaning project," said Molly, trying to keep the wobbles from her voice as she headed to the sink, where she began to scrub her bowl and spoon. "It starts this afternoon."

Mum looked up. "Really? Good for you."

Molly rinsed the suds from her bowl with jittery fingers and put it on the drying rack. "I'm just going out for a bit to get some air and read my book. Sunday morning stuff."

She felt guilty for not telling Mum the truth about her plans. But Mum, as it happened, was hardly listening anyway. "Stay safe," she muttered, frowning at her receipts. "Don't daydream when crossing roads."

"I won't."

"Good," said Mum. "I worry."

Outside, walking through Howlfair New Cemetery, Molly found the gravestone behind which she'd been accosted. But something was amiss. The red lettering was no longer there. There was no sign that a twelve-year-old girl had thrashed around on the soil while a demonic fiend had tormented her. No footprints. And no indication that a windstorm had blown through the cemetery.

Molly frowned. She had expected to find at least some trace of last night's ghastliness.

She touched the gravestone — wincing at the memory of the ghoul — then rose and headed to Wetherill's Weaponry Store.

The shop wasn't open, it being a Sunday, but beyond the foggy window with its displays of old monster-slaying weapons, the lumbering shape of Mr Wetherill shifted. He lived above the shop and spent his Sundays sitting behind his counter, reading. Molly tapped on the door. Wetherill opened it with a frown, his long hair a state, his sideburns frizzy. He wiped his gold-tinted spectacles on his sleeve, put them back on and said in his gruff, untested morning voice: "It's Sunday. Shop's shut. Come back tomorrow."

"I'm not here to shop," blurted Molly, wedging the door with her foot. "Unless you've got any Lassiter's Old Plague-Repellent Peppermint Cream Fudge, in which case I'll take as much as I can buy with…" – she rummaged in her pocket – "one pound twenty-three. But mainly I'm here because I need to know the truth about ghouls."

Wetherill scratched his neck. "The truth —"

Molly squeezed past the massive man, into the shop. "About ghouls, Mr Wetherill. I need to know if they're real, how to kill them, and whether you have any proper weapons. I'm guessing something silver is best…"

"Ms Thompson…"

Unconsciously Molly plucked a plastic pistol from a shelf and pointed it at Mr Wetherill while she spoke. Mr Wetherill raised his hands, blushed, and lowered them. Molly babbled on, waving the pistol with great drama. "And don't give me any baloney about not having real weapons because they're illegal and this is a souvenir shop and blah, blah, blah. Everyone knows you're one of the few people in this town who believes that the old stories about monsters are true. Everyone reckons you've got real weapons stashed somewhere in case the monsters ever return."

Wetherill wiped his forehead and stood rubbing one mutton-chop sideburn with a shovel-like hand. "Everyone thinks all that about me?"

"Yes," said Molly. "But nobody dares ask you about it, because you're so huge and scary."

Wetherill snorted. "If everyone's so scared of me, why are *you* in here, Molly Thompson, threatening me with a plastic pistol?"

She coughed and put the gun back on the shelf.

"Last night a shape-shifting ghoul lured me into Howlfair New Cemetery."

Wetherill made a face. "You what?"

"I know — it's hard to believe, isn't it?" said Molly. "But it's true nonetheless. I'm almost certain that Benton Furlock set it on me. He must've set ghouls on Mrs Fullsway, too. Furlock did some kind of black magic that put me under his control, and he made me shimmy down a drainpipe. And that's not all! There was a gravestone and—"

"Woah there, girl," said Wetherill, waving his hands. "Slow down. Did you say Benton Furlock?"

"That's right! His posters say he wants to make Howlfair scary again, but he isn't just talking about tourist attractions — he's talking about terrorizing our town with real monsters! He's got actual ghouls working for him, and they've been frightening people to death... He might even have threatened my dad with ghouls, and that's why Dad looked so scared before he died..."

Wetherill shook his head. "Molly, your father had no enemies whatsoever in this town — and he was on perfectly civil terms with Benton Furlock."

Molly flapped. "Well, *something* fishy's going on around here, and I'm going to prove it."

"You're going to prove that Benton Furlock — a local do-gooder who's trying to become mayor — is secretly an evil magician of some sort?"

"Yes!"

Wetherill spluttered dismissively. "It's not much of a secret if he'd risk setting a ghoul on a twelve-year-old girl right outside the Excelsior Guesthouse."

"He didn't think I'd dare tell anyone!"

Suddenly Wetherill laughed, which Molly found extremely annoying. "You're Molly Thompson! Holy mackerel, girl, everything you ever discover gets broadcast to the whole town."

"Hey, listen to me, Mr Wetherill —"

"No — listen to *me*, young lady." The shopkeeper frowned, stepping forward so that Molly was entirely in his shadow. "You are aware that Mr Furlock runs the Ghoul Tour at Loonchance Manor, and that he hires actors to play the ghouls?"

" 'Course I am."

"And is it not possible that the creature you met last night was an actor who'd been out drinking after his shift ended?"

"No, it is *not* possible, actually! The ghoul turned into my friend Lowry, and it could float, and then it flew away, and—"

"And if we went to the graveyard this minute, you could show me traces of all this supernatural ghoul activity?"

" 'Course not! Ghouls don't leave a trace! Why do you think Furlock's using them to execute his evil plan?"

"What evil plan? To become mayor?"

"No — to raise *monsters* and—"

"So you're alleging that Furlock has raised some monsters to help execute his evil plan to raise some monsters? And even though his magic monster-raising skills are a secret, he's using them to attack twelve-year-old blabbermouths who are guaranteed to run straight into town and start talking about him?

142

And he's doing all this right before the election?"

"I saw it with my own eyes, Mr Wetherill!"

Mr Wetherill held up his hands. "Ms Thompson, what you described to me was obviously a *dream*. A very bad dream. Accompanied by sleepwalking."

Gasping with frustration, Molly backed into a display of amulets. "I've never sleepwalked in my life."

Advancing, Wetherill reached out and took something from Molly's hair. "Tangletree spores. Couple of days old. Don't you ever wash this curly mop?"

Molly blushed. "Of course! Not *every* day, 'cause it's frizzy and I'd turn into a dandelion, but—"

"Well, you should definitely consider washing it after you go climbing in tangletrees. Some folks can have a terrible allergic reaction to the spores. They make you dizzy. The poison can linger in your system. The effects get progressively worse. Vertigo. Fevers. Blackouts. *Hallucinations*."

Molly thought about how Gabriel had kept sniffing her hair. "But I haven't been climbing any trees! I never climb trees! I..."

And then she remembered the tree she'd fallen through while fleeing Furlock's dog. The spores she'd inhaled. Cripes — could Wetherill be right?

"Listen, Mr Wetherill, Benton Furlock is up to something evil. He came to the Excelsior and threatened me after he caught me hanging around the orphanage."

"Threatened you specifically with ghouls?" said Wetherill, raising a brow.

"Well, no, but... Where are you going?"

Sighing, Wetherill trudged across the shop to the decommissioned butcher's cold-cabinets that contained sweets. "Time for a mug of tea and a couple of slabs of peppermint cream fudge. I'm going to teach you something about ghouls, Molly Thompson. And something about our town."

Orders and Guilds

MR WETHERILL OPENED THE DOOR TO HIS cramped, tinpot-cluttered kitchen and stooped through, beckoning Molly to follow. Bringing the kettle back to the boil, he made tea and then led Molly through another low doorway, down a corridor and into a study lined with sagging bookshelves. There were no windows, so Mr Wetherill lit an oil lamp to dispel the gloom. He pointed to a well-used armchair and left Molly to nibble a crumbly slab of chocolate-marbled peppermint cream fudge while he ran a finger along a bookshelf, holding up his lamp.

"A secret stash of ancient manuscripts!" Molly gasped.

Wetherill snorted. "All the ancient manuscripts are in Howlfair Library — and the secret stashes are in private rooms, where only the mayor can get to them."

"So what are those?"

"Modern copies of old almanacs," muttered Wetherill. "Tourists used to buy them. They're records of alleged monster sightings in Howlfair, from the end of the Dark Days till today." He turned and lowered his glasses. "You *do* know what I mean by the Dark Days, don't you?"

Molly swallowed a lump of fudge and nodded. "'Course. The period between the silver crisis of 1465, when miners first came to Howlfair and discovered priceless oquiel and supposedly stumbled on a gateway to Hell, and 1736, after the ghouls which Daphne Loonchance set free were supposedly banished from Howlfair."

Mr Wetherill stared, sniffed, and pushed his glasses back up. "A textbook answer," he grumbled. "Yes, that's what I meant. And I suppose you can tell me how the Dark Days started? What happened when those first miners accidentally found a gateway to Hell and opened it?"

"A horrible mist came out," said Molly, "and polluted everything in the valley."

"Nowadays, scientific-minded folks say that the mist was probably some kind of toxic gas which poisoned people and made plants and creatures mutate. They say that's what gave rise to Howlfair's legends about monsters. But there are still one or

146

two folks in this town — and I believe you're one of them — who think that the old reports of monsters have a ring of hard truth about them." He waved a hand. "Carry on. What happened next, according to those old stories?"

"The miners died," said Molly. "But they came out of their graves as vampires and zombies. Townsfolk began turning into werewolves. Ghouls started appearing. Evil spirits filled the town."

"And how, according to the old legends, did the people of Howlfair fight back?"

"They started forming groups," said Molly. "They called them Guilds and Orders. Each Guild or Order had a special talent. Some were experts in fighting specific monsters. Some protected certain buildings."

Mr Wetherill located a large tome, blew the dust off, sneezed, and brought it to Molly. It listed all of the Guilds and Orders that had been created to fight the evil creatures who'd supposedly plagued the town. It showed their insignias or coats of arms, and listed their founding members and their most famous exploits.

"Here we have the Order of the Silver Bullet, to whom my ancestors supposedly belonged," Wetherill intoned with pride. "See — there's the Wetherill name on the list! And here's the Order of Knights Astronomical, which guarded the Astronomy

Tower — the old Mayor of Howlfair himself was its patron. There's the Guild of Soothsayers. The Order of Tehuti — those folks guarded the library. The Order of Noble Vampire Hunters, founded by the Chillings family. The Guild of Asphodel, which nobody liked very much…"

"Really?" said Molly. "Why not?"

"They were miners — and folks agreed that miners were the ones to blame for the whole mess. Finally some brave members of the Guild of Asphodel managed to go down into the poisoned mine and shut Hell's gate so that no more mist would come out. They put a special lock on the gate and wouldn't tell anyone else the secret way to open it — and that *really* got the townsfolk mad. Everyone thought the Asphodels were acting like the portal to Hades was their personal property. Then there was the Guild of Gravediggers, which was hated even worse than the Asphodels."

"Gravediggers? They're the ones who fought ghouls, aren't they?"

"Yes — but they were corrupt. The townsfolk killed them."

"Oh yeah."

"But listen — if it turned out that the old legends about monsters were true, and the monsters ever came back …"

148

"Or if someone deliberately set them free!" Molly cut in, with venom.

"… then it would probably be a good idea for the folks of Howlfair to start forming Guilds and Orders again, to drive the monsters away. Don't you think?"

Molly stood up. " 'Course! We should do it right now!"

Mr Wetherill bit off some more peppermint fudge. "It's already been done."

Molly sat down. "Huh?"

"Not too long ago, some folks tried to re-establish one of the old groups."

"Who?"

"I won't name names. It was a small bunch of people who suspected that the legends might be true, and who wondered if maybe the monsters of Howlfair hadn't gone for good, just gone into hiding."

"Really?" gasped Molly.

Wetherill nodded. "The group conducted an investigation of the whole valley. And do you know what they found?"

Molly shook her head excitedly. "What did they find?"

Swallowing his fudge, Mr Wetherill sniffed and said, "Nothing."

"What?"

"Nothing! They found *zip*. No monsters. No danger. Eventually the group lost members to old age and boredom and infirmity and illness. They disbanded."

Molly frowned. "Mr Wetherill, were *you* a part of this group?"

He turned away, replaced the dusty volume about the Orders and Guilds, and ran his finger along the spines of the books on a lower shelf.

"No comment," he said. He withdrew another book. "But you can trust me when I say that there are no monsters in this valley any more — if there ever were."

He turned and handed Molly the book.

"What's this?"

"Copy of an almanac of alleged ghoul sightings in Howlfair. Keep it. If you ever come across a ghoul in real life, not just in a dream, you can update it yourself."

Molly took the book and stood up. "I know what I saw, Mr Wetherill," she said firmly. "And listen — I was lying awake last night giving it lots of thought, and I think Benton Furlock took over Loonchance Manor because he knew that the secret to raising ghouls was somewhere in there. I think he found the missing page from Daphne Loonchance's diary, and he's summoned ghouls to help him terrify people, sometimes scaring them to death." She felt herself blushing. "I admit I don't know what he's doing it for, but I'm going to get to the bottom of it."

The huge man sighed and headed to the study door. "Molly, I'll tell you this before we say our goodbyes. Benton Furlock may be a curious and somewhat spooky individual …"

"No kidding!"

"… but it's just an act. He wants to promote Howlfair as England's scariest town, and a scary town needs a scary mayor. But listen to me well. If *real* ghouls ever showed up in Howlfair, I can't think of anyone who'd defend this town with more commitment than Benton Furlock."

"You're joking! He's so obviously dodgy! He —"

Wetherill held up a vast hand, the fingers iced with peppermint cream fudge. "Enough, Molly. Last time Benton Furlock ran for mayor, the reason he lost is that —"

"The Workers' Union voted against him," Molly butted in.

"You've done your homework, I see. So you're probably aware that since last year *I've* been on the board of the Howlfair Workers' Union."

"You have?" blustered Molly. "I didn't know that."

"Well, now you do. And listen: *this* time I've

151

convinced our people to vote *for* Benton Furlock. He could help turn around the fortunes of this town, bring in the tourism we desperately need."

Molly stretched herself to full height, which admittedly was not high. "Mr Wetherill, if I could get you proof that there are ghouls in Howlfair and that Furlock has something to do with it, would you help me to stop him?"

"Help you how, exactly?"

"Set up a new group. An Order, a Guild, whatever — a ghoul-killing squadron."

Wetherill rubbed his face and sighed. "Molly, if anybody ever proved to me beyond any doubt that real ghouls had invaded my town, I'd make those ghouls wish they'd never been spawned."

Molly leapt with excitement. "I knew you would! Thanks, Mr Wetherill — I'll get you the evidence, I promise, and—"

"I haven't finished!" Wetherill growled. "Listen to me, Molly. I'm sure you'll do whatever your overactive brain tells you to do, but I warn you: if you cause any of your usual mischief investigating Benton Furlock, I'll go straight to your mother and tell her what you're up to."

"I hear you loud and clear, Mr Wetherill. I'll be as stealthy as a panther."

"Well, you haven't got long to make your case, Molly. The elections are five days away — and unless you can convince me not to, I plan to help make Benton Furlock our mayor."

The Great, All-Knowing Molly Thompson

AFTER SPENDING AN HOUR THAT AFTERNOON looking for her Doris de Ville's Street Cleaning Crew tee-shirt, Molly remembered that she'd left it at Lowry's and headed to Little Valley Drive, where she found Frances's birthday garden party in progress. Lowry was in the kitchen wearing a party hat, drinking lemonade through a straw shaped like a treble clef and looking bored.

"If you've come for some of the cake I made, I'd strongly advise you not to bother," she told Molly. "It's literally worse than death."

"Actually, I left my Doris de Ville tee-shirt in your room."

Lowry's dad tramped into the kitchen. "Hi, Molly. Cripes, you look like one of the undead. Do you want a job with the tourist board?"

"Dad!" Lowry scowled. "Instead of coming in here

and insulting my friend, you should be in the garden, eating the hideous cake that Mum and I made with our own hands."

"That's why I came in here — to get away from the cake," said Mr Evans, removing a chocolate éclair from the fridge and walking to the hallway with it. "None of the guests wants to eat the icing picture of Frances's face. It just sits there staring at everyone with its big googly eyes."

"Rather like Frances herself," Lowry reflected. "You do look a bit peaky actually, Molly. What was going on last night? I rang you, and Mr Banderfrith told me that you didn't want to speak to me."

"That fibbing fiend! I asked him to tell you that I was ill! Except I wasn't ill, I was…"

"Molly, you're quivering. Has something happened?"

Molly put her shaky hands over her face. "You could say that."

"Let's go to my office," said Lowry. "You need to tell me everything."

Lying on Lowry's bed like a patient on a therapist's couch, wearing Mrs de Ville's tee-shirt and clutching Wetherill's almanac while her friend listened from her gingham armchair, Molly told the whole story of Furlock's threat, the ghoul attack, and her visit to

Mr Wetherill's. When she'd finished, Lowry sighed and shook her head.

"Tangletree spores, eh? I never knew they could make a person go loopy."

Molly sat up. "Loopy?"

"You know, imagining ghouls and stuff."

"I didn't imagine the ghoul, Lowry! It really happened! A ghoul probably scared Mrs Fullsway to death, and one nearly scared me to death. For all I know, ghouls scared my dad to death too."

Lowry looked confused.

"But you told me that Mr Wetherill said —"

"I didn't say I thought he was right! Don't you see, we've got four days to convince him to stop people from voting for Furlock and to create a special ghoul-slaying team. Otherwise, Furlock's going to take control of our town. He's got something horrible planned for us! He said that the moment he becomes mayor, everything's going to change!"

"But, Molly, Mr Wetherill *could* be right about the tangletree spores, couldn't he?" Lowry ventured. "I mean, what's more likely — that corpse-eating decorators were summoned to attack you in the night or that you had a funny turn after falling through a tree?"

"Lowry, it's *always* made sense to me that there

might be something dodgy going on in this town," said Molly. "And I've always believed that my dad didn't just die of some random illness."

"I know." Lowry chewed her lip. "And *I've* always wondered if you're just torturing yourself for no reason."

An uneasy silence stretched.

"Torturing myself?" Molly said at last.

"Yeah, torturing yourself trying to see plots and conspiracies everywhere."

"Are you kidding me?"

Lowry tutted and crossed her arms. "Hey, stop getting so uppity," she said. "How come you're allowed to never take me seriously when I ask you to investigate my family's connection with the Kroglin Werewolf, but I'm not allowed to have even the slightest doubt about whether *you're* right?"

"Because I know about werewolves, Lowry, and I know you're not even the least bit wolfish. You don't even have a temper! You're the most laid-back person I know."

"Yeah, and why do you think I'm laid-back? Huh? Why don't I get annoyed when you fill up my room with your rubbish or when you say you'll read my research and then break your promises again and again? I'll tell you why. It's because every time I start to get angry, I feel something *nasty* and *wolf-like* rising up in me — so I force myself to calm down and smile and act like everything's hunky-dory. You never take me seriously, Molly, but you expect me to agree with everything you say."

"Wait, is that what this is about? Are you getting your own back on me for not believing you?"

Lowry was red with annoyance by now. "Yeah, Molly, that's it exactly," she said. "If I ever dare question the wisdom of the great, all-knowing Molly Thompson, it must be because I'm *spiteful*. *Obviously*. Because it's impossible that sometimes you might just be plain wrong."

Molly looked at her watch. "Well, thanks for clearing that up," she grumbled. "I'd love to stay, but on second thoughts I'd rather go and pick up rubbish with Felicity Quick." She hoisted herself off the bed.

"Don't forget your book."

Molly squirmed. "Can't I leave it here?"

"Might as well," said Lowry, laughing bleakly. "Everything else of yours is here. But you can flipping well collect it afterwards — I'm not taking in any more of your stuff. This isn't your personal storage room any more."

"Fine," snapped Molly. She left the book and started to climb through the window. "I'll pick it up when I'm finished — unless I get attacked by ghouls on the way and I let them devour me, because obviously I'm too stupid to know if they're real or not."

Feeling wretched, and definitely not in any mood to deal with Felicity Quick, Molly stalked in her silly tee-shirt to the town square.

"Molly Thompson, I'm pairing you with Felicity Quick."

Molly couldn't believe her bad luck. Neither, it seemed, could Felicity. Both girls groaned.

The early sun had heated the town square, known locally as the dance square (though dances were no longer held there), and a lid of cloud had slid over the day to seal the warmth in. To one side of the square reared a giant gallows from whose beam hung a mighty bell known as Old Mercy. The pupils had been sorted into pairs and were assembled in their grey *Doris de Ville's Street Cleaning Crew* tee-shirts next to the large white bandstand in the centre of the square, on which sat a set of wooden stocks. Doris had handed out bin liners, mechanical litter-grabbers, gloves and route maps.

"Your route map will show you the roads you'll be cleaning," called Doris. "Each route ends at a drop-off point. A friend of mine from the council will be picking up your full bags in a lorry. Don't pick up anything sharp, dead or explosive. We'll meet back here at four o'clock. Now go and beautify our town!"

Felicity gave Molly a look of disgust. In pairs, the pupils sallied through the fence of tall, ancient street-lamps, which hemmed the dance square in.

With four days to stop Benton Furlock from becoming Mayor of Howlfair, Molly felt she had more important things to attend to than picking up litter. But up in the nest of streets towards the northern hills, a discovery was waiting for her.

Hesperus and Phosphorus

AFTER NEARLY AN HOUR OF TRAMPING through the old grim streets around St Fell's, during which Felicity neither spoke to Molly nor picked up a single piece of litter, Molly wanted to throw her rubbish bag in the air and scream.

Then, at last, trudging past the apothecaries on narrow, steep Hesperus Street, Molly got so tangled in dark daydreams about pushing Felicity Quick down a well that an accident became inevitable. She tripped over a cobble and sent her bin-bag flying. Litter spewed forth and tumbled down the hilly street; Molly put out her palms to stop her head from bouncing off the road, and skinned them raw. She squealed with pain and frustration. The northern hills ahead looked down on her.

Felicity merely tutted and said, "Why d'you have to be so flipping clumsy?"

Molly got up and retrieved her grabber. She stuffed a fallen sweet wrapper into her bin liner. "Why don't you help me?"

"My granddad's going to find out about his housing development next week, and I've got a feeling it's going to be bad news — so you'll have to excuse me if I don't feel like helping the brat who's ruined my family. Anyway, I'm too busy planning how I'm going to kill your cat. My dad's a locksmith, so I might just use his tools to break into your hotel at night. I know how. I've broken into places before."

"Why are you so mean?" Molly snapped, fighting the urge to cry. "Why did you turn mean?"

Felicity's face bloomed purple. She marched forwards and gave Molly a shove; it was all Molly could do not to fall over. "Me? What about you! Nasty, nosy Molly Thompson with her miserable little scowl, snooping around in everyone's business, starting rumours, not caring who gets hurt by her evil investigations! My granddad's almost mad with fear, you horrible toad! He thinks he's going to lose everything, and —"

"Hey! Felicity!"

Molly and Felicity turned to see Belinda and another of Felicity's hound-like friends arriving with their rubbish bags from the direction of the cider orchards. "We finished quickly so we could go to the café. Are you coming? I reckon Thompson here has everything under control."

"Definitely," sniffed Felicity, slinging her empty bin bag at Molly. "In fact, I think she could probably handle a bit more rubbish."

Belinda took the hint. Grinning, she opened one of her bin-bags and dumped the rubbish over the cobbles. Gleefully Felicity's other follower followed suit, emptying her bags along the street. Then, tittering like imps, they tore away, leaving Molly standing on Hesperus Street, stunned.

Nasty, nosy little Molly Thompson.

Snooping around, starting rumours, not caring who she hurts.

Was that how people saw her?

She remembered Furlock's words: *I can see why the people of this town despise you.*

Suddenly somebody behind her spoke.

"At least they left the bin-bags."

Molly jumped, dropped her bag, whirled around and found herself nose-to-nose with a boy in a parka jacket. He was standing lopsided on account of the heavy, moth-munched cloth satchel hanging from one shoulder. The fur-lined hood of the coat was up, the drawstring pulled so tight that his facial features were squashed together. He picked up the fallen bag and handed it to her.

"Carl! What are you doing sneaking up?"

"I need to talk to you," said Carl, loosening the drawstring so that his face expanded. He rubbed his bright, hopeless eyes and nodded towards the top of the road, in the direction of Sibyl Hill. "I was just coming down Phosphorus Street and I saw you."

Molly picked up a fallen bin bag and began clearing up rubbish. "It's Hesperus Street," she said. "Not Phosphorus Street."

Carl adjusted his satchel, grabbed a couple of the discarded bin-bags and joined Molly in her efforts. He picked up a torn chunk of bicycle tyre. "Haven't you ever read the sign at the top? The road has a different name depending which way you go."

Molly said, "I've never been that way."

"You've never been to the end of this road?"

"No, Carl! Why is that such a shock? It's a big town, you know."

Carl shrugged and bagged a well-wrung toothpaste tube. "I thought you'd been everywhere and knew everything."

"Well, I haven't, and I don't," Molly said, reaching for a crisp packet with her grabber. A breeze puffed it away and she gave a grunt of annoyance.

Carl followed Molly as she tracked the fleeing crisp bag.

"Your dad's up there, isn't he? In Howlfair Old Cemetery?"

Molly tripped. The crisp packet escaped. "Yeah," she said.

"My folks are up there too." He looked to the hills. "I like it up there. It's nice."

"I've never been," muttered Molly, stabbing ineffectually at some rubbish with the grabber.

"What, you've never —"

"I don't see the point in visiting ugly bits of stone with writing on them," she snapped — and then she flushed with sudden shame. "But I'm, um, sorry to hear about your parents..."

"It's OK. I understand. About not wanting to visit the grave."

Now Molly felt wretched again. She struggled to soften her face. "How long have you, um, been without them? Your parents?"

"They died in an accident when I was three," Carl said, shrugging. "I've always had these amazingly clear memories of them, though. Really nice memories."

"That's good."

"But one day at school I was telling a friend about my parents, and she started laughing and said that

I was describing some parents from an old children's television programme. And she was right. Somehow I'd taken some grown-ups off the telly and put them in my memories. I realized that I don't remember my real parents at all. My friend thought it was hilarious." Carl looked utterly bleak. "I suppose it is."

"No, it's not," said Molly, angry. "And even if it was, your so-called friend didn't have to laugh."

Carl shuffled and shrugged again. "I gave up on having friends that day. I decided to stick to drawing comics. People can seem nice, but they're usually nasty." He stared at his shoes. "Then sometimes a person who *seems* nasty turns out to be the only person who gives a damn about you."

Molly took a breath. "You mean Benton Furlock?"

Carl stamped on a drinks carton and put it in the bag. "He was at yours, wasn't he, when you came to Mr Wetherill's shop? He was at your guesthouse."

"Yeah," frowned Molly. "How do you know?"

"We all heard the commotion that night — the dog barking and running off with its chain, and Mr Furlock legging it off into the town. He came back afterwards and told us not to worry. He said that he'd chased off an intruder and that he was going to visit the young scallywag's mother in the morning."

"He actually said scallywag?"

166

Carl nodded. "He may also have called you a scapegrace."

"A scapegrace? Woah."

"And a rapscallion. Anyway, that's why I told you to go home."

"But why would you want to warn me?"

"Dunno," shrugged Carl, stooping to arrest the fugitive crisp packet. "I felt like I should." He drew something invisible on the road with his foot. "And I just want it to end. I don't want to help Mr Furlock anymore."

"Want what to end? How are you helping him?"

"I used to think he wasn't doing anything wrong. Now I'm not sure. But I can't escape. I owe him a lot, but I'm also scared of him." He looked up. "I'm even more scared of him than I am of you."

"I don't want you to be scared of me!"

Carl snorted. "'Maybe you and Mr Furlock can share a cell in prison'," he quoted, affecting Molly's tone. "'You'll wish you'd helped me instead of covering up for your precious Mr Furlock...'"

Molly picked up a milk carton and bagged it.

She thought: *Nasty, nosy little Molly Thompson, not caring who gets hurt...*

"I shouldn't have tried to scare you," she said at last. "I'm sorry."

Carl seemed surprised by her apology. "Well ... OK," he frowned. "But listen, whatever it is that you know about him—"

"I don't know anything."

"What do you mean?"

"I was bluffing," Molly confessed. "I accidentally found a letter from Mrs Quincy to Mrs Fullsway and it mentioned you and it mentioned ghouls and it mentioned something bad that's going to happen, but I don't know how the pieces fit together." She picked up a crushed can. "I will find out, though, eventually. I don't give up. If you let bad things hide in the dark, they grow stronger and stronger. I learned that from horror novels."

Carl nodded almost imperceptibly and chewed his lip. "I never thought of it like that," he said. "Listen, Molly, something awful's happened."

"Hey, hey!" came a shout. Carl jumped and grabbed Molly, then released her, embarrassed. They both turned to see Lowry climbing the steep street, holding a carrier bag that Molly could see contained books. "I thought I'd come and help you," Lowry called. She drew near, looking miffed. "Turns out you're here canoodling with the enemy."

"We were just talking," said Molly. "And he's not the enemy."

"If you say so," said Lowry coldly. "Either way, it looks like I'm not needed after all."

"Lowry, don't be silly."

"No, no, it's fine, I understand. I'll be off. You've got Carl to talk to, and Mr Wetherill, and then there's your *real* best friend, Gabriel the wonder-cat."

"At least Gabriel believes me about the ghouls!"

"Gabriel's a cat, Molly. He doesn't believe anything. That's like me saying that at least Sheila the bull terrier believes me about the Kroglin Werewolf. Which she *does*, by the way."

"Hey, maybe Sheila's the Kroglin Werewolf!" Molly cried. "Makes as much sense."

Carl cleared his throat loudly. "Excuse me, but could you two stop bickering for five minutes?"

Lowry turned to Carl. "Grobman, what are you doing?"

Molly looked. Silent, grim-faced, Carl was pushing up the sleeve of his jacket.

Then he peeled off the grubby bandage that Molly and Lowry had spied in Mr Wetherill's Weaponry Store.

"Satan's socks!" Lowry cried. "What's that?"

Carl's flesh bore a curious black pattern.

"Carl, did Benton Furlock do this?" Molly said.

Miserably, shamefully, Carl nodded. Something

169

like sickness rose up in Molly. "Have you told anyone about this? Mr Wetherill? Or Mrs de Ville?"

"No."

"What about your friends?"

"I don't have any," shrugged Carl.

"We're your friends now," Molly said. "And you have to tell us everything. I promise that—"

"I found out today about Mr Cromble," Carl blurted.

"Stan?" said Molly, her innards suddenly roiling with dread. "I saw him yesterday. Carl, what's happened to Stan Cromble?"

Carl looked like he was going to cry. "He's in hospital. They're not sure if he's going to make it. He burnt himself. It was an accident with a deep-fat fryer."

"Oh no!" cried Molly. "Poor Stan!"

"The thing is, it was all my fault," sniffed Carl.

"How could it be your fault?" Lowry asked.

Carl just stared and shook his head. He couldn't bring himself to speak.

"Let's drop off these bags and head to the Circuit," said Molly. "I know the perfect place to share secrets."

The Timbrel Tearooms

THE TIMBREL TEAROOMS, FAMILY-RUN SINCE 1788, were famed not so much for their tea as for their tea leaves, which were excellent for fortune-telling. Colourful Victorian adverts hung framed on the walls:

TIMBREL TEAS:
The Fortune-Teller's Choice

RUBY TIMBREL'S
FULL MOON BLEND
A tea with lunar powers

MRS TIMBREL'S
STORMCLOUD BREW
A strong oracular cuppa for
seekers of dark truths

Generations of soothsayers had met with clients in the little lamp-lit booths that filled the five floors, to share a pot of Timbrel Tea and then read the leaves at the bottom of the cup. Some teas were good for predicting romance or happy turns of fortune; some could help foresee trouble. Others — stronger teas for stronger stomachs — opened the gateways to darker knowledge. The place was no longer licensed for fortune-telling, though Molly had heard rumours that after midnight, the current owners (spectrally pale siblings with a habit of suddenly appearing at your table) would secretly admit local seers and their customers. Molly had not managed to verify or disprove these rumours.

It was in a booth on the otherwise empty top floor that Molly, Lowry and Carl sat this afternoon as the sun struggled to filter through the ghostly window drapes.

Carl unfastened his satchel and withdrew his tatty sketchpad. He opened it. It was full of doodles — comic-book art and different styles of handwriting, including what looked like forged signatures. He found a particular page and pushed the book towards Molly and Lowry.

"I'll start at the beginning," he said. "Our dorm prefect at the orphanage caught me drawing demons one night after lights out. I can draw in the dark — it's one of my skills. Anyway, my book got confiscated and I was sent to Mr Furlock. I was petrified. But he didn't shout at me. He didn't even seem angry. He returned my book and told me that I had to work for him."

The present Mr Timbrel appeared suddenly at the table with cakes, scones and tea. The children jumped. Mr Timbrel gave Molly an odd look (he and his sister *always* gave Molly odd looks), set the tray down and migrated away.

Lowry snatched the biggest scone.

"What did he want you to do?" Molly asked.

"He didn't say. But he said he'd pay me. So when he told me to meet him at Loonchance Manor at midnight, I said OK."

"Are you deranged?" said Lowry through a mouthful of scone. "You went to Loonchance Manor to meet a man who looks like he ties damsels to railway lines?"

Molly had taken out her own notepad and pen. "What's Loonchance Manor like inside?"

"It's really creepy at night," said Carl. "We got in through a secret back door behind a black rosebush. I got tangled on the thorns. Then we went down this spiral staircase to the crypts underneath the house."

Lowry sprayed scone crumbs. "You went with him into the crypts? Carl, you are an absolute..."

"Lowry, shush," said Molly. "Carl, what happened next?"

Carl slurped his tea shakily. Although he should have been hotter than a baked potato in his parka, he was turning paler and paler as he recalled that night. "We went through the crypts. I don't think they were the same crypts that the Ghoul Tour visits. There weren't any signs or displays or waxwork figures. But I could hear sounds."

"What like?"

"Cogs moving. Liquid bubbling. I got the sense that Mr Furlock was running some kind of secret operation down there. He was dragging me by the arm and we went down some dark corridors. Then he opened a door and there was a round room with a fire in it — but the fire's flames were blue, and the room was cold... And there was a picture on the wall of a weird, horrible woman. Horrible but kind of beautiful. And ... and..."

Carl scrunched his eyes shut and rubbed his forehead, as though the memory was giving him a migraine.

"What happened, Carl?" Molly whispered, her pen poised.

Carl put a hand to his arm. "Suddenly Mr Furlock dragged me to the fireplace and took something from the freezing cold fire. It looked like one of those old-fashioned pens — the ones made of feathers."

"A quill?" Molly looked up from her notepad.

"Yeah, one of those. A *quill*. But it was made of metal, and really long, and the pointy end was glowing blue. He held it near my arm and it was icy cold but it burnt through my jumper. Then he sort of drew a picture in the air with it, and I felt this crazy coldness go right under my skin."

"Couldn't you run away?" asked Lowry.

"He was holding me by the other arm."

"What next?" asked Molly, doodling a picture of Furlock clutching Carl and brandishing the frozen quill.

"Then he dragged me back up the stairs. I was screaming all the way. But by the time we got back to the lobby, my arm was OK."

Molly stopped doodling. "What do you mean, OK?"

"Obviously my jumper was ruined, but there was no mark on my arm. No pain, no coldness. Nothing. Then Mr Furlock told me that I was one of his workers now, and that it was a great honour and I should be proud of myself. He said that I should report to him by the tree behind Loonchance Manor whenever he summoned me. I asked him how he'd summon me, but he just told me to leave. Then, a couple of days later, the mark appeared again. Next my arm started to go icy cold and I realized: the symbol on my skin is how Mr Furlock summons me. I went to Loonchance Manor and Mr Furlock was there, by the tree near the rosebush, and he gave me a job to do. I've been working for him ever since. I get the feeling that my arm's going to start going cold again soon…"

"What kind of jobs does he make you do?" Molly asked.

"Always the same thing. I deliver letters."

"To who?"

Carl looked distressed. "That's the thing. I delivered three letters to a man named Gerald Keepmoat. Then he fell off a ladder and now he's in a coma. I delivered about ten letters to Mrs Fullsway — and she died. I delivered five letters to Stan Cromble —"

"And he had a deep-fat fryer accident," said Lowry. "Coincidence?"

"Doubt it," said Molly. "Flipping Nora, Carl — you never delivered letters to my dad, did you? David Thompson?"

"No!"

"Has Furlock ever mentioned him?"

"Never."

"And have you ever opened one of the letters?"

"I can't," said Carl. "They've got those old-fashioned wax seals on the back."

"And you say Furlock has others working for him? Other kids from the orphanage?"

"He said I was *one* of his workers, but I don't know if the others deliver letters."

"But there could be more people getting these letters? More people in danger?"

"Maybe! I don't know! I've told you everything I know now." He ran his hands through his oily mop. "I swear, Molly, you're like a bloodhound."

Molly glared thoughtfully at the ceiling and tapped her teeth with her pen. "We're going to have to find a way into the crypts underneath Loonchance Manor. We'll take pictures of whatever it is that Furlock's doing down there — get some hard evidence that Furlock's up to something evil. Carl, d'you think we could sneak onto the Ghoul Tour and then slink off and find Furlock's secret crypts?"

"Too risky. The tour guides would catch us." He rubbed his eyes and checked his watch. "I need to go now. What are you doing on Tuesday?"

On the back of Mrs de Ville's street map was a list of other tasks planned for the summer. Molly checked it. "At midday until four I'm helping to clean Howlfair Museum with Doris de Ville's crew."

"I'll meet you afterwards. I'll try to think of the best way into Loonchance Manor. But don't breathe a word of any of this to anyone until I see you. Promise?"

Molly promised.

As the children left the tearooms, Lowry leading the way, Carl slipped Molly a crumpled note. Molly opened her mouth to say something, but Carl silenced her with a glare. The note was for her alone. He pulled up his fur-lined hood and headed back to the orphanage.

"I'm not sure I trust him," said Lowry when Molly caught up with her, having pocketed the note. "There's something dodgy about his story."

"Dodgy?"

"I can't put my finger on it. Let's just … be careful. That's all I'm saying." She stopped and checked her watch and then handed her carrier bag to Molly. "I've got to go. But listen, I wanted to make you a deal."

"Oh yeah?"

"I promise I'll be more open-minded about your ghoul visit if you'll just look at my research into the Kroglin–Evans werewolf connection. I've been thinking that maybe my gran is a *new* kind of werewolf, one that hasn't been studied yet."

Molly looked into the bag. It contained Mr Wetherill's almanac and one of Lowry's scrapbooks full of pictures and notes. She was tempted to roll her eyes, but she thought about how Felicity Quick had called her *nasty*, and she stopped herself. "Deal," she said, and held out her hand.

Lowry shook it, then tightened her grip. "Promise you'll read it? Before the blue moon? Just in case there's a chance that the blue moon will make me change into a slavering hairy beast of doom?"

Molly thought that she had more important things to attend to before the blue moon, such as saving Howlfair from a man who could summon ghouls. But her friend looked so hopeful that she felt compelled to agree. Also, she was afraid that Lowry would crush her fingers if she said no.

"Promise," Molly said.

On the way home, she stopped in the doorway of Ablemarch's Department Store for Children and unfolded Carl's note. Here's what he'd written:

If you need to talk about anything in secret, come on your own to the lamppost outside the orphanage any time after nine o'clock and make an

owl noise. I will come down, even
if it's late.

Molly frowned. Why would she need to go to the orphanage alone? Without, say, Lowry?

Maybe Carl didn't trust Lowry any more than Lowry trusted Carl.

She stuffed the note back into her pocket and headed to Howlfair Infirmary to visit Gran. She had an important question about cats to ask her.

All the Secrets

GRAN WAS NOT IN GOOD SPIRITS. SHE HADN'T slept in twenty-four hours, and Molly arrived just as she was finally dropping off.

"Gran, why haven't you been sleeping?"

"I've been worrying about Stan Cromble," Gran grumbled. "Have you heard? He's in intensive care in Charnton Hospital with burns all over him."

"Yes, I heard. Poor Stan."

Gran began to nod her head thoughtfully, then snored suddenly.

"Gran!"

"What? Who? Huh?" She rubbed her eyes. "Ah, Molly, it's you. I'm so cream-crackered I keep bobbing unconscious. What was it you were saying?"

Molly decided to get to the point. "I was wondering about something you mentioned yesterday."

Gran yawned again. "Uh-huh?"

"You said you once had a cat who saved Mrs Fullsway's life. Flea, or something."

"Fleance? The Excelsior cat."

Molly stared blankly.

"You *do* know that special cats come to live at the Excelsior, don't you?" Gran asked.

"First I've heard of it."

Gran shrugged. "They just turn up. They protect whoever takes them in."

"Really?"

"Yeah, really. Take that one you've got now. That scrawny creature."

"Gabriel."

"Protects you, does he?"

"Sometimes," said Molly.

"They're very brave, Excelsior cats. And they have this knack of getting into locked rooms – don't ask me how."

"Gabriel does that!"

"They follow you around everywhere, unless you command them not to. And they seem to enjoy danger. I got the feeling that Fleance was only happy when he was putting himself in peril to protect me. You can't let yourself get too fond of Excelsior cats – they don't last very long."

Molly shuddered. "So what happened to Fleance?"

"Fleance got through his nine lives pretty quickly," Gran sighed. "Odd place, the Excelsior. As soon as I get out of here, we need to have a serious talk about that guesthouse. Hectoria said I won't be in this hospital much longer." She yawned hugely.

"Wait, Gran — is there something I should know about the guesthouse? Can't you tell me now?"

But Gran's eyes were closing. "Need some kip, Molly. Been awake for ever..."

"But—"

It was no use. Gran had nodded off, leaving Molly with that peculiar sense of frustration that comes when you try to investigate something and end up with more questions than you started with.

Molly and her mum usually ate meals in the kitchen, after the guests had had theirs. Sometimes they sat in a draughty corner at the small square table next to the freezers, or on the wooden crates near the boiler. Sometimes they leaned against the long kitchen surface over to the left, eating leftovers. Mealtimes, since Dad passed away, were never leisurely. Today Molly sat eating at the table while Mum, over by the oven range, gobbled the remainder of the day's pasta and sauce from the big pan with a wooden spoon.

"How did street cleaning go?" Mum asked. "Was

Mrs de Ville pleased with you?"

Molly frowned. "With just me or with all of us?"

"I mean you. Was she happy with you?"

Molly spotted Gabriel on the thin windowsill, trying to keep his balance. "Well, I cleaned up more litter than anyone else."

"That's good. How many bags?"

Molly had just inserted a mouthful of pasta. She held up five fingers.

"What happened to your palms?" asked Mum, noticing the rawness.

"Nothing," Molly mumbled through her food. "I fell over."

Mum sighed. "Can't you do anything without some sort of calamity or injury?"

Molly chewed glumly.

"Are you ignoring me?" Mum asked.

Molly swallowed. "I'm just concentrating on eating my dinner without causing any calamities or injuries."

"That's not funny, Molly," said Mum. "I just want to be able to go through a day without worrying about you."

Molly wolfed down the rest of her pasta, feeling a stirring of spitefulness (or indigestion) in her stomach. Her skinned palms throbbed.

"I went to see Gran today," she said casually. "She

says there are special cats that guard the Excelsior."

Mum gagged. She looked up with a livid expression, made more livid by the ring of tomato sauce around her mouth, which gave her the look of an evil clown. "She what? When?"

"I visited her today and she was half asleep, and she started telling me things," said Molly slyly.

"What kinds of things?" Mum blurted.

"Oh, nothing," said Molly, trying not to look alarmed at the vehemence of Mum's outburst. She got up to put her plate in the sink. "I'll do the washing-up in a bit. I've just got to call Lowry and tell her about the magical Excelsior cats."

Still holding her wooden spoon, Mum trotted after Molly as she headed for the door.

"Molly! Molly, wait. What did your grandmother tell you?"

Molly stopped, shrugged. "Oh, just bits and pieces. About the Excelsior. About Fleance and the other cats who've lived here."

She felt an acid flush of satisfaction. After spending such a long time suspecting her mother of keeping secrets from her, it felt right that Mum should get a dose of her own medicine.

But Mum was looking awfully distressed as she detained Molly by the kitchen door. The hand that gripped Molly's arm was shaky. "Molly, you can't listen to that woman."

"*That woman?* Why not?"

"She's ill. She'll be blurting out all kinds of —"

"What — secrets?" said Molly, feeling miserable for enjoying herself so much. "Like you've always said, the Excelsior doesn't have any secrets."

"Don't get funny with me, Molly Thompson," said Mum, brandishing the spoon. "The only secrets I keep are the ones that every good parent keeps."

"Why should parents keep secrets at all?"

"Oh, I suppose you'd want me to tell my twelve-year-old daughter everything about everything, would you?"

"You don't tell me anything about anything!"

"Because you're twelve!"

"Mum, I can handle secrets. Haven't I proved that by now? I've handled every secret in town!"

"Molly, you investigate other people's lives because you don't want to think about your own."

"What!"

"You don't want to think about how unfair it is that Dad isn't here and you're stuck with a boring mother, in a house where nothing interesting has happened since Mr Quinby tried to do the splits at Mrs Marrable's birthday party."

"How do you know what I don't want to think about?"

"I know it because you can't even bring yourself to come to the cemetery with me."

Molly rocked, shaken. "Well, what about you? You threw all of his things away! You don't want to think about Dad either!"

"I threw them away because I needed to start to accept that he's gone. You need to start to accept it too. You don't have to *like* it. You don't need to *understand* it. Just start to *accept* it. You'll never be able to move on with your life until you stop acting like every story in Howlfair is true except your own."

Molly stood glaring. The silence in the kitchen stood glaring. Eventually Molly narrowed her eyes and spoke. "Gran says she's going to tell me all about the Excelsior, and about all of the things you're keeping from me. Everything. When she gets out of hospital."

Mum sighed. She'd run out of energy. "Molly, I'll tell you everything myself — when you're ready to hear it." She made her way back to the sink. "Till then, don't believe everything your grandmother tells you," she added without turning, waggling the spoon. "She's a stirrer."

Don't Mess With a Girl Who Knows Flags

MOLLY DIDN'T LIKE STORMING OFF. IT WAS such a *teenage* thing to do, flouncing off to your bedroom, slamming doors along the way. Especially when nosy Mr Banderfrith was lurking in the lounge, and flouncing would give him something to gossip about to the other residents.

But she couldn't seem to slow her stride or strike the indignation from her face. She stamped up to her room and flopped onto her bed with her notepad, Lowry's book and Mr Wetherill's almanac. On the desk, Gabriel emerged from behind her curtains as though he was hosting an evening of light entertainment.

"No, Gabriel, I don't want to talk about my annoying mother. I'm going to distract myself by reading Lowry's stupid research."

Gingerly, the cat joined her on the bed.

Molly opened the book and squinted at the photographs, urgent notes and newspaper cuttings. "To be honest, though, I don't know why I'm even humouring her."

Gabriel looked at the photographs without interest. Molly flapped impatiently through the pages of the scrapbook.

"There are seven signs that a person might be a werewolf, and Lowry's gran doesn't display any of them," she told the cat. "But now Lowry's saying that her gran is a *new* kind of werewolf." She scanned the notes. "Lowry thinks the curse of the Kroglin family is somehow going to pass to her. But that's just not how werewolfism works. It's not a magic curse; it's more like a virus. But I don't know how to convince Lowry that she's wrong."

Gabriel stretched and settled and watched her.

"I'm going to have to pretend to take her seriously, aren't I? Maybe I can find a harmless werewolf remedy in one of the old botanical books and tell her to take it before the blue moon. What do you think?"

Gabriel stared blankly. Molly watched him until at last he blinked.

"Good — that's settled, then."

Molly shut Lowry's book and frowned. She took

up her notepad and stared at her crude sketch of the already crude mark on Carl's arm:

She showed Gabriel the sketch. "This symbol could tell us what Furlock's up to. It could help me to figure out his secret. Any ideas what it might mean?"

Gabriel looked.

"It looks like some sort of wonky … crucifix? Or maybe a phantom with big sleeves? Why do phantoms always have big sleeves? It's not like they need to keep tissues handy." She frowned. *"Or do they?"*

Gabriel had no opinion.

"Oh, I don't know where to start!" She glared at the wall. "The maddening thing is, I feel like I've seen this shape before."

She doodled. She tried to turn the shape into phantoms, crosses, trees, seesaws. She pondered the angle of the cross-beam. She wondered why the outstretched arms had horizontal flat bits. She paced the room. She read Wetherill's almanac. Eventually she gave up, sat at her desk, opened Lowry's scrapbook to try to unblock her head by reading some more of her friend's silly research, turned a few pages, and fell asleep.

She woke hours later with her head stuck to a page; the gummy glue used to attach a newspaper clipping had oozed onto her face. She lifted her head and heard a rip as the clipping tore away from the scrapbook. In the window she saw her reflection. The torn scrap of newspaper on her cheek featured a photograph of Lowry's grandmother in a parade, holding a flag.

"Oh, crud!" she said to Gabriel, who was reclining on the bed looking entertained. "Now I've got to explain to Lowry why I've spoiled her scrapbook. And to top it all, I've got a picture of Lowry's gran on my head." Gabriel looked at Molly's reflection in the window and cocked his head.

Molly peeled off the paper and banged the table with her fist. "I've wasted the whole night!"

Then she looked closely at the picture.

"Some sort of parade," she said.

Gabriel purred.

"She's holding a flag…"

Purrrr.

191

"A flag…"

Gabriel yawned.

"A *flag*. *The* flag. The Howlfair — oh, flipping Nora, I've been studying it for the past three months! The Howlfair flag! That's where I've seen it!"

Breathlessly she wrenched open her desk drawer.

Withdrew a vellum scroll.

Unfurled it and laid it flat on the desk.

The Howlfair flag was divided into quarters. In one quarter were three ravens carrying, between them, a banner containing the town motto in arcane script. One quarter was almost completely black, with mysterious grey vertical streaks; it was like a picture of night-time rain. In the third quarter was a picture of a hand holding a gem. But the bottom-right quadrant was a crowded mess of tiny signs and pictures, and nestling among them Molly found the following symbol, surrounded by a blue circle:

"Gabriel, it's here! It's right here on our flag!"

The cat hopped onto the desk. Molly pulled her magnifying glass from the drawer and put her face to the vellum.

"These squiggles dotted around the main shape — they can only be one thing," she said. "They're *sigils* — magical symbols or words turned into pictures to hide their meanings. In old magic books you always find that demons have their own sigils. They're kind of like signatures."

She pulled back from the page.

"Gabriel, this whole thing is a sigil! And I'd bet any money that it belongs to a demon — see the spikes that look like curling devil tails? I don't know *which* demon, but trust me, I know *exactly* where to look to find out."

Gabriel appeared impressed.

Molly set down the magnifying glass and narrowed her eyes. "Gabriel, we've had a breakthrough," she announced. "Benton Furlock should've known better than to mess with a girl who knows about flags."

With a twinge of guilt, Molly stuck the piece of ripped-off newspaper back into Lowry's scrapbook. Then she climbed into bed and sank almost immediately to the bottom of the ocean of sleep.

She slept well that night, and dreamt vividly. She dreamt that a beautiful grey-haired woman was leading her through a misty, silver-lit grove. The woman turned and smiled at her. Molly had trouble seeing the woman's face clearly, for it was partially obscured by what looked like butterflies. The lady stretched out her hand and pointed to the sky, and Molly looked up to see a glorious full moon, bright as a mirror. Somehow Molly knew that this was a *special* full moon, the second one in a month — that is, a blue moon. It turned dazzling cyan as Molly watched.

Suddenly the lady was beside her. A strong hand grabbed her shoulder. Butterflies orbited Molly. The moon blazed.

Then, just before Molly was woken by a *real* hand shaking her shoulder, the mysterious lady spoke some words to her in a kind but authoritative voice.

"Friendship, Molly," she said, "is a sacred thing."

Knitting for Pooches

"**M**OLLY, WAKE UP..."

She woke in morning brightness to find Lowry shaking her. Or was it another infernal fiend *impersonating* Lowry? Instinctively Molly cried out and thrashed upon her bed and made the sign of the cross with her index fingers.

"Begone, ghoul!"

"Very funny," said Lowry. "Here, I brought you a piece of French toast with icing sugar, but it got a bit squished in my bag. Your mum let me in. I couldn't wait any longer to hear what you think of my research."

Molly took the toast. A ghoul, she reasoned, wouldn't give her breakfast. "Sorry, I've been on edge lately."

"No problemo. So — what's the verdict? On my research?"

Molly thought guiltily about how little time she'd

spent studying Lowry's scrapbook. "Um... Well, I thought it was actually really interesting, and I think we should definitely find a way to make sure that you don't turn into a werewolf. So I've decided that today we'll go to the library and get a copy of Follington's *Botanicals* — the 1612 edition — and we're going to make you a cure."

Lowry looked as though she might faint with joy. "So you believe me at last! Oh, I'm so relieved I could swoon! Look, I'm swooning!"

She swooned.

"Get off my floor, Lowry."

"This is the traditional behaviour of werewolves when someone agrees to cure them," explained Lowry, sprawling dramatically. But then Gabriel walked over her face and she squirmed away, spitting fur.

Molly rolled her eyes. "Listen, I figured something else out last night. The mark on Carl's arm is a *demon sigil*. And you'll never guess what — it's right there on the Howlfair flag! I know exactly what book to look in to find out about it. It's a book I read a thousand times when I was deciphering the Howlfair motto: *Demonology and Heraldry in 17th-Century England*, by Hayden Drake. It probably won't tell us much — it's more about flags than demons — but I should be able to find out at least the *name* of the demon whose mark is on

Carl's arm, and when we explore the crypts underneath Loonchance Manor, we… Lowry, are you listening?"

"Sorry, I'm still busy being excited about my cure. Are you sure that it'll work on my kind of werewolf? I don't want to end up poisoned."

"All of the recipes in Follington's *Botanicals* are perfectly safe herbal remedies. No poisons involved."

"Hooray!" Lowry spat out some more cat fur. "Yuck. If this is what being a werewolf feels like, I'm glad I'm getting cured. Come on — get dressed and I'll meet you in the lobby. You can tell me about your boyfriend's demon on the way to the library."

But Molly had been barred from Howlfair Library!

Barred, that is, from everywhere but the children's section. Her mother, it turned out, had been to see the librarian, Mrs Brank, and had advised her that Molly was not to use the library for anything resembling investigative research.

It was a great blow for Molly, and not just because she was on the verge of discovering the identity of a demon linking Carl Grobman and Benton Furlock. The ancient library was her favourite place on earth.

Some people thought that Howlfair Library, built in 1537, resembled a sort of castle, or church; Molly thought it looked rather like an odd magical bird. Its plump body, made from huge stones, was solid and low with irregularly spaced feather-shaped windows that glowed orange with silence-thickened light. From one side of the body a long slender tower (or neck, if you will), added around 1710, rose way too high and terminated in an oval observatory (the bird's head). There were flags that looked like plumage. It's true that unlike most real birds, the library never flew away. But it could transport you anywhere you wanted to go if you stepped inside.

And, oh, the innards! Winding guts of corridors; arterial passageways connecting snug reading chambers, firelit, which bulged with portraits and lamps and legends and, of course, *books* — the lifeblood of the beast. Books bound in hide and double bound with dust. Books piled high, sent speeding down corridors on trolleys steered by silent staff. Many rooms contained private collections and were locked. As for the library tower — well, not many people in town were allowed in there. Some rooms in the tower, according to legend, could not even be found unless you had special maps.

Of course the place was lavishly haunted, if the old stories were to be believed.

Anyway, Molly didn't think it fair that she was not allowed to consult a couple of harmless books about heraldry and herbs. So she did what any sensible investigator would do in her shoes: she asked Lowry to sneak into the grown-up part of the library in her place (Lowry was a gifted sneaker).

Timing her entry to coincide with the arrival of a local reading group assembling to pay homage to the works of Hectoria Fullsway, Lowry Evans slipped past the librarian with ease.

Molly waited in an armchair by a cavernous, gusty fireplace, scanning a book of ghastly rhymes, creepy old dolls watching her from the shelves.

Outside, the day grew windy and the window frames rattled and thumped, and the fireplace breathed unholy groans.

"What took you so long?" Molly asked when Lowry finally reappeared.

"I found loads of books on werewolves and I wanted to bring them back with me, but Mrs Brank caught me and made me put them back because she thought I was getting them for you."

"Don't worry, Lowry, I've read them all anyway. So, what did you manage to get?"

Lowry sat down in the armchair opposite. "Mrs Brank let me keep Follington's *Botanicals* — the 1612 edition — because I said I needed it to look up herbal remedies for my sister's toe infection."

"Superb work, Agent Evans. Mrs Brank's so squeamish that she probably let you have the book just to shut you up."

"My description of Frances's toe was so vivid I almost made *myself* sick. But Mrs Brank took the book on demonology off me, I'm afraid. She only let me keep this." Lowry showed Molly a book about knitting cardigans for one's dog.

"Flipping Nora!" tutted Molly. "I really needed that other book. Most books on demonology in Howlfair were burnt in 1800 by the vicar of St Fell's, and the only books that he spared were really dry academic ones. *Demonology and Heraldry in 17th Century England* is the one book I know of that has any information about demon sigils."

"I bet he didn't burn *all* of the demon books," said Lowry. "I bet there are some locked in the library tower."

"Yeah — where only the mayor and a few other people are allowed to go." She frowned. "Hey, maybe that's why Benton Furlock wants to be mayor! To get hold of forbidden black-magic books!"

"Maybe *you* should run for mayor."

"I should. Meanwhile, I'm stuck with *Knitting for Pooches*."

"It's so cute, though!" Lowry sighed, opening the hardback. She gasped loudly. "Oh, wait — what's happened here? Someone's swapped the cover! Oh, what a catastrophe! So now poor Mrs Brank is returning *Knitting for Pooches* to the History section, and here we are with a copy of *Demonology and Heraldry in 17th Century England* by Hayden Drake."

"Lowry! You are a genius!" Molly cried, taking the book eagerly.

"A genius, and possibly a werewolf."

"Right — I'll look for that mark on Carl's arm, and you find me the chapter on lycanthropy in Follington's *Botanicals*. Then we'll compare notes."

The Mistress of Ghouls

THEY SAT AND READ. AFTER A FEW MINUTES, Lowry gave up. "Molly, I'm not sure this is even written in English."

"I'll look in a minute," said Molly, her eyes wide. "I've just found the symbol that Furlock branded onto Carl's arm."

"Ooh! Tell all."

"It's not a cross or a phantom, like I thought — it's a set of weighing scales."

"Weighing scales? Weird."

"It's the mark of a demon named Lady Orgella. Want to know her alternative title? Wait for it: *the Mistress of Ghouls*."

"Ghouls!"

"There's a whole paragraph about her!" Molly marvelled, taking out her notepad and copying information down. "She must be really flipping important."

"But why weighing scales? Is she a demon baker from Hell who's always burning cakes? Like my mum?"

"She's a lawyer in Hell, and sometimes a judge. The scales are the scales of justice."

"They have lawyers in Hell?" said Lowry. "Actually, that makes sense."

"She specializes in Ghoul Law. Remember, ghouls are demons who've been given horrid bodies and sent to earth to exist on a diet of corpses as a punishment for crimes against Hell." She read on. "Lady Orgella decides how long a demon who's found guilty must live on the earth as a ghoul before it's allowed back into the underworld."

"I like to see women in positions of power."

"She's definitely powerful. Ghouls are desperate to impress her so that she'll let them back into Hell. And get this: like ghouls, she's a desecrator — she enjoys spoiling things that people hold precious. Apparently she's also very vain — there's a quote from an old *grimoire* here, a magical book for calling up spells. It says that she 'taketh an interest in whosoever taketh an interest in her'."

"She soundeth like a proper big head."

"Her lesser-known title is the Lady of the Double Mirror, whatever that means. Various mayors of

Howlfair are rumoured to have paid occultists to summon her to give them secret knowledge. It's said that one of them agreed to put her symbol on the Howlfair flag to thank her for her services."

"Is there a picture of her?"

"No pictures. But get this – there's supposed to be a portrait of her in Howlfair Museum! It's not labelled, though. It was painted to look like a portrait of a normal aristocratic lady, but there are clues that it's actually the Mistress of Ghouls."

"What kind of clues?"

"It doesn't say."

"So how are you going to find her picture?"

"I've no idea."

"And why did Furlock brand Carl with this Lady Oregano's symbol?"

"It's Lady *Orgella* – and I haven't the foggiest. Maybe Furlock's set up some sort of secret club in honour of her, and he decided that Carl might want to join it."

"Doesn't sound like he gave Carl much of a choice. Hey, do you think Furlock is some kind of demon worshipper? Maybe Lady Orgella is the one who gives him the power to control ghouls?"

"I definitely wouldn't rule it out."

"So… Furlock worships a demon lawyer who has

something to do with ghouls, and he runs a kind of evil church underneath Loonchance Manor, and he enslaves children and brands them with the mark of Lady Orgella and he gets them to deliver letters to people, who then end up dead or in hospital." She faked a big yawn. "To be honest, Molly, I was hoping this investigation would lead somewhere more interesting. But since we've come this far, tell me: if Furlock really is a demon worshipper who controls ghouls, how are we going to defeat him?"

"Defeat him?" frowned Molly. "We're not dragon slayers, Lowry, we're investigators. We're going to get hard evidence about what he's up to, and then we're going to give it to Mr Wetherill so he can stop Furlock from becoming our mayor." Molly finished copying the notes from Hayden Drake's tome. "Now give me that copy of *Botanicals*. I'm going to find you your werewolf cure."

Lowry sat giggling into a picture book about mischievous elves while Molly scrutinized *Botanicals* and made notes on her pocket notepad. The fireplace coughed out echoes and dust. Window frames shuddered. Outside, the day was darkening as a coven of clouds debated whether to smite the town with rain.

At last, Molly slammed Follington's *Botanicals* shut.

"I'm done."

"Really?"

"It's a simple recipe — good for all kinds of lyncanthropy. No harmful ingredients. We need to get to Hesperus Street. Do you have any pocket money on you? I've made a list of roots and oils we need to get from Bodle and Sharnyard."

"Will this recipe definitely cure werewolf curses? I was saving my money for a massive blow-out at Cakes and Shakes."

"Yes, it'll stop any curse from passing to you."

"And you're *absolutely sure* the potion won't kill me? You're definitely not just fobbing me off, are you?"

"Lowry, Follington's *Botanicals* is a highly respected work. Everything in it has been tested."

"In that case, yes. I have pocket money."

"Good. Let's go."

First Lowry returned the books, swapping the covers back, and then the girls headed out through the mizzle to Bodle and Sharnyard, the apothecary on Hesperus Street, to buy small quantities of fifteen oils and roots from old Mr Bodle.

In the pungent, bark-scented little shop, Lowry informed Mr Bodle that she was hoping to create her own brand of toiletries.

"I'm working on a special moisturizer," she told him. "Softens skin and, um, removes excess hair."

Somehow she got away with it.

"We'll go to yours and make a tincture, and you can start taking a few drops a day," Molly said as they walked back to the heart of town. "But you have to stop using it if there are any dodgy side effects..."

They passed the museum, with its three appalling spiky spires of different heights. The black stone faces of the building were crowded with little windows, flags set into holders and furious gargoyles. Black columns held up a porch over the main doors. Gold ravens were painted on the columns, beaks skyward, swirling around as though being drawn into a cyclone. A sign outside advertised an exhibition called The Silver Forest.

"I've always been a bit scared of the museum," Molly admitted. "And Mrs Dalby on reception always glares at me."

"D'you want me to come along and help you clean the place tomorrow?" said Lowry. "We can try to find Lady Orgella's portrait."

"That'd be fab," said Molly. "Although I don't know how we'll be able to tell her picture from all the others."

"You're Molly Thompson. You'll figure it out."

They headed to Little Valley Drive with the ingredients, and in the cosy kitchen of Lowry's bungalow, pretending to Mr and Mrs Evans that they were making their own special food colourings, the girls worked happily to cook up a harmless anti-werewolf remedy.

Through the kitchen window, Molly saw the waxing moon glowing in the summer-blue sky, clear as a mirror. It seemed to Molly that it was *staring* at her. And some words swam into her mind:

I taketh an interest in whosoever taketh an interest in me.

The Last Drop

THAT NIGHT, FOR THE SECOND NIGHT running, Molly fell asleep at her desk.

She'd been reading Wetherill's almanac. She'd lit her desk lamp, locked the window, drawn the curtains, charged Gabriel with making sure that nothing — *nothing* — succeeded in luring her out of the window and down the drainpipe and settled in her chair to go through every single official ghoul sighting in Howlfair's history.

A few hours and several pages of scrawled notes later, she'd identified some interesting patterns in the accounts of ghoul outbreaks. But her eyes hurt from squinting at tiny writing, and she felt as though someone had tightened a belt around her forehead. Meaning to restore herself with a brief doze, she put a cushion in the middle of her desk, laid her head on it — and fell immediately into a deep sleep.

For the second night running, she had vivid dreams.

Molly dreamt that she was walking through Howlfair on a rainy night. She arrived at Lastmead Lane, a winding hilly road of smugglers' pubs, mostly terraced buildings, with cryptic names like The Cat o' Knaves and The Old Ghost Gateway. They were the kind of pubs where folks with gold teeth and eye patches would go to plot acts of murder and banditry and the running of contraband. A fair number of folks through the ages had gone to a Lastmead Lane pub to plot a murder, only to get murdered themselves before last orders, silently strangled in some unlit nook.

If you managed to escape one of these pubs alive, you still weren't in the clear. The bumpy cobbles had tripped many a wobble-legged drinker over the years, and sent countless tumbling down the hill towards the ancient statue of a hooded monk. Numerous people had died over the centuries by rolling head first into the monk and cracking their skulls. But despite the perils of Lastmead Lane, it was hard not to be enchanted by the colourful pubs with their strange old signs swinging in the wind; the small leaded windows, conspiratorially mottled and glowing with caramel firelight; the low doors and beams; the wafting murmur of a motley medley of sounds — jokes and raspy laughter and music and clinking glasses.

Molly found herself outside the northernmost pub, near the bottom of the road, where the hill fell steepest. Like the other pubs, its timber exterior was colourfully painted, as gorgeous as a gypsy caravan. But unlike the other pubs, it had no sign, only a hangman's noose dangling from a wooden strut. The pub was called The Last Drop Inn.

Her dad had run a weekly book club here.

In the dream she opened the door and a blast of warmth coated her. The shady-looking drinkers at the curved, silver-railed bar fell silent. For a moment Molly felt dreadfully scared; then she noticed a short and messy-haired boyish man grinning widely at her. In front of him was a glass of limeade with a slice of orange. "Dad?" she gasped. "You're not dead?"

He laughed. "Dead? 'Course not, silly — I've been in here!"

A butterfly landed on the barkeeper's head.

Molly wondered how she could ever have thought that her father was dead when he'd been here at the Last Drop Inn all this time with his rowdy friends.

"Don't just stand there frowning, Moll — come in!"

But as she walked forward she was ambushed by a fluttering gang of dark moths. She shooed them away. The pub door shut behind her with a prison clunk. The lamps blinked, failed and came on again. Molly noticed that grey moths and pale butterflies were settling on the bar and on the heads of the drinkers.

"Dad, I can't believe it — you've been here all along, in the... Dad, what's with these butterflies?"

Her father looked around. "What butterflies?"

Molly could have sworn that one flew out of his mouth when he said that. She was about to mention it, but the lights blinked again and failed altogether. In the darkness, Molly heard the sinister laughter of Dad's friends. Unseen wings brushed her face. Dimly the light pulsed on for a moment, and Molly saw that Dad's friends weren't Dad's friends any more. They had *changed*...

Darkness again.

What was going on?

She was overpowered by sudden panic. She stumbled backwards and bumped into the door. She realized she had her torch clipped to her belt, and she fumbled for it. Then she saw something glowing in the dark.

Blue spangles of light. Small, like eyes.

Molly pointed the torch, pushed the button with her thumb and illuminated a scene of horror.

The pub's patrons were shroud-clad ghouls, leering and rotten, each with a glowing left eye. And Molly's dad — well, he wasn't Molly's dad any more. In his seat sat a woman dressed in a tomb-grey gown made fussy with lacy frills. Her face was even greyer than the gown, beautifully sculpted and sombre. One eye socket was covered with a round blue eye patch made of something like velvet and studded with blue gems. Her ash-hued hair was pinned up, and impaled moths wriggled on the pins. Many other moths circled her head and emerged from her mouth as she opened it impossibly wide and began to *inhale*.

All of the pub's air seemed to flow into that awful maw. Molly staggered forwards, drawn towards the vast mouth, and all the while she heard the woman's voice in her head, a voice both sickly sweet and sinister.

"Molly, wouldn't you like to know the secret of Daphne Loonchance? The secret of Tom Taffler? The secret of Benton Furlock? Come close so I can whisper it in your ear. Would you like some ghouls of your own, Molly? I'll gather a lovely flock for you and tell the naughty fiends that I won't let them back into Hell unless they obey little Molly's every command. As long as you're willing to pay my fee — on the night of the blue moon!"

Molly dropped her torch. She grabbed ineffectually at chairs and tables, trying to resist the draw of the woman's breath. But her fingers failed to grip; she staggered towards the black tunnel of the huge open mouth.

"I don't want ghouls!" she cried, back-pedalling frantically.

"Ah, Molly!" the voice chirruped delightedly inside her head. "Please — accept my generosity! A gaggle of ghoul slaves who'll obey your wishes is the least I can give you! After all, it's you who'll seek to summon me this blue moon…"

"No flipping way!"

"Our friend Mr Furlock will help me bring the Dark Days back to Howlfair and make this valley a place fit for a demon to dwell. But once that is done, *you*, Molly, are the one who will one day open the Gates of Hell and let me take possession of your town."

"No!"

"*My* town…"

"No way!"

"The capital of my new kingdom…"

Molly stumbled, and into the slipstream of wind she flew, the pub pitching from side to side as she was sucked towards the cavern of the lady's mouth.

"Molly Thompson — the solver of mysteries!" hissed the voice in her head. "Tireless seeker of hidden knowledge, unable to resist the lure of the strange! A girl enslaved by curiosity, destined to sniff out the secret of the Guild of Asphodel, the secret that unlocks the doors of Hell… *My own dear, doomed Molly.*"

There was an almighty crash to Molly's rear, and her torch beam suddenly blazed somewhere close behind her. She felt hands upon her. The one-eyed lady's mouth shrank and snapped grimly shut, and her face clouded with shock and fury. Then, from over Molly's shoulder, the metal bezel of her torch (it was Molly's beloved Firefly Shadeshifter tactical torch) whipped through the air and smashed the vile woman in the jaw. And as Molly was being hoisted back towards the door, she heard a familiar voice, a man's voice, saying brightly, "Evening, Orgella, me old mucker! Don't know if you noticed, but this is a *Guild* pub – and this is my little girl you're messing with."

Molly's heart jumped. It was Dad. The real Dad. Not an impostor.

The lady's eyes blazed with fury and shock.

Whack! The blinding torch clocked Lady Orgella again, right on the chin.

Gasping, Molly turned to look over her shoulder as she was dragged towards the busted door, and for a moment she thought she saw Mrs Fullsway standing among a small mob of villagers.

"It's OK, Moll – I've got you," Dad said.

She looked over her other shoulder, trying to catch sight of her father as he wrenched her away from the woman — from the *demon* — but as she tumbled through the doorway, back into the rain and the darkness —

She woke.

Gasping, wild-faced, her curls drenched and stuck to her forehead, she heard meows and sought Gabriel in the darkness. She found him on the desk in front of her. Leaping from her chair, she began to throw on clothes over her pyjamas. Gabriel interrogated her with yowls.

"Stay here or come with me — doesn't matter. I need to speak to Carl. I've seen his demon, Gabriel! I know what she looks like. And my dad — my dad came and rescued me from her. He knew who she was…"

Molly grabbed her torch from the drawer and clipped it to her belt.

Gabriel strongly disapproved. Nevertheless, moments later Molly was tiptoeing down the corridor, clutching her keys and a satchel full of books over her shoulder, Gabriel following with a scowl. Soon she was out in the night, heading through the empty streets to Howlfair Orphanage.

Twit-twoo!

IT WAS OFFICIAL – MOLLY COULD NOT IMPER-sonate an owl.

She'd assumed it would be easy. But after standing by the lamppost outside the orphanage for five minutes experimenting with different noises, she was growing frustrated.

She tried again. No use – she sounded like a dove being flushed down the toilet.

Tried again. No, that sounded like a steam train.

Tried again. No. That was a Wookiee trapped in a car boot.

"Stop giving me that I-could-do-a-better-owl-impersonation-and-I'm-a-cat look, Gabriel," she hissed.

There was only one solution: just shout *Twit-twoo*.

"Twit twoooo!"

From behind a nearby tree came a giggle.

"Carl!" Molly whispered. "How long have you been standing there?"

"Seems like for ever," said Carl Grobman in his oversized parka, grinning as he headed towards her. "I was already outside."

"Doing what?"

"Walking. Thinking. Trying to stay awake." He lowered his fur-lined hood and blew his scruffy fringe from his eyes. "Why are you here? You look upset."

"I need to know whether you've dreamt about her too."

Carl blanched. His dark eyes twitched. "You mean the lady with the moths."

"Her name is Lady Orgella. The Mistress of Ghouls. She's a demon. Furlock put her mark on your arm."

Carl looked appalled.

"Follow me," said Molly. "Let me show you something."

"Where are we going? And why is that cat following us?"

"The museum," said Molly. "And he's protecting us."

"You have a cat protector?"

"He's my oldest friend, I'll have you know," said Molly. "And he's a tough cookie."

Howlfair Museum was a great three-horned silhouette. The trio of turrets grasped clawlike towards the dark sky. Flags flapped in the escalating wind storm;

Molly shone her torch towards the biggest of them.

"The mark on your arm — it's on the flag. Bottom right corner. You can check it out tomorrow when it's light. Sit down — I'll show you."

They sat on a bench below a yew tree and Molly withdrew the vellum print of the flag from her satchel, along with her notepads.

"It's hard to see without a magnifying glass," Molly said, directing her torch beam at the print of the flag, "but you can just about make out the shape." The vellum's edges flapped in the wind. "It's the mark of Lady Orgella. She gives people the power to control ghouls. She told me in a dream. Tonight."

"She told you?"

"Yeah," said Molly. "She said that Benton Furlock is going to help her to bring back the Dark Days — the days when there were monsters in our town. And when the Ethelhael Valley's dark enough for her, she's going to come up from Hell herself, and set up a new kingdom, with Howlfair as its capital."

"Flipping heck," said Carl miserably. "Since I got branded I've seen her every time I sleep, in my dreams — but we never chat about her plans to take over the world."

"So what happens? In your dreams?"

"She always starts out as a really nice teacher —

I'm at school and everyone in the class is my friend. But then the lady changes, and the kids in the class change. Into monsters. *Ghouls.* They have blue left eyes. The lady's just like the one in the painting I saw in the crypt underneath Loonchance Manor. She's got grey hair and a blue eyepatch, and she opens her mouth and breathes in and I get dragged towards her..."

"That happened to me, too!"

"So you know what happens next..."

Molly looked at him. "Um, do your parents ... come and save you?"

Carl frowned, confused. "Nobody comes to save me. The lady's mouth gapes really wide as she breathes me in... I go into the darkness and I go into Hell and I scream until I wake up."

"Flipping Nora," said Molly. She felt a wave of desperate pity for Carl Grobman, and put a hand on his shoulder. He flinched, then settled. "This happens every night?" she asked.

"Not every night — only if I sleep," Carl said. "I try not to sleep if I can help it." He rubbed his eyes. "So ... in your dream, did someone save you? Was it your dad?"

"Yeah. He already knew who Lady Orgella was. He..."

"What's he like?" Carl blurted. "I mean, what was

your dad like when he was alive? He must've really cared about you if he turned up in your dream."

Molly rolled up the map. "He was lovely. And very silly. But in a good way. And friendly — he liked to make friends with people that everyone else avoided. He was always laughing and smiling." She put the map back in her satchel. "I wanted to be like him."

"Maybe if you ever smiled, you would be."

"What? I smile! I smile all the time! Look."

She attempted a smile.

"That's not a smile," said Carl. "That's just showing me your teeth."

"Listen, Carl, I'm going to find a way to get this demon out of your life. That's a promise. And whatever evil mischief Benton Furlock has in store for this town, we're going to stop him from becoming mayor, and we're going to get him to spill all of his secrets."

"How?"

"You're going to find a way into Loonchance Manor and I'm going to photograph everything down there, and we're going to give the evidence to someone who can help us reverse whatever black magic it is that Furlock's doing."

"But who can help us?"

"Mr Wetherill."

Carl spluttered. "Mr Wetherill? What are you talking about?"

"Trust me — he knows how to help. But he won't help us unless we can get evidence. Now look at this."

She took out Wetherill's almanac and a notepad. "The blue eye patch," she said. "The blue ring around Lady Orgella's emblem on the flag. The blue left eyes of the ghouls you see in your dreams. Blue circles, blue circles. What does the blue circle mean?"

"Um…"

"The blue moon!"

"Ah."

"She's also known as the Lady of the Double Mirror. I think that's another reference to the blue moon — in old magic spell books you often find the full moon described as a mirror, and a double mirror would be two full moons in a month." Carl was looking confused. "You do know that a blue moon is the second of two full moons in the same month?"

"Um, no."

"Well, you do now," said Molly. "In the dream, Lady Orgella told me that I was going to summon her on the blue moon, and then I'd get some ghoul companions."

"You? Summon her?"

"She was bluffing. I'm hardly going to summon a

222

demon, am I? And I told her that I wouldn't like any ghoul friends, thanks."

"*I* would," Carl muttered. "Imagine having ghouls who did whatever you told them to! I could get my own back on a few people at school..."

"Not funny, Carl." Molly flapped through the pages of the almanac, cross-referencing with her own notes. "Now look at this. Every single recorded ghoul outbreak in Howlfair has taken place after a blue moon. If Lady Orgella is the demon who gives you control over ghouls, and you summon her on a blue moon, then Furlock must've summoned her at least three years ago, because that's when the last blue moon was. But I think he summoned her way earlier than that."

"Why?"

Molly turned the pages of Wetherill's almanac. "Every ghoul outbreak in Howlfair is linked to a person who's just experienced a *tragedy* — like when Daphne Loonchance's fiancé and best friend died. Or when Furlock's business partner died."

"Business partner?"

"There used to be a property surveying company called Furlock and Halfstar — I read about it in an old copy of the *Ethelhael Panopticon*. Preston Halfstar got ill and died eleven years ago — just two months before

223

a blue moon. It was a big tragedy in Furlock's life. And if Furlock summoned Lady Orgella right after that tragedy, then he's been controlling ghouls for…"

"Eleven years."

"Exactly. He probably keeps them locked up in those secret crypts under Loonchance Manor. If we can just find a way into the crypts, we can take photos of his dodgy operations."

Carl suddenly looked shamefaced. "Molly, I'm not sure I could face going into those crypts again."

Molly said, "I'll be with you."

Carl smiled weakly.

He took some deep breaths.

"OK, I'll try to find us a way in," he said at last. "I'll see if I can pick the lock of the secret door."

"How come you know how to pick locks?"

Gabriel was weaving around the legs of the bench, and Carl reached down to stroke his head. "Remember I told you about a friend from school who laughed at the memories I thought were of my parents?"

"'Course."

"She's the daughter of a locksmith, and she taught me some basic skills."

"Wait — you were friends with Felicity Quick?"

"Not for long," he said, looking at Gabriel, who was now leaning against Molly's leg. "By the way,

224

what was Lowry talking about yesterday? You were arguing about werewolves…"

Molly sighed. "She thinks a werewolf curse runs in her family, and she's going to inherit it from her grandmother."

"And you think she's making it all up?"

"I think it's all in her imagination," said Molly. "Werewolfism isn't a magical curse that runs in families and skips generations — it's more like a virus."

Carl mulled this over. "Maybe you don't want to take Lowry seriously because everything else in your life is so strange. Maybe you want one thing in your life that's normal."

Molly scoffed. "What, you think I should seriously consider the possibility that Lowry Evans might be plagued with a curse that isn't mentioned in any book ever written about werewolves?"

"Maybe there's a book on werewolves that hasn't been written yet," he reasoned. "Are you going to tell her about your dream?"

"I don't think so," said Molly, remembering how she and Lowry had argued about the tangletree spores. "She'd probably just say I must have eaten too much cheese for dinner. Which happens to be true, but that's not why I dreamt of Lady Orgella."

Carl nodded. He looked at the moon. "I need to get back to the orphanage," he said. "As soon as I've had a look at the lock on the door to Loonchance Manor and found out how to break in, I'll get in touch with you." He stood up. "You're the nicest friend I've ever had," he stammered, blushing profoundly after the words were out, and then he hoisted up his hood and headed into the night.

Mayhem in the Museum

TUESDAY DIDN'T START WELL.

Molly and Mum exchanged little more than grunts at breakfast, except when Molly dropped a glass and Mum accused her of smashing it on purpose. Then, up in her room, Molly couldn't locate her *Doris de Ville's Street Cleaning Crew* tee-shirt. Eventually she found it behind the bass guitar she'd inherited from her dad, which was propped against the amplifier by her wardrobe, and when she tried to shake the dust from it, she knocked over the lamp, breaking the shade. She tripped over her chair and cracked the face of her watch, nudging a half-full mug of tea from her desk onto the carpet in the process. Gabriel watched with some alarm.

"Don't worry, Gabriel," she grumbled. "Hopefully I'm getting all the clumsiness out of my system so that I don't end up destroying the museum today."

She yanked the whole drawer from her desk while searching for her camera.

Gabriel gave a concerned mewl.

"You can't come with me, Gabriel — cats aren't allowed in the museum."

Meow!

"I'm sure I'll be safe — it's not like Lady Orgella's going to crawl out of her portrait and attack me." Molly shivered, remembering the nightmare wherein the demon had tried to inhale her. "Anyway, if she does leap out and attack me, I'll just do what Dad used to do when he was my age and bullies attacked him. I'll play dead!" She stretched out on the floor and let her tongue loll out. "How's this?"

Gabriel wasn't impressed.

Molly sat up and shoved her camera into her rucksack. "I've got to go — I want to visit Gran before I meet Lowry at the museum. Stay here and practise playing dead in case you're ever attacked by demons. Or bears. I'll be back in a few hours, safe and sound. If I'm lucky, I might even help clean the museum without burning the place down."

"Gran, why does everyone in here look so miserable today?" Molly whispered in the Genevieve Wakely

Wing that morning. "I mean, apart from the fact that they're in hospital."

"Haven't you heard?" said Gran. "Stan Cromble died."

Molly put her hands to her mouth. "No!"

Gran used a wisp of frazzled hair to wipe her eyes. "They say his sister Lesley visited him in the hospital over in Charnton, and he woke up and started shouting about the blue moon, and ghouls, and then he died, right in front of his sister."

Molly noticed that Gran's hands were shaking as they drew the bedclothes up to her chin.

"Is something happening, Molly?" Gran asked. "Are you investigating something that's happening?"

Molly lowered her face to hide the redness rushing into her cheeks. "What d'you mean, Gran?"

"The blue moon. I don't know why, but I'm scared of it. Is something going to happen to me? When Hectoria said I wouldn't be in here much longer, did she mean I'd be getting out of here alive, or..."

"Gran, calm down," said Molly, laying a hand on Gran's quivering arm.

"Hectoria said a horrible horror is coming to Howlfair. It's going to come on the blue moon, isn't it? The vanity moon, my grandma used to call it, because it's like the full moon is showing off by

229

popping up twice in the same month..."

Vanity, thought Molly. Lady Orgella was known for her vanity.

"I won't let anything happen to you, or to Howlfair," Molly said. "And neither will Granddad, or Dad, or Gabriel. And I even have a feeling Hectoria's looking out for you. That's enough to scare away any horrible horrors."

Gran managed a limp smile, but Molly could tell she wasn't reassured in the slightest.

It was a confused day: warm, bright and cold and windy and calm. The farmland hills were mooing in the north and clouds were clustering in the centre of the sky like backing singers around a microphone, then sweeping away into the wings like stagehands changing a theatre set between acts. Doris de Ville, dressed memorably in lime-green dungarees, led the twelve members of her Street Cleaning Crew – plus Lowry Evans in a borrowed tee-shirt – past the sign which read CLOSED FOR CLEANING 12–4PM and into the museum. Molly looked up at the gargoyle-guarded, doom-coloured walls and felt an inner lurch of dread.

"Thanks for coming," she said to Lowry as they mounted the steps, glad of her company.

"My pleasure," Lowry said. She lowered her voice.

"Hopefully we can sneak off and try to find the painting of this mystery demon, eh? Oh — I took some of your potion, by the way."

"Huh?" Molly had forgotten about the werewolf remedy. "Ah, the potion... Um, how do you feel?"

"A bit seasick, but basically OK," said Lowry, as Mrs de Ville held open the museum's door for the children to go in. "Feeling sick is probably a sign that it's working."

"It can't do you any harm," Molly reassured her.

She followed Lowry through the entrance, trying to ignore the jackal scowl of Felicity Quick, who was stalking the lobby.

The candlelit interior of the museum was claustrophobic and close, the walls rough and jagged. The cave-like, circular front office had a ceiling so low that it made even Molly feel tall. Mrs de Ville passed around cloths and cans of spray polish, then spoke to the diminutive mole-like woman behind the front desk, who handed her a stack of pamphlets. Mrs de Ville transferred these to the ever-dependable Kiran Birring to hand out, while she briefed the children on their mission.

"We've been asked to do a clean and polish of the railings, metalwork and windows before the opening of an exhibition by Kaspar Van de Werhe, a world-famous artist who I've never heard of." The mole-like woman looked up, frowning over her spectacles. "You can read about him in your brochure," added Mrs de Ville, waving a hand.

Molly took a glossy brochure from Kiran and turned to the section on Kaspar Van de Werhe.

Mrs de Ville went on. "His main exhibition of trees made of silver is on the other side of the museum. On this side, around the regular exhibits, you'll find cobwebs that he's made out of spun silver. They're trailed all around the place and they're very expensive. Your challenge, in case you haven't guessed, is to clean this side of the museum without sweeping away any priceless cobwebs. Now look at the map near the back of your brochure."

Pages flapped.

"Molly Thompson, Lowry Evans, Kiran Birring and Felicity Quick — you'll be cleaning the Murmuroth Wing."

Molly couldn't believe it. Felicity Quick again! Why was Mrs de Ville always hurling them into the same cooking pot? Clearly Felicity was equally disgruntled — Molly heard the bully tut behind her.

Doris put the other children into trios and sent them off with a warning: "Don't anybody — *anybody* — stray one inch from the areas I've given them, or I'll set Mrs Dalby here on them."

Mrs Dalby spotted Molly and gave her an unwelcoming glare.

"Guess we won't be sneaking off to find that picture of Lady Oregano today, then," Lowry muttered to Molly as they headed into the first of the creepy exhibition rooms.

Molly said, "We'll see."

Molly felt momentarily dizzy as she passed through the door into the torch-lit Olden Days exhibition. She felt a headache coming on. No — not a headache, a slow-blooming pressure inside her skull. An expansion, as though something was shouldering its way into her consciousness. She wondered if she was coming down with something.

"Molly, are you OK?" whispered Kiran, who'd drawn up alongside her.

"I just don't like this place, that's all," said Molly, which was true enough. "I prefer the library."

Off to her left, she heard Lowry giggling at an exhibit and Felicity scolding her.

"I thought you'd have loved it, Molly," said Kiran, adjusting her very fashionable glasses. "All this history about the Dark Days and the monsters that everyone believed in, and all the weapons that they used to fight vampires and goblins!"

"There were never really goblins in Howlfair," mumbled Molly. "Though some miners in 1675 claimed they were attacked by something goblin-y..."

"So why don't you like the museum?"

Molly glanced at a display case full of necklaces — lucky charms made of children's milk teeth hung on cords fashioned from the plaited hair of the dead. The information board on the inside of the cabinet mocked the vulgar superstitions of the medieval makers of the charms. This was partly what Molly disliked about the museum: the sneering, sceptical information boards that treated the olden folks of Howlfair like gullible idiots seduced by old wives' tales.

"Reading stories about the Dark Days in the library is one thing," said Molly, "but seeing all this stuff... It reminds me that there were real people once who lived in really horrible times." The girls moved on into a corridor lit by squat candles set in skulls. Molly examined a little sign beneath one of the glowing skulls.

```
Child's skull used as lantern to
scare away "crib-cranks", vampires
believed to prey on infants.
```

"It makes me sad to think of how desperate people must have been back in those days," she added.

"Imagine if those days ever came back."

Molly wasn't sure how to respond. She couldn't tell Kiran that she thought the next mayor of Howlfair might be a man who *wanted* the Dark Days to return to their town. A man who could command the monsters from Howlfair's scariest legends, and who served a demon who seemed keen to open the Gates of Hell...

"They won't," she said firmly.

They ascended a short staircase to a chamber that sizzled with shadows. Spotlights picked out glass cases of ancient books, splayed to display gory woodcuts. There were hideous grimoires and despairing journals; there were pacts with demons, written and signed in terror-shaken script, some countersigned in sinister lettering. Down a further corridor the girls found the Asphodel Rooms.

Molly led the way into a spacious octagonal hall, cavernous and gloomy. The hall's displays weren't all on one level; little flights of stone steps took you up or down to different exhibits. Spun-silver cobwebs spangled atop some of the displays. The girls chattered and cleaned. Spray-polish hissed through the air. Molly's head felt as though someone was inflating a balloon inside it. She scrunched her eyes shut — and she realized that the pressure in her skull wasn't a merely physical sensation. It was a *desire*.

A desire to see the picture of Lady Orgella.

Suddenly Lowry screamed.

Molly looked up to see Lowry pointing towards the ceiling. The other girls looked too. Over their heads, rusty gibbets were swinging in an unfelt breeze. Each one contained an unhappy-looking skeleton.

"That's what they did to grave robbers in the olden days," snorted Felicity Quick. "Hey, and look what they did to werewolves!"

Felicity was standing beside a complicated human-sized contraption.

"Satan's socks, what's that?" Lowry warbled, nearly raking her cloth through one of Van de Werhe's silver cobwebs as she staggered backwards.

"It's called a wendy-hut," Felicity said gleefully, checking the information board. "From the German *wende-haut*. Listen to this: 'If the authorities thought your family were werewolves, they'd kill you all, even the children, unless one of you volunteered to get inside the wendy-hut to prove your family's innocence. They'd pull this lever and it would turn you inside out, so they could see if you had fur on the inside of your skin!' Anyone want to try?"

"Of course not!" cried Lowry. "That's the most horrible thing I've ever heard."

Molly could barely concentrate on the conversation. Her curiosity about the demon portrait had become a persistent mental itch.

"Me too," Kiran said. "What if you were found innocent?"

"Then your family wouldn't get killed," Felicity shrugged.

"Barbaric!" Lowry wailed.

"Ha — wouldn't it be great if the people of Howlfair all got really paranoid again and started accusing each other of being werewolves like before?"

"No, Felicity, it would not!"

"Did you know that old Wetherill keeps a secret stash of real silver bullets in the back room of his shop? I'd love to be in a militia of werewolf hunters."

"And I'd love to be a werewolf eating your stupid werewolf hunters one by one," Lowry growled. Felicity countered with a colourful description of her preferred werewolf-hunting methods, and Lowry counter-countered with the claim that back in the olden days, seventeen werewolf hunters were killed for every werewolf slain. Molly knew that the true figure was twenty-six hunters killed for every werewolf eliminated, but she didn't feel like contributing to the conversation. The urge to find Lady Orgella's painting had turned miasmic and sickly inside her head, and she fancied that words were forming in her skull.

Aren't you curious, Molly?

I'm waiting in the Dark Chambers.

She felt a need to flee the others and head to the portrait galleries on the other side of the museum. It seemed that if she just found the painting, the pressure in her head would cease...

"I'm just going to see what's, um, over here," she mumbled while Felicity teased Lowry, and Kiran tried to intervene. She slipped away through the nearest archway and discovered that the room beyond it — circular and filled with torture devices — led to a passageway. She headed for a nearby corridor, consulting her map as she walked, looking for the quickest way to the Dark Chambers.

She wasn't yet halfway down the corridor before she heard Lowry behind her.

"Molly! What are you doing? Why did you just abandon me?"

Molly stopped, and turned. "I — I just wanted to see something..."

Lowry's eyes were bright with confusion. "Felicity Quick was tormenting me, and you just went off to see something?"

"The portrait, Lowry! I need to see the portrait of Lady Orgella! I didn't want to get anyone else into trouble, so I thought while you were all arguing, I'd—"

The door behind Lowry opened, and into the corridor spilled Felicity Quick, Kiran behind her.

"Oi! What's going on?" Felicity demanded. "Where do you two think you're going?"

"None of your business, Flick Quick!" Lowry roared over her shoulder with a ferocity that Molly had never witnessed her friend exhibit before. It shocked Felicity, too. For a moment she stood quake-faced; then she mastered herself and made fists, storming down the corridor.

"Don't call me that!"

And then, just like that, Felicity and Lowry were fighting — or, rather, Felicity was fighting and Lowry was cowering against a wall, covering herself with her arms. It took Molly a few moments to recover from her shock and stumble forward to aid her friend; by then Kiran had hurtled forward, grabbed Felicity's shoulders and wrenched her backwards. The bully spun around and launched herself at Kiran, who fell to the floor and kicked out at Felicity's knees, and now Lowry leapt onto Felicity's back, and Molly—

Molly ran.

The Last Archway

MOLLY FOUND HERSELF IN THE ARCHAE-ology Exhibition in Middle Museum.

She ran around the mock-up of a Viking settlement, through the double doors.

I'm waiting, Molly.

Down a further corridor she flew, her feet clopping on the wooden flooring as she ducked beneath a display of hanging vines made of silver. Molly stopped, raw-breathed, to consult her map and find the way to the Dark Chambers. Then she pressed on.

At last, at the end of a chilly corridor, was a door with the sign: MIRROR ROOMS AND DARK CHAMBERS.

She gulped when she saw the hall beyond.

It was not particularly large, but its walls (the misshaped hall had many walls, some jutting out in wedges, others curved) had been plated with mirrors, and the mirrors made the space infinite. The ceiling, too, was mirrored. The main sources of light were the lanterns hanging from the silver trees that made up Kaspar Van de Werhe's art exhibition. Reflected in the mirrored walls and the mirrored ceiling, the trees formed a silver forest that fell away from the eye in every direction and vanished to nothing.

But there were archways as well, set in some of the walls, and these glowed with deep ruby light – beyond them (Molly knew) were Dark Chambers, which housed claustrophobic galleries of creepy portraits.

I can satisfy your curiosity, Molly.

Molly struggled to calculate how to get across the room – with every step, the forest tilted and lurched around her. If she spun, it spun the other way; it loomed and fled and swirled and disobeyed her senses.

I'm in here, Molly…

She wobbled her way through the glimmering landscape of lamp-lit trees, peering into the red-glowing chambers, scanning the paintings on the walls, looking for the grey-faced lady with the eye patch.

She heard a voice speaking directly into her left ear.

The last archway, Molly.

Gasping, she spun. The mirrored hall spun. The trees flew and the lights streaked as Molly wobbled across the hall, until at last she tripped through the last archway, into the chamber beyond.

She was surrounded by eerie glare-eyed portraits lit by torches set in metal holders on the walls. Thick velvet curtains hung from a silver railing that ran around the chamber; at present the curtains were tied back to reveal the portraits. The torches were made of red darksbane, which produced a deep scarlet flame.

And there, on the wall, was Lady Orgella wearing her circular blue sapphire-studded eye patch. Just as in Molly's dream. Molly thought that the other paintings looked drab by comparison; Lady Orgella glowed with astonishing lunar beauty.

Molly stared.

The longer she stared, the stronger her fascination became. She didn't know how long she looked up at the portrait, gazing into the one good eye of the Mistress of Ghouls, spellbound. But eventually she was wrenched from her reverie by a horrid, shrill noise.

"Thompson! Where are you, Thompson?"

It was the furious voice of Felicity Quick.

The Flaming Face

"**Y**OU'D BETTER HAVE A GOOD EXCUSE FOR legging it, you little germ — there's a search party out looking for you!"

Felicity was too flushed with indignation to even notice the portraits scowling down at her. Molly came to her senses; the pressure in her skull had gone.

"A search party?"

"Mrs de Ville's gonna rip your arms and legs off when she gets hold of you. She said not to leave the areas she wanted us to clean, and here you are looking at... What *are* you looking at?"

"Nothing," Molly blurted. "I just came to look at this, um, picture here."

Felicity looked up and jolted to see Lady Orgella glowering at her. "Why would you run off just to look at a weird picture of a one-eyed woman?"

Molly fidgeted. "I just... I'm..."

"This is one of those stupid mysteries you've been investigating, isn't it?" Felicity narrowed her eyes. "There's something special about this portrait, isn't there? A secret panel behind it, or something." She strode towards the painting. "Get me one of those torches."

"Um … what?"

"A torch, you idiot!" Tutting, Felicity yanked a darksbane torch from its iron holder and held it aloft. "I want to see what's so special about this painting before the search party gets here."

She stood on tiptoes and scowled at the picture, then thrust the torch into Molly's hands. "Hold this, Thompson — I'm going to get something to stand on."

Molly clutched the darksbane torch and complained under her breath. From outside the chamber there came a clang and a curse.

"Felicity?" Molly called. "Are you OK?"

"Stop shouting!" Felicity shouted. "Keep your voice down."

Molly stood grumbling for a couple of seconds, and then she realized she could smell something funny.

Felicity came through the archway and dropped the chair she was lugging. "Molly! What the hell are you doing?"

"Huh?"

Molly turned and cried out with horror.

By accident she had touched the torch flame to the bottom of the portrait's canvas!

She yelped and leapt back, flinging the torch aside, while the flame romped over the features of the vain demon.

"Get out of the way!" Felicity spat, shrugging off her jacket and whipping it at the burning face. But the flames gobbled up the image in seconds, the canvas curling and bubbling. And meanwhile ...

"Flipping Nora!"

... the fallen torch had set fire to a curtain; and soon another portrait's frame was aflame, the old wood splintering. Now it seemed the whole room was blazing: the wallpaper was on fire, the curtains were on fire, the tasselled ropes on the barriers were on fire, the portraits were on fire...

The worst thing was the portraits. As the features melted, the faces contorted, and Molly was certain that she heard the writhing faces scream as the oil paint slid down the walls like gore. Only Lady Orgella remained unmoved in the inferno. From behind her wall of fire she glared, her one good eye squinting with ineffable badness at Molly, her lips tight, her skin blackening until there was nothing left of her image but that single bewitching eye.

A picture frame fell flaming at Molly's feet, and suddenly the burglar alarm, electronically imagining that a portrait was being stolen, began shrieking. And the portraits were shrieking. The whole museum, it seemed, was shrieking.

"Molly, get out of there!"

It wasn't until she heard Felicity shouting at her from the other side of the archway that Molly realized she was standing frozen in the middle of a furnace. Till that moment it had seemed like a hallucination: the thick tar-like oil pouring from the paintings and streaming down the walls; the air full of the screams of painted faces; the image of Lady Orgella receding into blackness but somehow still glaring — it was all too nightmarish to be real. But Felicity's voice brought Molly back to her senses. Now she felt the broiling heat enclosing her. She looked up and saw the wooden beams about to fall. And then, even over the wail of the alarm, she heard fresh commotion as adults poured into the Mirror Rooms. Somewhere overhead a red iron pipe wheezed and an ancient sprinkler system (at last!) came alive, so that Molly found herself amidst a steaming monsoon. Then an unseen hand — cripes, the grip was cold! — grabbed her arm and pulled her back through the archway.

"Somebody get in here, quick!" cried a familiar,

horrid voice. "Save the painting! The portrait! O my Lady! Don't let her portrait be harmed!"

Molly knew now why the hand's touch appalled her. It belonged to Benton Furlock. His glacial grip softened and he began laughing gently as two members of staff rushed past him, into the chamber; one of them disconnected Lady Orgella's picture from the burglar alarm while another covered it with a heavy fallen curtain — but not before Molly caught sight of something so strange that at first she assumed she was imagining it.

The portrait of Lady Orgella that Molly had burnt was mended.

Apart from a few fading singe marks, the face was intact, and glaring even more wickedly than before.

Furlock's relieved tittering sounded like the gossip of tiny birds.

"That's impossible," Molly muttered as the curtain obscured the rejuvenated visage of Lady Orgella.

From the archway, Felicity Quick said, simply, "Her face."

She'd seen Lady Orgella's miraculous reappearance too.

Felicity stepped aside as Furlock dragged Molly into the mirrored hall.

"She's safe!" he cried to the adults who had now

thronged into the smoky room, none of whom knew that Furlock was talking about the portrait of his beloved Lady Orgella, not about Molly. "Oh, praise the powers, she's safe!" And then Molly heard him whisper to himself: "I should have known that her vanity would not permit her image to burn!"

Molly pulled away from Furlock's grip. Her jacket tore as she spun around — and then her stomach flipped at the sight of Furlock holding a ripped-off swab of her jacket in one hand while raising triumphantly the hand he usually kept tucked in his coat. The latter was not a real hand at all. It seemed to Molly to be made of *glass*, fragile and dainty. Molly let out a gasp and Furlock stuffed the glass hand back into his jacket.

Molly had no time to ponder the significance of the glassy hand. For by now the staff members in attendance were barking at the children to make their exit immediately through the fire door.

"You — stop dithering!" shouted the mole-like receptionist at Molly. "Out!"

So out Molly hurried, Felicity following, into the gravelly car park, the sky a bombastic blue in which the moon bobbed like a lifebuoy. Already the other members of Doris de Ville's Street Cleaning Crew — variously frightened or furious or flummoxed — were being stewarded from the museum by the teacher. Still the burglar alarm howled, and now another howling could be heard across the town, as if in reply: Howlfair's sole fire engine was hurtling hither.

Molly saw Kiran heading towards her. But Lowry — where was Lowry? Molly spun, her eyes sweeping broadly. She spotted Carl Grobman on the other side of the car park, his fur-lined hood up, hands thrust into his pockets. He slipped behind the grasping branches of a Judas-root tree with its rough, curled leaves like shut purses.

But Lowry was not to be seen.

"Molly!" hissed Kiran. "We've been looking for you! Lowry's poorly! One of the museum staff took her to the infirmary."

"The infirmary?"

"She — Oh, crumbs!"

Kiran backed away, and Molly turned to see a fearsome figure rounding the car park barrier and rushing onto the scene: her mother.

What was she doing here?

Mum's rose-gold hair hovered aloft as she broke into a sprint. The crowd parted; Benton Furlock stepped back and hurriedly bowed. It was obvious to everyone that Mrs Thompson was in an exceedingly bad mood. Even Mrs de Ville kept her distance, counting the other children and trying to keep them together in an orderly assembly.

"Uh, hi, Mum."

"You've poisoned her!" Mum shrieked, gripping her daughter's shoulders. "The hospital called, Molly! Lowry's been rushed there! Werewolf medicine, Molly — have you gone insane?"

The crowd watched enthusiastically.

"Mum, listen to me — is Lowry OK? Can I see her?"

"Thank God Lowry's mum found your herbal witchcraft recipe in time so she could tell the doctors what poison you fed her! And Mrs Evans found your stolen newspapers and your notebooks too, Molly, the ones you've been hiding in Lowry's room! Your mad scribblings about ghoul conspiracies and some boy named Carl who's burnt his arm off…"

Benton Furlock's eyes widened.

"Mum, stop!" Molly pleaded.

"You're grounded for the summer. Under lock and key. No sneaking out. No telephone calls. No —" Suddenly she looked up at the museum and gasped. Her eyes followed the rising drift of the smoke from the skylights in the exhibition hall. "What's going on here? What have you done now?"

"It was an accident!"

Sirens neared. Mum grabbed Molly's arm and led

her to the car, which was parked haphazardly on a grass verge on the other side of the car park barrier.

"Mum, what's going on with Lowry?" she squealed, trying not to cry as she stumbled over a cobble and her mother yanked her upright. Mum wrenched open the back door of their red Mini and shoved Molly in as though she were a criminal under arrest. Then Mum squeezed into the front seat, her furious fingers fumbling with the key in the ignition.

She yanked the key and the car growled to life. Gears complained noisily. "Her poor parents are going frantic. Mrs Evans threw your notebooks at me! Gave me quite an earful, and I can't blame her." Mum reversed the car like a stuntwoman, engaged the handbrake and spun the car noisily to face home. "I promised her that you'll never see those books again."

"Mum, you don't understand!" Molly grabbed the sides of her seat as the Mini roared around the corner of Flayer's Lane. "This isn't just some everyday investigation! It's life or death!"

"You got that right." The car bumped and skidded over the cobbles. "It's Lowry's life you've put at risk."

"Mum, please — you're driving like a nutcase."

The car mounted the kerb as they rounded a corner. Molly's teeth rattled in her skull.

"Don't talk to me about behaving like a nutcase,

Molly Thompson. Because of your disobedience, an innocent girl is in hospital. And what about the museum! Molly, you burnt down Howlfair Museum!"

"Not the whole museum, Mum — just a bit of it. And listen, Mum, the maddest supernatural thing happened! There's this picture of a demon—"

"Enough!" Mum shouted. "For heaven's sake, Molly, no more mad supernatural nonsense."

"Mum, I've got proof this time. A painting of a demon mended itself right in front of me, and I think the whole town's in danger, including—"

"Molly, can't you see? *You're* the most dangerous thing in Howlfair!" They arrived outside the brooding dark guesthouse, and Mum brought the car to a jolting halt. "Take a good look at the outside of the Excelsior," she snapped. "You're not going to see it again for the rest of the summer."

Guesthouse Arrest

ELLIS, THE LOCAL HANDYMAN, WAS SUMM-oned immediately to make terrible alterations to the Excelsior Guesthouse. Silently he trailed Molly's mother through the corridors, jotting notes on a notepad, while Molly objected.

"Mum, this is worse than putting me in prison!" she complained as Mum scrutinized the window at the end of the third floor east corridor.

"Don't be melodramatic," Mum snapped. "Ellis, could we get iron bars over this window?"

Molly choked. "Bars! That's monstrous!"

"I'm trying to make sure you get through the rest of this summer without killing yourself, Molly. I refuse to let anyone else in this family die!"

Mum marched on, leaving Ellis inspecting the window.

"The whole town might end up dead if I don't carry

on with my investigation," Molly said, trying to keep up with her.

"What investigation, Molly? The ghoul conspiracy, the character-assassination of our next mayor or the werewolf scandal?"

"All of them! All of the ones you blabbed about in front of the whole town!"

Mum wasn't listening. "Ellis, I want a sign in the snug saying that the telephone is out of order, and directing residents to the phone in the lobby."

Ellis gave Molly a sheepishly apologetic look, and scribbled on his notepad.

"Mum, we live in a guesthouse. People have to be able to get in and out. What are you going to do, lock me in a room? Or lock the guests in too?"

The look on Mum's face made Molly fear the worst.

"Funny you should ask," said Mum.

Downstairs, Mum ordered Ellis to cart the Excelsior's cosiest armchair into the lobby. Then she called a meeting of several long-term residents, with the purpose of making them an alluring offer: free board and meals for the rest of the summer in return for agreeing to spend three-hour shifts sitting by the front door between morning and bedtime, making sure Molly did not leave.

Mr Banderfrith managed to be the first to put his hand up to volunteer, partly because he was already halfway through a stretch.

"Mrs Thompson, I would be honoured to help you keep this recalcitrant child captive," he said, adjusting his wig. "You can put me down for triple shifts."

And so it was decided: Molly would be shut up in the house for the rest of the summer. This arrangement struck Molly as so horrifying that she couldn't quite believe her mother would insist on it. But she was wrong. By the time Mum had finished introducing Molly to her cruel new regime, it was past bedtime, and Mum marched her to the bathroom Molly used to sleep in whenever Mrs Fullsway stayed. She locked her in without the slightest sign of scruple.

It wasn't until Mum's footsteps had faded that Molly noticed an intruder, who'd appeared from nowhere.

"Gabriel! I thought Mum'd locked you out!"

The cat leapt onto the linen basket.

"Any ideas, Gabriel? What the heck am I supposed to do?"

Gabriel meowed.

"No, Gabriel — I most certainly should not have told Mum the whole story of what's going on. It's bad enough that she blabbed to the whole town that I've been investigating ghouls, and — oh, flipping Nora,

Furlock knows about Carl! He'll kill him!"

Gabriel curled up.

"I'm going to have to escape as soon as possible and break into Loonchance Manor before Furlock kills Carl. The election's in three days' time — so I have less than three days to prove to Mr Wetherill that Benton Furlock is a demon-worshipping ghoul-botherer, or he'll become mayor!" She frowned hard. "Gabriel, there's no other choice. I want you to go and protect Carl until I can escape. Maybe get together a posse of cats…"

Gabriel sat up and objected.

"I mean it, Gabriel! I'm firing you! You're not my personal protector any more! You know how to sneak into locked rooms, so you can blooming well sneak out of them too, starting with this one!"

"Meow!"

"Look — it's my fault that Lowry's in hospital. I'm a terrible friend. I've put everyone in danger. I don't deserve to have a magical cat guardian. I'm not asking you to do anything silly or brave — just go and watch out for Carl. Oh, and make sure you keep away from a girl named Felicity Quick. She might try to kill you."

Gabriel stared.

"She looks like, um…" Molly took some nail scissors from the cabinet and trimmed off some of her hair at an angle. She lifted Gabriel from the linen basket, pointed him at the cabinet mirror so he could see his reflection and held the hair over his head. "Kind of a slanting haircut like this, but less curly, obviously."

Gabriel scratched her.

"Fine — be like that. I don't want you here anyway! Scram! Do that magic thing where you sneak through locked doors or whatever it is you do!"

The cat sniffed and settled down again, some of Molly's hair still attached by static electricity. "I'm going to close my eyes and count to ten. If I open them and you're still sitting there like a lemon, there'll be serious trouble."

Silence. She counted to ten.

She opened her eyes. Scanned the bathroom. Gabriel was gone.

Feeling suddenly very alone, Molly climbed into the bath, pulled the bedsheets over herself and tried to think how she could escape from the Excelsior Guesthouse.

Cruxton Keys

THE POLICE VISITED ON WEDNESDAY MORNING to hear Molly's account of the accident in the museum. Luckily, her reputation for clumsiness and nosiness meant that nobody suspected her of deliberate wrongdoing. But the police stayed a long time, and so Molly's first opportunity to try to escape the Excelsior came later that afternoon, when Mum had gone upstairs to have a bath.

Mr Banderfrith was on duty in the lobby, but Molly found him asleep, his mouth gaping as though he was undergoing dental work, snoring so loudly that the rippling airwaves set the glass chandelier above him shimmering. It was the perfect opportunity for Molly to make a run for it.

Molly wafted her hand in front of Mr Banderfrith's face to see if he'd wake, and he didn't. She lowered a finger into the cavern of his mouth and withdrew it unscathed. She took off his wig and turned it back to front.

"I'd say he's asleep," she whispered to herself.

Then she slipped towards the door, tripped over the rug and crashed into the pamphlet stand beside the coat racks, dragging the brochures and flyers on top of herself.

"Halt, or there'll be hell to pay!" warbled Mr Banderfrith, sitting upright and instinctively flinging the first thing he could find at Molly, which happened to be his wig. It landed on Molly's upturned face. She screamed and hurled it away. The hairpiece landed on the white telephone beside the guest book, where it sat looking oddly mischievous.

"Don't you dare leave this house, wicked child!" Mr Banderfrith quivered, feeling down the side of the armchair for a large brass bell as Molly climbed to her feet. "If I ring this bell, that mother of yours will eat you alive. Now fetch me my hair."

Grumbling, Molly headed to the desk. But as she was lifting the toupee, she spied an unfamiliar pencil — the bat-shaped eraser at one end suggested it was from Wetherill's Weaponry Store — lying next to the guest book.

"My hair, scoundrel!"

"Won't be a minute," she mumbled. She opened the

guest book to the most recently written-on page and found the following words in light pencil:

> *Found way into LM. Know how to save town. Stay tuned!*
>
> *P.S. your cat keeps following me.*

LM?

Molly frowned. Of course! Loonchance Manor!

The note must have been from Carl!

He'd visited!

He was still alive!

And Gabriel was protecting him!

Molly felt, and suppressed, a strong urge to dance.

"Oi!" rasped Mr Banderfrith. "Give me my blasted wig, you vile child!"

"All right, keep your hair on," Molly muttered, rubbing out Carl's writing with the bat-shaped eraser and shutting the book. She scooped up the wig and turned. "Here, catch."

Mr Banderfrith's eyes widened as the wig flew.

So the front door, apparently, wasn't an option. At least not for the time being. But Molly wasn't out of ideas yet.

There was a small room at the back of the guesthouse, originally a boot room, which had its own patio door leading to a small outdoor seating area with a single wrought-iron table and two rusty chairs. Nobody ever went out there. It was to this door that Molly headed. She checked the lock, which bore the maker's inscription: CRUXTON.

Then she headed upstairs to steal a key.

It was a risky move, hiding in the broom cupboard down the corridor from Mum's bedroom, waiting for Mum to emerge after her bath. At one point the housekeeper walked past, and Molly was certain that she was going to be discovered. But the housekeeper strolled by.

Suddenly Mum emerged from her room, humming a tuneless tune. She shut the door but didn't lock it.

Eyeball to the keyhole, Molly watched Mum stride down the corridor.

When Mum had gone, Molly stumbled from her hiding place and headed for Mum's bedroom. Mum only ever left her door unlocked when she knew she'd be back within a few minutes. So there wasn't much time for Molly to find the...

"Keys, keys, keys..."

Maintaining this muttered mantra, Molly stole into Mum's gaudy bedroom with its rows of shoes and scarves everywhere and the hanging rugs and the giant potted cactus named Louis. The ash blanket box painted light green. The tallboy, snow-white with seven drawers. The white oak dressing table by the window with the long oval mirror.

"Drawers, drawers, keys, keys..."

With fumbling fingers she dislodged every drawer and dug her hands into whatever lay inside, ploughing up papers, underwear, handkerchiefs, jewellery. Her ears were tuned to catch the slightest sound of footsteps. She'd decided she would scoot under the bed if Mum returned. That always seemed to work in films.

Bah! Nothing in the drawers. Where else could the dratted key be? The pockets of the jackets hanging on the back of the door? No. The pockets of trousers? No. Inside the decorative wooden bowls on the bookshelves? No, no, no...

Just as she was beginning to give up, Molly thought she heard a familiar sound from outside.

Meow!

She dashed to the window.

"Gabriel?"

Her gaze swept left, right, trying to take in every outdoor detail at once — the lane, the forecourt, the trees, the parked cars. She put her hands on the dressing table, leaned forward and put her face to the glass.

There was no sign of him. Her mind must have been tricking her.

Suddenly she became aware of a distinctive sensation in her right palm. She lifted her hand and there, on top of a shabby book of short stories by Poe, was a set of keys.

Molly gasped.

"OK, which one of you keys is named Cruxton?"

Jangling her way around the loop, she found two keys bearing the Cruxton moniker. She decided to take both and was attempting to remove them from the keyring without snapping her fingernail when she heard the sound of footsteps in the corridor outside.

The Trooper

PANICKING, MOLLY DROPPED THE KEYS AND dived onto the floor. There she discovered that there wasn't enough space under the bed for her to conceal herself.

"Drat!"

The footsteps stopped. The door handle turned. By now Molly had thrown herself onto the bed and was scrambling across it like a mad monkey, towards the nearest wardrobe.

Mum pushed open the bedroom door.

Molly pulled open the wardrobe door —

and Mum came into the room, her frown-puckered eyes seeking out the source of the strange scrabbling noises.

By now Molly was in the wardrobe; with great skill she'd pulled the door silently shut — and then she cried "Flipping Nora!" as an avalanche of clothes fell from hangers onto her head.

With a raider's rage Mum stormed forth to ransack the wardrobe. Flinging open the door, she loomed over Molly in silhouette as Molly cowered beneath her covering of black tee-shirts.

"Mum, it's not what it looks like!" Molly squealed. "I mean, it's exactly what it looks like, but I didn't know what else to do! I came up to see if there were any keys, and — Mum, say something!"

The silent silhouette simmered with rage. Molly fully expected Mum to smite her like a vengeful Fury. Instead, she seemed suddenly to crumble. One lanky leg gave way momentarily at the knee, and she grabbed the frame of the wardrobe. She bumbled backwards and bumped into the bed, then sat clumsily down.

"Mum, are you OK?"

Mrs Thompson put her head down in her palms and quietly started to sob.

"Mum?"

Molly threw the tee-shirts off her head and crawled out of the wardrobe. Briefly she inspected the tee-shirt that was wrapped around her forearm. It definitely wasn't one of Mum's. It pictured the album cover from a record by a famous heavy metal band. The artwork showed a ghoulish soldier rushing forward, gripping a union flag and a sword.

"Mum? Whose clothes are these?"

Molly crept closer.

"So you've found me out," Mum said bitterly. "I didn't throw all of his stuff away. Happy now?"

Molly sat down next to Mum on the edge of the bed, the tee-shirt on her lap.

"What — these horrible tee-shirts are Dad's?"

No answer — just noiseless tears.

"And you kept them? A whole wardrobe of them?"

Mum hiccupped, but said nothing.

"I never saw Dad wear them," said Molly.

Mum sniffed and glared for a long time. Molly wondered if she was supposed to get up and leave.

"Do you want me to leave you alone, Mum?"

But before Molly could get up, Mum started to speak in a small, tense croak.

"Molly, your dad had a secret."

Molly jolted with alarm. "What?"

"He was a heavy metal fan."

Molly spluttered with relief and disbelief. "No way."

Mum nodded slowly. "It's true, I'm afraid. He used to wear these tee-shirts when he went to those rough pubs on Lastmead Lane for his reading group."

"I can't imagine Dad wearing one of these," Molly

said, "laughing and joking with smelly blokes who've got tattooed knuckles."

"Heaven knows," muttered Mum, shaking her head and staring at her clasped hands. "Heaven knows."

Molly waited. "Um, heaven knows what, Mum?"

Another span of silence.

"Heaven knows … how he got them to join his book club, those reprobates who drank there. He loved befriending people like that. He once said that you can't really know a person until you've tried your best to care about them. So he tried to care about the people who nobody else liked. He made them laugh with his silly magic tricks."

Molly turned a tee-shirt over in her hands. "I remember his silly magic tricks," she said. "They *were* silly."

Mum sighed heavily.

"People said that those rough toothless blokes changed when they were around your dad," she said. "That was the real magic trick: he knew how to get people on his side. He had a magic smile."

"I wish I had a magic smile," said Molly. "I wanted to learn how to be like him. He died before I had a chance."

"You have exactly the same smile as your father," said Mum. "But you never use it. Not since he died, anyway. If you combined your knowledge and your dad's smile, you'd be unstoppable."

Molly remembered what Carl said, about how she never smiled.

She remembered what Felicity had said about her *miserable little scowl*.

She remembered how Furlock had called her *earnest*. She didn't want to be earnest. She wanted to be fun and carefree, like Dad.

"Mum," Molly said, wishing to shift topic, "of all the things of Dad's you could've kept, why did you keep these tee-shirts?"

Mum sniffed bleakly. She swept her hair back from her damp, flushed face. "I always nagged him to get rid of them. We argued about them. It doesn't seem fair to get rid of them now, when he's not here to argue back." Suddenly she turned to Molly, red-eyed. "Is that weird? Should I give them to the charity shop?"

Molly was taken aback. Mum didn't often seek Molly's advice. Nervously she turned the tee-shirt over in her hands a few more times. "Don't ask me," she shrugged. "I mess everything up."

Mum sniffed and looked at her clasped hands once more.

"Yes," she said at last. "You're certainly a nuisance, just like your father."

Molly held her tongue.

"And," Mum went on, "you're the best investigator in Howlfair. Or so people say."

Molly looked at her mum. "What people?"

"Mostly the same people who say you're a nuisance," Mum said. She pondered and frowned. "Molly, why do you bother with all of your investigations?"

"I knew there was something wrong," Molly said. "Even before Dad got ill. He seemed different. He looked so scared and desperate. I knew there was something going on that I didn't understand, and I hated not understanding. I still think that if I'd figured out what was going on, I could've found a way to help."

"Like burning down the museum, or poisoning us all with werewolf potion?" Mum sniffed. "Molly, don't you realize that the reason I get so angry at your crazy shenanigans is that I'm scared to death I'll lose you too?"

Molly shook her head. "I didn't know that." She stared at the tee-shirt. "I just feel like helping Dad was the one thing in my life I could've got right if I'd figured out what was wrong with him, but I missed my chance. Now I feel like I have to figure out *everything*."

Mum said, "Sometimes there's nothing to figure out. Your dad got ill, that's all."

"But he looked so scared!"

" 'Course he did! He'd never been ill before in his life. He'd always had so much energy. And like a typical man he refused to see a doctor until it was too late. Molly, you have to trust me: there's nothing you could have done."

Molly looked down at her feet. A tee-shirt was wrapped around her leg. "What are you going to do about these?"

Mum tugged at a strand of hair and thought. "Give me a couple of days to say goodbye to them, and then I'll put them in the bin. It's time to move on."

"Are you sure?"

"I'm sure. I'll need you to do something, though."

"I know, Mum: stop hiding in wardrobes."

"I want you to keep a tee-shirt for yourself," said Mum. "You can choose which one. You can wear it when we go to visit Lowry in the infirmary tomorrow. I've heard she's doing a bit better."

"Is she?" said Molly. "That's brilliant news!"

"Go on then — pick a tee-shirt."

Molly scooped some of the garments off the floor. "But they all horrify me equally."

"Wear it under a jumper if you like. Dad would be happy just knowing you're wearing it."

After pulling faces at a number of them, Molly

chose the one with the skeletal soldier and the flag. "This one."

"Ah, he loved that one."

Molly folded it and stood up. "Are you going to be OK?"

"'Course," said Mum, scooping up a long-sleeved tee-shirt and grimacing at it. But as Molly began to head for the door, Mum said, "Molly, wait."

"What is it?"

"I'm sorry I don't take more of an interest in the things you investigate," said Mum. "When this summer's over, maybe we could find some local historical thing that we can investigate together."

Molly brightened. "Really? What kind of historical thing?"

Mum said, "Ask me in September."

Well, September seemed a long way off to Molly. It wasn't even August. It was the last day of July. In a few hours the second full moon of the month — the blue moon — would show its face; and after that it would be too late to convince Mr Wetherill to help her. Benton Furlock would be voted Mayor of Howlfair, and the Dark Days would return, unless —

Heading down to the lobby, Molly tiptoed across the flagstones while Mrs Jones — a kindly woman, presently unconscious and snoring — was on door-watch. Molly went straight to the guest book, hoping to find, but not daring to expect, another message from Carl inscribed within.

The following note was written in pencil:

> He's releasing them.
> We need to save Howlfair.
> COMING TO GET YOU TONIGHT.

The Night of the Blue Moon

AT JUST AFTER TEN O'CLOCK, THE WEATHER turned. The wind snorted and kicked its hooves, raising dust, and it put its head down and began storming through the streets of Howlfair. Rusty, squeaking signposts swung. Trees applauded. Above the Ethelhael Valley, a single sponge-like cloud wiped the sky clean. The moon dazzled the town and gave the streets a mercury hue. The wind inflated the jacket of a tall, athletic girl on a bike as she flew wobbling madly over the dark cobbles, a carrier bag full of clothes bouncing as it hung from her handlebar. The wind carried the girl down Stayhand Walk, towards the junction where it collided with the Circuit, and nearly dashed her into a wall; she braked, skidded, and stopped inches short of a lamppost. She had her father's cloth locksmith's bag slung over her shoulder. It clanked when she shrugged to adjust its position.

She scowled. *What was all this blue mist?* Felicity Quick set off again on her urgent business, while behind her a cat scrambled from an alley, chased by a wafting whoosh of fog — and a huge hound.

Felicity rode on.

What a chase took place! Through the cobbled streets the hound pursued the cat under the blue moon's ghastly grin, down grim, depressing Mine's End Road, sometimes overtaking and blocking the cat's path, as though steering it towards a pre-decided destination.

Around Moon Crescent they sprinted, and back to Pennythief Lane, knocking over a tin dustbin, then down Ghulfost Street and onto The Cobblings, claws clattering.

Down Bonebroth Avenue with its famous soup kitchen. Heading towards Sellheart Road, the night's eerie blue mist spewing slowly from alley and crawling down the streets. The cat sharply rounded the corner, its little face determined and tired, and the dog closed the distance just as Felicity Quick was approaching the top end of Sellheart Road. The shadowy hound finally caught its prey outside a grey-windowed, abandoned shop.

The hound's amber fangs caught the cat's collar. *Chomp!* A swing of the dog's dire head pitched the poor cat high into the air. The collar flew; the little silver disc bearing the cat's name spun into the air and landed in a groove between the cobbles. If you'd looked, you would have seen the name: GABRIEL.

Gabriel landed badly, and lay motionless. The dog picked up the floppy feline in its teeth.

A nearby doorway hissed.

The dog looked left, looked right, then padded towards the doorway of a boarded-up house.

It dropped the limp body and sat down obediently.

Eyes glowed from the dark recess.

"Good girl, Hecate," said the man in the black doorway. He began to emerge from the darkness. But before he could step into the street's dim lamplight, a girl's shout echoed down the quiet lane.

"Hey! Shoo, dog! Leave that cat alone!"

A perfectly pitched stone arched through the night air and clipped the dog's head. The dog sprinted away, hurt, slipping down an alley. The tall figure in the doorway scowled hatefully and receded into the darkness as Felicity Quick, captain of the school rounders team, pedalled over through the thickening blue mist.

Felicity jumped from her bicycle and approached the twisted moggy, one hand pressed against her heavy locksmith's bag to stop it swinging around.

She saw that the cat was still alive.

"A stray," she muttered, noticing the lack of collar. "Hey, cat, it's OK, the dog's gone."

She knelt, and Gabriel glanced up at the girl's jagged fringe.

The cat remembered Molly's warning.

Only feet away, the figure in the dark doorway was silently drawing a weapon. Then he frowned with surprise as the cat, summoning its last bit of energy, hissed and swiped at the girl, sharp claws carving the air.

"Hey! I'm trying to help, you stupid cat!"

But Gabriel, forewarned against Felicity Quick, was putting up a desperate fight.

"Fine — be like that!" Felicity backed off and picked up her bicycle. "Ungrateful mammal."

The moment Felicity cycled off, the man in the doorway put away the cruel weapon he'd drawn and re-emerged from the shadows, a jute sack draped over the crook of one arm. Benton Furlock (for the figure was he) snapped his fingers, and a boy in a parka coat slipped from a nearby alley and trotted over. Furlock lifted Gabriel by the scruff of his neck and dropped him into the sack.

"I've got the cat," Benton Furlock told the boy. "You get the girl."

* * *

Tucked up in a narrow bed in the children's ward of Howlfair Infirmary on the night of the blue moon, Lowry Evans lay fretting and wondering if she was about to become a werewolf, while her fellow patients slumbered and the loon-faced moon leered through the silver-lit window.

Suddenly she heard something moving outside in the darkness.

Jolting upright, Lowry looked over at the window to see —

The face of a monster!

The face, that is, of Felicity Quick.

Scowling, Lowry padded to the window in her hospital gown. Felicity gestured for her to open the window, but it was locked. Rolling her eyes, Felicity unslung and opened the bag containing her father's locksmith tools, and within moments the lock was mastered.

"What in the name of Beelzebub's bathrobe are you doing, breaking in here?" Lowry hissed.

Felicity threw her plastic bag full of clothes through the window while the children of the ward looked on with alarm. "Put these on and come with me."

"Felicity, I don't know if you've noticed, but I'm in hospital."

"Are you still ill?"

"Well, not particularly, but—"

"Good. I'm going to set Thompson free and I need you to convince her to come with us."

"Come with us where?"

"I'll explain everything on the way."

Lowry folded her arms. "You'll explain some of it *right now* — or I'm not going anywhere."

Felicity sighed angrily. "My granddad got permission to build his houses. Benton Furlock smoothed over the problem with the plague pit."

Lowry shrugged. "So?"

"So it turns out that Benton Furlock has been blackmailing my granddad. Furlock *forced* him to buy that land. He *wants* Granddad to build houses over a plague pit."

"What for?"

"I don't know! Because he's a sicko," said Felicity. "Or maybe he thinks it'll be good for tourism if he builds a load of houses that he can pretend are haunted. I was telling Granddad tonight about the weird thing I'd seen in the museum — long story short, Molly set fire to a painting and it mended itself — and when I described the painting, he had a complete breakdown and confessed everything. He said that Furlock's been blackmailing half of

Howlfair, threatening to set ghouls on people if they don't give him money and do what he says. He's trying to get control of the whole town. Granddad says that Furlock sends people letters with his demands, and if they don't give him what he wants, he sends ghouls round to *scare* them. After that, he sends ghouls to *hurt* them. If they still won't play along, he sends ghouls to *kill* them."

"No way!"

"Furlock desperately needs money — not just for the campaign, but for something massive he's going to do as soon as he becomes Mayor of Howlfair. Granddad's got this mad idea that Furlock's going to send ghouls out to kill all the people he's been blackmailing now that he's bled them all dry. I tried to tell him that ghouls aren't real — that Furlock's probably just hired actors to pretend to be ghouls — but Granddad's convinced that actual ghouls are going to come out during the blue moon and murder everyone who knows what Furlock's been up to."

"But … *tonight* is the night of the blue moon."

"Exactly! Now tell me straight — has that annoying best friend of yours been investigating all this stuff?"

Lowry felt a twinge of pride. "She's *Molly flipping Thompson* — she investigates *everything*. She was planning to break into Loonchance Manor to get evidence of the evil things Benton Furlock is doing so she can stop him from becoming mayor."

Felicity chewed her lip anxiously. "I need her to tell me everything that she knows. Get dressed — we're going to the Excelsior Guesthouse to bust Molly out, and we're going to stop Furlock tonight."

Lowry put on the tracksuit Felicity had brought, and after swearing the other children in the ward to secrecy and saluting them farewell, she climbed through the window and got onto the back of Felicity Quick's bike (she never imagined she and Felicity Quick would be sharing a bicycle) — and off they rode, fleetly flying over the cobbles.

Lowry noticed that Felicity had a wooden bat strapped to her back.

"Are you planning on stopping to play rounders?" she asked as they careened through the streets.

"I'm gonna do some batting practice," Felicity growled. "As soon as I get my hands on Benton Furlock."

If Felicity hadn't stopped to rescue a strange cat that night, she and Lowry might have reached the Excelsior in time. But while the two girls were speeding down Poorhouse Lane, Molly was watching with excitement from her temporary bedroom as Carl Grobman, standing on a thick branch of the oak tree, picked her window lock to set her free. By the time Felicity and Lowry reached the guesthouse, Molly was gone.

The Hand That Grabbed

THE MOON MADE THE GRAVESTONES AND the blue mist glow as Molly followed Carl through Howlfair New Cemetery.

"We're lucky, you know," Carl said. "If we'd waited another day, it would've been too late."

Molly dodged a headstone. "What would've been too late, Carl? You need to fill me in."

"I'll tell you everything as soon as we get to Loonchance Manor." They passed through the graveyard's gate and emerged on the northernmost end of Squint-Eye Lane. The blue moon grinned overhead in a sky forlorn of clouds. All around the valley gleamed the glossy walls of night.

"Can't you tell me anything now?"

"We're going to break some evil spells," said Carl. "We're going to save the town and rescue your friend Lowry."

"Lowry?"

Carl stopped and, momentarily silhouetted against a streetlight, looked back. "Mr Furlock cursed her family, Molly. He's turning them into werewolves so he can control them."

"What!" coughed Molly. "You mean Lowry was right?"

"I've found the hidden room where he's doing his werewolf spell, and I know how to stop the curse from working. I even know how to make it rebound on him."

"I don't want to turn Furlock into a werewolf," said Molly. "He's ugly enough without a snout."

"He's got a whole lair underneath Loonchance Manor — with bubbling potions and runes and magic circles drawn with blood. Mainly they give him power over ghouls. If you can help me decipher the coded message around Furlock's magic circles, we can send his ghouls back to Hell and stop his curses."

"Really?"

Carl began to move up the street. "I've been pretty busy while you've been locked up, you know. Oh — by the way: the only reason Lowry hasn't started turning into a wolf already is that potion you gave her. You did her a massive favour. I thought you might want to know."

Molly felt a bit more at ease now. As at ease as anyone can feel when they're on their way to break a werewolf curse in a secret chamber in a mansion famous for hosting a historic ghoul feast.

They slipped down a quiet narrow side street. Shadows and silent cats watched them. Molly felt a pang for Gabriel. What had happened to her guardian cat? Where had he gone? Had he run away? Or run out of lives?

"Molly, keep up," Carl hissed. "Stop daydreaming."

"I wasn't daydreaming," said Molly. "I was just wondering…"

"About what?"

She didn't feel inclined to confess that she was thinking about her cat. "I was wondering what kind of scumbag tries to turn twelve-year-old girls into wolves."

"The same kind that enslaves twelve-year-old boys and forces them to help him blackmail people," said Carl, jumping over a pothole.

They headed down Witherway Street. Then up Lastmead Lane, past the pubs. The silhouettes of candle-lit revellers moved behind the drapes.

"The Last Drop," said Molly.

"What?"

"That pub — The Last Drop. My dad ran a book club

there. That's where I met Lady Orgella in a dream."

"A book club?" said Carl. "That was a smugglers' pub. The people in there are dead dodgy."

Dodgy. For some reason the word chimed in Molly's mind. She remembered that *dodgy* was how Lowry had described Carl's story about how he got marked with the symbol of Lady Orgella.

"My mum said he never had any trouble," said Molly. "He knew how to make friends with all kinds of people. He smiled at them and slapped their backs and made them laugh with magic tricks."

Carl said, "I don't think magic tricks would work with Furlock's ghouls."

They didn't speak again until they arrived at the roundabout where the hideous wooden house of horror, silver and slanted, stood beside its yew tree bride.

At the gate, Carl took something from his pocket, shoved it into the padlock and cursed under his breath as he struggled to open the lock.

"Aren't we going through the secret back door?" Molly asked.

"I checked the back door — it looks like Mr Furlock's booby-trapped it," said Carl — and something fell to the cobbles with a chime. Molly saw it was a key. Hastily Carl scooped it up and reinserted it into the lock. "I've found out how to get in through the front door, though."

"What was that?" asked Molly, wary.

"My lock-picking tool," mumbled Carl, grunting as he worked on the lock. Suddenly the gate swung open.

It hadn't looked like a lock-picking tool to Molly. It'd looked like Carl had a key to the gate. But there was no time to question him, for by now he'd run up the path and ascended the steps to the narrow front door of Loonchance Manor. And now Carl was using another key — or, rather, his *lock-picking tool* — to open the front door. He was holding the frame with his left hand and attacking the lock with his right, as though it was stuck. But it seemed to Molly that when the lock at last opened, it did so pretty smoothly.

Carl pushed the door open. A wedge of pure darkness appeared. Carl fumbled in his jacket for a torch, and beckoned Molly over.

She closed the gate behind her and trotted to the door, feeling dreadfully uneasy.

Molly didn't know quite what inspired her, at that moment, to ask the question. Perhaps fear and curiosity had conspired to shove the question out of her mouth.

"Carl — can you show me how Furlock did it?"

Carl, already moving into the darkness, his torch

not yet activated, turned. "How he did what?"

"How he put Lady Orgella's mark on you with that metal quill."

The boy narrowed his eyes suspiciously. "What for?"

Molly scratched her curls. "If I'm going to go through with this, I need to make myself hate Furlock more than I'm afraid of this house."

Carl pondered, then stepped out of the doorway. "He grabbed my arm with his hand, and he held the quill, um, like this…" He lifted the torch.

"Grabbed you how? Show me."

"You want me to grab you?"

"Yes," said Molly.

"Like this." Carl took hold of Molly's upper arm with his left hand. "And he pulled my arm. Like this…"

Suddenly, unexpectedly, Carl lurched back through the doorway, wrenching Molly into the mansion. A foreleg flicked past Molly — Carl had kicked the door shut. He switched his torch on. A dreadfully dreary cobwebbed hallway spread before them, populated by waxwork ghouls.

He still had hold of her arm. "You're hurting me," Molly said, scared.

"He waved the quill over my arm like this to make the mark."

287

Molly flinched as the torch's light danced across the sombre hallway and the waxy faces of the ghouls. Then Carl slipped past her. He locked the front door, no longer hiding the fact that he had a key.

"Carl, why are you locking it?" Molly said. "How did you get a key to Loonchance Manor?"

"I don't want Furlock following us in here," Carl mumbled, pocketing the key and pushing past Molly, striding towards the reception desk. "Let's get this over with."

Molly didn't move.

"Come on, Molly! What are you waiting for?"

Molly said, "You've never seen Furlock's other hand, have you?"

Carl's face was scrunched up with annoyance now.

"His hand? Of course I've seen his hand."

"The one he keeps stuffed in his coat," said Molly. "It's made of glass, or crystal, or something. It's not real. He couldn't have grabbed you with it the way you showed me."

Carl stared, his torch beam stretching across the floorboards towards Molly. He had the look of a wild dog about to leap at a tasty throat.

"You didn't bring me here to save Lowry, did you?" Molly said. "All that stuff about her really being a werewolf — I can't believe I fell for it."

Carl looked away.

"Mr Furlock's the only person who's ever given a damn about me," he said, avoiding Molly's eyes. "Did you honestly think I was going to betray him?"

A shudder of dread pulsed through Molly. "What?" she coughed. "Carl, *I* give a damn..."

"Yeah, right!" Carl laughed humourlessly. "You were just using me. You don't care about me or anyone else. You don't care about this town. Everyone knows that all Molly Thompson cares about is solving mysteries."

"That's not true! Anyway, Furlock *hurt* you, Carl!"

Now Carl was advancing. "I *asked* him to give me the mark of Orgella. I *want* to be a servant of Lady Orgella, just like Mr Furlock. The mark is her seal of ownership. When she sets up her kingdom on earth and Mr Furlock is her Prime Minister, I'm going to be a general, with an army of my own ghouls!"

"Carl, listen..."

He lifted the torch, blinding Molly.

Then the torch went off, and everything was abysmally black.

The House of Ghouls

FOOTSTEPS ON THE FLOORBOARDS. WHISPERS and feral breaths as something cold crept close. Any summer-night warmth left in the hallway flew away with the stinging suddenness of a ripped-off plaster. Molly spun — a mistake, because a freezing unseen hand grabbed her as she spun, and spun her some more, kept spinning her; and she screamed — an even worse mistake, because while her mouth was wide open, something like rope (she was pretty sure it was rope) was wrapped around her lower head, wedging between her teeth so that she couldn't shut her jaws.

Now she was being dragged by the head, lassoed, herded, with no idea which direction she was going in. It was like spinning through space. The fear was cosmic. Thought was impossible. Then the torchlight blared, and Molly saw who was pulling her: it was

Benton Furlock, his delighted white face as shiny as a melting ice cube. He was walking backwards, dragging Molly towards him; Carl must have been behind Molly, aiming the torch.

"Well done, Carl!" Furlock laughed. "And well done to *you*, Molly — for figuring out that Carl has been working for me all along." His pale, evil face glowed as he yanked the rope. "Unfortunately, you found out too late."

Molly tried to claw at the rope wedged in her mouth, but it was too tight. Besides, she needed both hands for protection — she was bouncing off walls and furniture. She stumbled, knocking over a waxwork of that crooked old viper Grandma Loonchance. She knew that if she fell over, Furlock would yank her to her feet, and it would hurt. She put her hands out and fended off a flapping cobweb as Furlock wrenched her through a doorway.

"At least you get to go on my Ghoul Tour before you die, eh, Molly? Look! This is the room where Daphne Loonchance told her family that she would be marrying a gravedigger..."

Molly was unable to take in the features of the drab, miserable room. Furlock hauled her like an anchor and her hand sliced through the glass of a grandmother clock. She moaned as the glass slashed her flesh to free a flow of blood. The clock toppled behind her.

"Daphne, of course, discovered the secret of gaining control over ghouls — her fiancé gave it to her before the Loonchance family murdered him. She wrote it in her diary, on a page that went missing. And I found the missing page when I took possession of Loonchance Manor. Took me months to find it…"

Molly wanted to beg Furlock to let her go, but the rope was wedged tight between her jaws.

"The secret of gaining power over ghouls, Molly, is a *sacrifice* — performed on the night of a blue moon." Furlock's voice faded as he moved into the darkness of a side corridor. "A sacrifice made to a very special demon — Lady Orgella. A sacrifice that will persuade her to command a mob of ghouls to obey your every wish, ghouls desperate to win the Lady's favour and return to Hell. Ah, and do you know what you must sacrifice to meet the Mistress of Ghouls' demands?"

Molly felt a surge of centrifugal force as Furlock swung her around a corner. The torch beam followed, bobbing.

"You must sacrifice *your best friend*, Molly. Friendship, you see, is a sacred thing, and Lady Orgella loves to desecrate that which is sacred. Daphne Loonchance sacrificed her best friend on the night of the blue moon. I poisoned Mr Halfstar — my business partner and closest friend — on an altar beneath this manor. And tonight, Molly, you are going to sacrifice your best friend on the same altar."

Molly thought: *Lowry!*

"I've had my eye on you for some time, Molly — your investigations have caused me much amusement. But then you began meddling in my affairs, telling everybody about the plague pits underneath a plot of land on which I wish to see a new housing estate. Helping Doris de Ville by spying on me. And then Carl told me that you were investigating Mrs Fullsway's death — I never meant for my ghouls to give her a *fatal* fright, by the way — and I knew I had to get rid of you. Not only get rid of you, but destroy your reputation so that nobody believes anything you've ever said."

"Scumbag!" Molly tried to shout — but the rope didn't allow her to form the word. Her palm slammed into a wall, leaving a bloody print from her cut. The rope creaked as Furlock dragged Molly up a short flight of wooden steps. She stumbled, cracking her knee on the splinter-riddled wood. A sob of pain and terror and fury escaped her.

"Your body will be found underneath a pile of

fallen timbers in a vault undergoing renovation," Furlock continued. "An investigation will reveal that you discovered the secret of Daphne Loonchance, the secret of raising ghouls, and broke into Loonchance Manor to enact a horrific ritual. What's more, a note will be found in one of your school books, forged by Mr Grobman here, and will suggest that it was Doris de Ville — the mayor's own wife! — who first encouraged you to break into my manor to spy on my operations ahead of the mayoral elections."

Molly's head thumped against a sinister ebony cuckoo clock. Her skull sang.

There was an old-fashioned paternoster lift halfway down the corridor. Furlock yanked Molly towards him, and with great dexterity he spun her around like a ballroom dancer and coiled her in the rope, pinning her arms. Hooking the rope over the crook of his elbow, he wrenched aside the cage door and gestured for Carl to enter the lift, then pulled Molly inside.

The torchlight roamed as Carl found the right button. Furlock's presence seemed to freeze the air. Molly searched frantically for a means of escape. Furlock's casual ease betrayed a certainty that no such means were available to her.

The lift lurched, falling. Molly's stomach rose. She

dreaded to think what horrid chambers awaited her beneath Loonchance Manor.

The lift gathered speed.

"Think of the scandal, Molly! The mayor's wife encouraging a meddling youngster to spy on her husband's rival... A morbid-minded young girl breaking into Loonchance Manor and murdering her best friend as part of a macabre black-magic ceremony intended to raise ghouls! Then dying in a horrible accident before the ceremony can be concluded!"

The lift thumped to a stop. Carl pulled the lift's cage door aside and directed his torch down a tunnel studded with black archways.

Furlock followed. He gave the rope a tug, and Molly followed too. She found she was whimpering with fear. Her legs wobbled and danced wildly. She thought of Lowry trapped down there in some hideous vault, awaiting the fate that Furlock had planned. The evil philanthropist's voice echoed as he led her down the tunnel.

"You're playing along so nicely, Molly, that I'm tempted to tell you the thing that you most want to know: what happened to your father. But that is one mystery you will die without solving. I will only say that I cannot, unfortunately, take any credit for his death. I say *unfortunately* because your blasted father caused me a great deal of distress — not least because he cost me my hand."

Over one of the archways was a metal sign, curved like a shallow rainbow. Furlock paused beneath it. The writing on the sign made Molly think fleetingly of fairground rides. It read:

CATACOMBS & CRYPT

Another sign below it read:

DANGER — NO ENTRY
RENOVATIONS IN PROGRESS

Furlock pulled Molly into the darkness beyond the archway, towards a spiral stairway of freezing stone. As Furlock trod, lamps set in little alcoves in the walls sprang alive. Carl switched off his torch. Furlock disappeared round the corner and gave Molly a tug.

"Keep left," he barked as she jerked forward.

There were metal plates on every fifth step, one on the left, one on the right; stepping on a plate on the left caused the lights further down the staircase to illuminate, and plunged the stairs behind Molly back into darkness. At last they reached the foot of the steps, where they found a corridor bearing a row of wooden doors with silver edging. Carl moved ahead to unlock one such door. He shouldered it open to reveal a circular stone-walled room lit by torches that nestled in iron holders. The room breathed out rancid air; it had the haunted stench of a stagnant midnight pond.

Furlock shoved Molly into the chamber and released the rope; she tumbled to the damp, cobbled floor. Instinctively she thrashed to release her arms. Carl shut the door. Wildly Molly looked around the ghastly vault, searching for Lowry.

Opposite her, with steps beneath it, was a portrait of Lady Orgella, flanked by torches. Orgella wore a circular, cyan eye patch. Butterflies and death's head moths were in her hair. Her face was grey and grave, beautiful and nightmarish. Circling the room were small booths, cut high into the wall, half of them empty, half of them occupied by — flipping Nora! — the skulls or leathery, embalmed heads of people sacrificed to the Mistress of Ghouls.

Above the booths were foggy, thick-glassed windows; Molly fancied she saw blue lights spangling behind the glass.

At ground level a large lever, the sort you'd imagine might open a lock, protruded from the wall. And in the middle of the room was a low altar...

There was a sheet draped at one end of the altar, the end nearest the demon's portrait, and under the sheet was —

Well, it wasn't Lowry, that's for sure.

It was the size of a small animal, and it wasn't moving.

Molly knew immediately who was under the sheet. It was her oldest and truest best friend.

The Altar of Sacrifice

THERE WASN'T TIME TO FORM A PLAN. Furlock was pulling the lever, and hidden cogs in the wall were emitting a rusty shriek. Presently the windows high in the circular wall began to hinge open like the slack jaws of zombies.

Creatures proceeded through the frames.

Some floated down from the windows. Some crawled face-first down the wall like geckos. All were shrouded, grey-faced; all had bright blue left eyes; all were weighed down with gold and silver jewellery robbed from the dead.

Molly whimpered and thrashed as one of the ghouls — female, long-haired — scuttled over to untie her. The ghoul's breath was eye-wateringly vile. "Wonderful, aren't they?" cooed Furlock. "It so tickles me when visitors say that the ghouls on my tour aren't *realistic*. If only people knew of the havoc my slaves wreak when I permit them to leave Loonchance Manor to perform my errands. In the eyes of my ghouls, I possess the authority of Lady Orgella herself." Furlock gestured to a pair of the creatures. "Get her in position."

Molly was free of the ropes now — but she was even less free than before; cold ghoulish hands were gripping her. Flicker-lit by the torch flames, Furlock's ghouls roughly shunted her across the chamber and forced her to her knees at the portrait end of the low altar. Molly's fingers were prised apart and an object thrust into her hand: something heavy. Then the clammy hand closed around hers, forcing her to grip the object. A vague and inappropriate image came to Molly's mind: her mum teaching her to write by enfolding her hand in hers as she held a pencil, helping her to form the words. She remembered how gently she'd guided her hand...

But the ghoul wasn't gentle, not at all. She knelt at the side of the altar near the wall-lever, to Molly's right, silver hair falling in straggles over her face. She drew aside the sheet of cloth, and revealed a cat barely alive, eyes glazed, staring, his little ribs pulsing with fast, shallow breaths.

"*Gabriel,*" Molly croaked, her jaws not really working.

The cat twitched as he tried to raise his head to look at Molly. Then his head fell still; but his nearly lifeless eye continued to seek her.

The ghoul lifted her hand high, so that now she was poised to bring the heavy object in her grip — some sort of cudgel or truncheon — down on Gabriel's head.

"Hold there — perfect!" cried Furlock. Molly realized that Carl, in the background, was whimpering with nerves.

"Gabriel," was all Molly could say, her voice catching in her throat. Her jaw felt dislocated.

"It was Carl who told me that your cat, not the Evans girl, was probably your real best friend. But don't worry; I promise that your other best friend is going to die tonight as well. Once my ghouls have staged the sacrifice of your cat and caused a little accident involving those loose timbers over your head, they'll erase all traces that I was here. Then, when I give them permission to leave this chamber, they will head into the night for the next stage of my plan. An anonymous caller" — he indicated himself — "is going to telephone the Chief of Police to say that he saw a young girl breaking into Loonchance Manor holding a cat. The police will arrive to find that you and your cat were killed while you were performing a ghoul-raising ritual."

Furlock smoothed his moustache in a manner that Molly might have found comical under other circumstances. The horrid clammy grip on her hand tightened.

"I have made a lot of money and accomplished a lot of devilry by blackmailing the people of Howlfair," Furlock continued. "It's time to put my ghouls into hibernation while I concentrate on winning the mayoral elections, as my mistress Lady Orgella has commanded me, and on the work that lies ahead. But first, I'll be authorizing my ghouls to leave their lair and undertake one last mission: to kill everyone who might know about them. While the emergency services are here, digging your body out from under a pile of timber, my ghouls will be burning down Howlfair Infirmary and causing a number of other witnesses — including Mr Quick, Mrs Quincy and your own mother, of course — to die in their beds..."

"Please — don't kill them!"

"Shush, shush, Molly!" laughed Furlock, revealing his glass hand and setting it to his lips. "Don't fill your furry friend's last moments with terror and anxiety! Spend your time comforting the poor creature."

Molly felt herself swooning. The ghouls' hands held her in position. Her head was full of fear and fog.

"You have thirty seconds," Furlock told Molly,

"to say goodbye to your pet."

Molly looked down at her beloved sidekick, her companion through a thousand adventures. The ghoul was resting a grey hand on Gabriel's flank, but there was no need to hold Gabriel down; the brave cat had no strength left. He could no longer move his head. But one little eye was straining sideways in its socket, looking at Molly.

"I'm sorry, Gabriel! It's all my fault! But it's OK — it won't hurt, and you won't have to worry about losing any more lives again, and I'll be right behind you, and then…"

And then what?

"Time's up," yawned Furlock, though only seven seconds had passed. "I honestly thought your death-bed speech would be more entertaining. Anyway, let's get this show on the road. It's almost a shame that you won't be around to see the unfolding of my mistress' plan. She has given me the prestigious job of bringing the Dark Days back to Howlfair, and this time there won't be any Guilds or Orders to fight her monsters. With me as mayor, our valley will become dark enough, evil enough, for the Mistress of Ghouls herself to come forth from the underworld and establish Howlfair as the capital of a new Hell. She will be its supreme queen — and she has promised to make me an honorary demon! But alas, you will be far too dead to see any of this. Ghouls — on the count of three, make the girl kill the cat."

"In a minute," Molly told Gabriel firmly, fixing her gaze on the little eye. "I'll see you again in a minute."

"One!" cried Furlock.

"You and Dad, and …"

"Two!"

"… and all the other brave Excelsior cats."

Furlock opened his mouth, drew a breath, and the heavy lump of wood came crashing down.

Rounders

AH, NOT THE PIECE OF WOOD IN MOLLY'S hand. No — that didn't have time to fall. For Furlock was interrupted before the count of three by the collapse of part of the ceiling.

It was a loose shank of timber that dropped, clonking the head of the ghoul who held Molly. Something — a rock — had been thrown across the room from the doorway, and had hit one of the ghouls who'd been leaning against a wooden strut up in the rafters. The door to the chamber stood open; Molly saw a shadow in the gloom beyond. Then it vanished.

"Who's there?" Furlock shouted, and Molly noticed with wild relief that he appeared somewhat discombobulated. The ghoul who'd been struck by the falling timber still held Molly in position. Molly looked down at Gabriel. The little eye had closed. The cat's tongue protruded slightly, as though Gabriel had wanted one last taste of life. The female ghoul who'd been holding him raised her head and grinned at Molly as if to say: *He's dead.*

The shadow in the doorway appeared again, and Molly saw the mysterious visitor expertly pitch another rock at a ghoul sitting in the eaves. The ghoul spun around, shoving a rafter, and a shower of bricks narrowly missed Carl. Another beam fell, slamming to the floor close to Furlock. Dust billowed, making Molly choke. Furlock scrambled coward-faced behind the nearest ghoul (his ghouls seemed unconcerned by the falling ceiling) and screamed at it to cover him. The ghoul wrapped him in an awkward hug that made Furlock scream all the more.

Watching Furlock, Molly didn't notice the gnarled lump of timber directly above Gabriel fall through the dust clouds until it was too late.

Crash!

"Gabriel!"

She looked down to see the hunk of wood lying on the altar where her oldest friend had been. The ghoul had slithered away and was now looking to Furlock for instructions. But he was trying to get to the door, locked in a sort of tango with his guardian ghoul.

"Who's that in the doorway?" Furlock shrieked. "Ghouls — kill the girl! Pull down the ceiling, all of you!"

306

Molly, eyes full of dust and tears, looked up to see Furlock break free from his bodyguard and lurch towards the chamber's entrance. And from the corner of one eye she saw a ghostly black shape skate along the wall.

Furlock scooped up a sharp stake of wood and bumbled through the storm of dust, flattening himself against the wall to one side of the doorway, where he stood ready to thrust the stake into the throat of anyone who tried to enter the chamber.

Then as the dust drifted aside, Molly saw a figure — no, *two* girl-shaped figures — in the murk beyond the doorway. It took her a moment to recognize them.

Felicity Quick — armed with a rock and her rounders bat — and Lowry Evans.

A strut of timber groaned and cracked overhead, for now the rest of the ghouls had climbed the walls and populated the rafters, where they were working deftly to dislodge the beams. The noise masked Molly's shout of warning:

"Watch out!"

Felicity didn't hear her — and as Carl Grobman swam pathetically across the floor in an attempt to clamber out of her path, Felicity rushed straight into Furlock's trap.

She caught the thrust of Furlock's wooden spike

with her rounders bat, dashing it aside, but as Felicity attempted a backswing, Furlock grabbed the bat in his right hand and ripped it from her grasp. Lowry sprang onto Furlock but was thrown against the wall, her foot twisting horridly, a torn scrap of Furlock's jacket and a couple of shiny buttons in her fist. And then Molly saw it again — the ghostly black streak crossing the floor. It wasn't until the black streak leapt up onto Furlock's back and scrambled aboard his skull that Molly dared to recognize what it was.

"Gabriel!"

Somehow he'd slipped off the altar before the chunk of timber had struck. The ghoul-woman had taken her hand off him, because —

He was playing dead! Molly thought. *Just like Dad used to.*

Furlock screamed and clutched at the cat whose front claws were in his eyes.

The two girls bumbled towards Molly, dodging a deluge of rubble, Lowry limping painfully. Lady Orgella watched from the wall. The torches writhed. Molly spied Carl Grobman slipping into a shadow in the corner of the chamber. At last Furlock, blinded, his face gored, managed to peel Gabriel from his head and lurched for the door, bouncing off the wall, feeling his way with his one good hand.

Meanwhile, a strut of wood above Molly was torn away and dropped.

"Molly!" Lowry cried — and Molly looked up in time to see the plank plummet. But not in time to get out of the way.

Instinctively she rolled over. The beam slammed into the side of her leg and for a moment Molly marvelled at how the falling wood had landed with a sound exactly like the sound of a bone cracking.

Then she realized that her leg-bone had cracked.

Bravely Felicity and Lowry wove their way across the collapsing chamber. Gabriel joined them at Molly's side. With a grunt, Felicity hauled the timber from Molly's leg.

"Get Gabriel and go!" Molly spluttered.

"What — that's Gabriel?" said Felicity, looking with distaste at the cat who'd previously attacked her.

The cat hissed.

"You can trust her, Gabriel — she's a friend," winced Molly as Felicity helped her up. Gabriel let Lowry scoop him into her arms, and the girls headed for the door, four creatures supported on five terror-tipsy legs.

"Ghouls — come down and eat those children!" Furlock sobbed at the fiends in the rafters as he found his way to the door.

Carl cried out. "Mr Furlock! What about me?"

"And don't let that useless orphan follow me!" Furlock commanded his ghouls as he fled — not up the stairs, but down the corridor. The silver-rimmed door swung shut, and now the ghouls were descending from the rafters, floating through the dust.

"Hurry!" shrieked Lowry.

Molly scooped up a length of fallen timber to use as a walking-stick, and half hopped, half pole-vaulted across the chamber with all her strength.

Felicity got to the door first and pulled it open — thank goodness Furlock hadn't managed to lock it — as the long-haired female ghoul drifted through the dust clouds. The ghoul was nearly upon the girls as they bumbled into the corridor with Gabriel in Lowry's arms. Felicity wrenched the door shut and the girls blundered towards the staircase.

"They're not following!" Lowry gasped with wild relief.

"They need Furlock's permission to leave," Molly croaked, lolling as Felicity, with an arm around her waist, heaved her onto the steps. "They can only do what they're told to do."

Lowry, wincing with pain, held Gabriel with one arm and clung to Felicity's shoulder with the other.

Molly was right. The ghouls remained in the

chamber. Furlock was gone. The only thing that followed the girls as they toiled up the stairs was the sound of Carl's screams as the ghouls closed in on him.

Me Old Muckers

"I CAN'T STAND IT!" LOWRY SOBBED AS THEY ascended, the metal plates on the left hand side of the staircase activating the eerie illumination, the sound of Carl's cries rising up the staircase.

"We need to get help fast," said Felicity. "In case Furlock comes back and lets the ghouls out."

Shock and fear had numbed Molly's leg till now; at last she was beginning to feel the pain blooming. But the screams from the chamber hurt more. Her coat was hanging half off, ripped; she shrugged it from her shoulder. She looked down at the top she was wearing: the heavy metal tee-shirt picturing the ghoulish soldier. Her mouth was terribly dry and the thought that her leg was almost definitely broken was making her feel very faint.

"Dad would've known what to do," she croaked, stumbling. Felicity kept her from falling. "He'd get the ghouls on his side…"

"Thompson, stop babbling," said Felicity.

Molly's head lolled. Felicity was struggling to support both her and Lowry.

"So that's how you found me," Molly muttered, looking down at her cut hand, which still gripped her makeshift walking-stick. "By my trail of blood."

"Yeah — and the trail of clumsy destruction you left all through the house," said Felicity as she hoisted Molly up another step.

Another scream from the chamber below and Molly squeezed her eyes shut. Opened them. "Leave me here."

Lowry choked. *"What?"*

Felicity said, "Thompson, don't be an idiot."

Molly summoned her strength and pulled away from Felicity. She toppled sideways, nearly fell, and hopped down a dozen steps, three at a time, before she planted her walking-stick hard and regained her balance, clinging to the bannister with her free hand.

"I'm slowing you down," she shouted. "I can't make it up those stairs — I'll probably fall and break my neck and drag you with me. Get Mr Wetherill and come back for me before Furlock returns."

"Molly, are you crazy?" Lowry shouted, struggling to retain her grip on the thrashing cat. "You can't stay down here!"

But Molly continued her hoppy descent, falling towards Carl's cries.

"It's OK – the ghouls can't get out and Furlock's gone blind," she called. "Just fetch Mr Wetherill – and be quick!"

"She's right," Felicity conceded. "I can't get you both up these steps. We need to get help."

Lowry tutted. "Just stay alive!" she shouted down the stairs. "We'll be back soon."

The pain and terror had nearly overwhelmed Molly by the time she'd hobbled with her stick back to the door to Lady Orgella's chamber. She could hear Carl whimpering and begging. The sound of her friends' footsteps receded. She wondered how long it would be before Furlock returned.

"I know what you'd do, Dad," she whispered to herself as she leaned panting against the door, listening to Carl beg for mercy. "You'd go in and try to save him. You'd find a way to get the ghouls on your side. But I'm not like you."

She closed her eyes as a wave of weakness unmoored her from her senses. She couldn't fight the dizzy faintness. She seemed to fall into a dream, a seductive and comfortable dream more vivid than her waking nightmare.

A voice inside her head: *You're exactly like me, Moll.*

In her imagination she looked down and saw some-one else's hand reaching for a door handle. She looked up and saw warm-lit windows. She heard shouts of revelry, the laughter of scallies in an old smugglers' pub down Lastmead Lane. She raised her eyes and saw a noose swinging, and a copper plaque over the door:

THE LAST DROP INN
FINE ALES
1622

Her dad's favourite pub.

Now she imagined the door opening before her. Two dozen gold-toothed, tattooed reprobates turned towards her.

Give them your smile, Moll, said the familiar voice in her head. *Get them on your side. Do a magic trick!*

She felt a grin stretch across her face. She couldn't remember the last time she'd grinned. And now the gnarly patrons were all beaming at her, welcoming her into the firelit pub. She felt herself shouting a greeting, but the voice wasn't her own.

Then the vision was gone. She opened her eyes,

and she was back in the bowels of Loonchance Manor. One leg probably broken. She thought of something her mum had told her:

If you combined your knowledge and your dad's smile, you'd be unstoppable.

"Blue moon — vanity moon," she babbled to herself. "A moon which goes away and comes back. A demon's mark which goes away and comes back. A face that comes back when you burn it... Smile — use my knowledge — get the ghouls on my side... Do a magic trick..." She took a breath. *"Save Carl."*

She grabbed the doorknob and turned it and pushed the door to reveal a scene of horror. Carl was squirming in front of the picture of Lady Orgella. On the stone steps, ghouls were snapping at him, scratching, pushing against each other. Then the ghouls turned to see a pale girl.

A pale girl who was *grinning* at them.

Molly shouted the first thing that came into her mind.

"Evening, me old muckers!"

She slammed the door behind her. The ghouls glared, stunned.

"All right," she shouted heartily. "Listen up, you horrible lot."

The Messenger of Lady Orgella

IN THE GRAINY TORCH-LIT GLOOM THE GHOULS glowered, jaws hanging. Molly's cheery tone had befuddled them. But they wouldn't stay fuddled for long.

"What's up with you all — don't you recognize me?" Molly boomed, laughing. "I'm a messenger of your mistress, Lady Orgella! She sent me to chase off that snake Benton Furlock and give you your new orders. Now stop mucking about and listen up — if you ever want to be allowed back into Hell."

Preston Halfstar's leathery head looked down from his alcove in the circular wall. The ghouls, though suspicious, began to move away from Carl Grobman (who looked even more confused than they). But one turned back towards the bedraggled boy, raising its claws —

"Oi, mate!" shouted Molly. "D'you think for a

317

minute that the Mistress of Ghouls will ever let you back into Hell if you disobey her messenger?"

The ghoul paused, but did not retreat. Carl cowered on the steps, looking at Molly as if she were completely mad.

"What, don't you think that I really am a messenger of Lady Orgella?" Molly said boldly, wobbling forward with her stick and trying not to shriek with pain. "Do you need proof or something?"

The ghouls looked at each other. One of them nodded.

Molly rolled her eyes. "Fine! Step aside, you lot, and let me near the portrait so I can summon a sign from our mistress."

The ghouls backed into the shadows; the darkness and dust swirled, and the unblinking eyes gleamed. Frowning, bewildered, Carl moved aside.

Somehow Molly managed to limp to the wall, where she looked up at the portrait of Lady Orgella, cleared her throat and spoke.

"Yo, Mistress Lady Orgella. Fancy giving my pals here some proof that you've authorized me to take charge of them?"

Beside her, slumped against the wall, Carl coughed, "Molly, what are you doing?"

Molly didn't answer. She dropped her stick and

hopped up the few steps below the portrait. She wobbled, lost her balance. Clenching every muscle in her torso, she steadied herself, and reached up to wrench the nearest darksbane torch from its metal holder.

The ghouls hissed. Some began to move towards her. Then she stretched upwards, feeling her sinews separate, swaying on the tiptoe of one foot – and touched the torch's flame to the portrait's canvas.

The ghouls screeched, aghast, as flames gobbled up the image of one-eyed Lady Orgella. They wailed and flailed and threw themselves to the ground. Lifting her eyes, Molly cried a request to the flaming face:

"Hey, Lady Orgella – if I am your chosen messenger, do me a favour and bring back your image from the flames!"

The portrait bubbled and blackened and smoked.

Nothing.

Anxiously Molly whispered: "*Come on, you vain cow.*"

The fretting ghouls fell silent as they watched the smoke dissipate. Their blue eyes blinked.

Molly watched the ruined portrait. Her torch flame dwindled. Occasionally a ghoul cleared its throat.

Nothing happened.

And as she lost her balance, dropping the spent torch, Molly managed to mutter, "Oh, *biscuits.*"

* * *

319

Carl caught Molly and together they toppled to the floor. From the shadows, the ghouls emerged, furious, and fell upon the pair. Claws descended, dragging Molly off Carl. Molly's leg roared with pain as the ghouls pinned her down like a flatworm under a brick.

Her vision swam. She saw fangs looming, and a shadowy mouth lowered towards her.

At that moment Carl cried, "Look at the picture!"

All eyes turned. Molly strained to look past the ghoul's grey face, up at the portrait, which had repaired itself, leaving Lady Orgella staring with her one baleful eye.

The miracle had occurred again!

And suddenly all the creatures were gasping and weeping. Clumsy ghoulish hands hauled Molly upright. Carl hastened over and gave her support.

"About flipping time!" Molly yelped, giddy with relief.

"You came back for me," Carl choked. "Why?"

"It's what I do," Molly said matter-of-factly. "I solve mysteries and I rescue boys who've betrayed me to demon-worshippers." The ghouls stood watching her. "So ... what shall we do now?"

Carl narrowed his eyes at the ghouls. "Leave this to me."

* * *

"Listen, you ugly devils," Carl boomed impressively. "I'm an ambassador of Lady Orgella too, and my mistress has got a command for you. Stay in this room and leave the people of Howlfair alone till it's time for you to return to Hell." He brushed himself down. "Mr Furlock's not your master any more. If he ever tries to speak to you again..." Carl looked at Molly.

Molly said, "Eat him."

"Yeah – eat him," Carl said. "Everyone got that?" He took a step forward, his fists clenched.

The ghouls, amazingly, nodded.

"OK, fab," said Molly, clapping. "Glad that's all clear." She took a big breath. "Right, we're off."

With a bloodied Carl supporting her, Molly proceeded slowly between the rows of frowning ghouls. She tried not to cry out with pain, or show signs of fear. Out of the corner of her eye she noticed the biggest of the ghouls watching her with suspicion, as though he saw through her ruse. She forced herself to look calm. At the doorway she looked back at the portrait of Lady Orgella, made a face at the Mistress of Ghouls, and then pulled the door shut behind her.

They found Benton Furlock entangled in a hedge round the side of Loonchance Manor, flailing blindly beneath the silken, navy sky, to which the blue moon was pinned like a brooch.

"Hey, Mr Furlock," said Molly as Carl helped her across the lawn. "I must say, the tour was fun, but those ghouls aren't very realistic."

Furlock cursed and thrashed. "How the hell are you still alive?"

"By the way," Molly went on, "I control your ghouls now. If you don't believe me, you can ask them. Although I should warn you that I've commanded them to eat you if you speak to them."

Furlock's face was contorted. "What? But—"

"Get out of Howlfair, Mr Furlock," said Carl. "Tonight. If you're still here tomorrow, we'll set our ghouls on you."

"Grobman? Are you raving mad? I'm going to be mayor!"

"Think again, Benton," said Molly.

Furlock managed to turn his grimace of pain into a toothsome grin, which he aimed in Molly's direction. The light of the blue moon was upon the crevices of his face. "You need me, Molly Thompson. Don't you want to learn the truth about your father?"

A wave of craving unbalanced Molly; that too-familiar craving for truth that had mastered her for so long.

But then something occurred to her.

Molly regained her balance. She lifted her head.

"I already know the truth about my dad," she said. "The truth is that he loved this town, and he'd want me to look after it."

At that moment a pale green van bellowed up the road, negotiating the roundabout on two wheels. Molly saw Lowry, Felicity and Gabriel bouncing around in the cab like bingo balls. Mr Wetherill was behind the wheel. The van mounted the kerb and crashed into the fence enclosing Loonchance Manor. The front end of the van sizzled as the huge man tumbled forth in his nightshirt, barking at Lowry and Felicity to stay put. Lowry, seeing Molly alive, began to flap frantically with joy.

"Right — what's this about ghouls?" Mr Wetherill growled, marching across the lawn. Molly noticed that he had a musket in his hand, the sort you'd expect a highwayman to carry.

"Wallace — is that you?" moaned Furlock from his hedge. "These horrible children broke into my manor, and—"

"Shut your trap, Furlock — if there's an ounce of truth to the children's story, you're *finished*. You'll have lost my vote, and you'll have lost the union's vote, and if I find anything dodgy underneath this house, I'll see you punished as a traitor to our town."

Furlock groaned as he crawled from the spiky hedge and flopped onto the lawn. "You won't find anything underneath Loonchance Manor."

"We'll see about that," said Wetherill, heading for the front door. "Molly, Carl — don't let this fink escape."

"We won't, Mr Wetherill," said Molly. "Just follow the trail of blood and destruction — the ghouls are behind a door in the crypts, at the bottom of the staircase. Be careful!"

Mr Wetherill held up the pistol. "I'm always careful," he said, opening the front door and striding into Loonchance Manor. Moments later a shot rang out. Molly jumped.

The door opened again and Mr Wetherill poked his head through briefly. "Sorry about that."

As it happened, Mr Wetherill also hadn't been careful enough to engage the handbrake after crashing his van, and the vehicle began to roll back into the road. Carl ran after it, shouting "Handbrake!", and between them, Lowry and Felicity just about managed to wrench the heavy, rusty lever and halt the vehicle before it gathered speed and vanished down one of the steep streets beyond the roundabout. Molly watched with high anxiety — and when the van lurched to a stop, she looked around and realized that Furlock had managed to escape.

"Oh, crud!" she hissed. Her injured leg filled with pain. "He's gone," she told Carl as he returned with Lowry, Felicity and Gabriel.

"Maybe it's for the best," said Lowry, flinging her arms around Molly while Carl searched the grounds. "Maybe he'll never come back. I'm so glad you're alive!"

Carl returned, shaking his head. "He got away."

Wetherill emerged in due course. "No ghouls," he sighed. "Lots of dust and rubble, bit of blood, and a painting of a demon, but if there were ghouls down there, my guess is that they've crawled into hiding places. We'll have to undertake a full search of Loonchance Manor to flush them out, and — where's Furlock?"

"He disappeared," said Lowry. "And I think Molly needs to get to the hospital pronto."

"You do believe us, though, don't you, Mr Wetherill?" Molly asked.

He shrugged and rubbed his jowls. "I don't know why anyone would make up a story like that."

"And you're going to set up one of your Orders again, to find out what Furlock's been up to and where his ghouls are?"

"I'll make sure that any ghouls in Howlfair are

located and dealt with, you can trust me on that," said Wetherill.

"And Furlock said that my dad cost him his hand." Molly saw the huge man flush with confusion. "What did he mean, Mr Wetherill? How was my dad..."

"Molly, I promise we'll get to the bottom of all these mysteries. But for now, let's get you to the hospital. Carl, you're staying with me. Wherever Furlock's scurried to, you can be sure of this: he's never going to be our mayor."

"What are you going to tell your mum?" Lowry asked Molly as she and Felicity helped her to the van. "The nurses will call our parents, you know."

Molly had no idea. She still had no idea later, when her mother burst into the consulting room while Ben was preparing a splint for her leg. X-rays had revealed only a fairly minor fracture, which was a small mercy.

"Molly, what happened to you? Where did you go?" Mum cried, wrapping her arms around her.

"Mum, I don't... I'm so sorry, I can't... You wouldn't..."

"It's OK — you don't have to tell me now. I'm just so happy you're alive. When the hospital called, I thought the worst. I've never panicked so much in my life — I had this awful feeling they'd found you dead, and I can't lose you, understand? I refuse to lose you as well." She burst into tears. "What was I thinking, locking you up like a criminal? What kind of a mother am I?"

"You're a great mum!" blurted Molly. "But I don't know how to tell you what happened tonight — it's ever so exciting, but there's no way you'd believe it, and it ends with me and Lowry and Felicity Quick saving Howlfair. But if you'd rather not know…"

"Molly, of course I want to know," said Mum. "I want to know everything. As soon as you think I'm ready to hear it."

The Mayor of Howlfair

RAIN THREATENED BUT NEVER ARRIVED. THE sky over Howlfair Old Cemetery remained clear and white and fresh as laundered linen. Three generations of Thompsons stood on five legs (seven if you count Molly's crutches as legs) at the grave of David Nathaniel Thompson. They laid flowers, which the breeze ruffled — much like Mr Thompson, in happier times, had liked to ruffle Molly's messy hair. Lowry remained at a respectful distance, swinging from the low branch of a tree. Eventually, Grandma Thompson spoke.

"He's not here, is he?"

Mum looked at her. "What?"

Gran yawned. "He's not here. Molly was right all along. This is just a stone. David's spirit is somewhere else."

Molly cocked her head. "It's a nice stone," she said, "as far as stones go."

328

Mum thought it over. "I'm sure he appreciates fresh flowers," she said. "And I bet he gets a kick out of the fact that Molly is wearing one of his atrocious tee-shirts."

They headed home, Molly and her best friend (or best *human* friend) trailing Molly's mum and gran, making their way slowly down the hill through the graveyard, Lowry still limping from her sprain.

"Quick question, Thompson," said Lowry. "What's happened to Carl Grobman?"

Molly frowned. "I haven't seen him. He's still staying with Mr Wetherill, but I think he's avoiding me. I suppose we'll see him at school in the autumn."

"And Furlock?"

"Haven't seen him either."

"Thank God," said Lowry. "Maybe we scared him off for good." She chewed her top lip. "And do you think Mr Wetherill's going to find out how your dad did that thing to Furlock's hand? Why it looked like it was made of glass?"

"If he doesn't, I will," said Molly. "But first I'm going to take a break from investigations. Just until I've got two working legs."

There were cheers from the streets below. Apparently the mayoral results had been announced early.

"Let's go and find out who our mayor is," said Molly.

Lowry smirked.

"Why are you smirking?"

"Because you're smiling," said Lowry.

"And what's so funny about that?"

Lowry shrugged. "I'm just not used to it, that's all."

G.O.A.

MOLLY'S STILL SMILING LATER, AT HOME, as she sits on her bed that evening, one leg in plaster, Gabriel beside her, and reads once again the headline article in the *Ethelhael Panopticon* about how Lawrence de Ville is still Mayor of Howlfair.

Barry Parrott came second place.

Benton Furlock? Well, he *would* have come second place, but nobody knows where he is. The local council has taken over the running of Howlfair Orphanage. Loonchance Manor has been closed until further notice.

Molly scratches Gabriel's head and looks out of the moonlit window with a strange sense that happy times await her haunted town. She doesn't want to think about ghouls or Benton Furlock or Lady Orgella or investigations. She wants to sleep soundly and dreamlessly under her duvet with the Dracula cover. And so she closes her eyes.

Out in the evening, Mr Evans is lowering the awnings outside the tourist office on Zaleska Street.

In a candle-lit attic in a neighbouring valley, Benton Furlock sits at a desk, a bandage over one eye, scratches circling the other, glaring at a crumpled old poster that reads:

FURLOCK FOR MAYOR

Back at the Excelsior Guesthouse, Molly's mother is sorting through her late husband's clothes. Her freckled face furrows with a frown as she holds up a long-sleeved tee-shirt that has a hole in one of the forearms. It looks rather as though something has burned through the material. She drops the tee-shirt into a bin-bag full of similar items, and within moments it is forgotten.

In his lamp-lit study, Wallace Wetherill is looking at an old framed photo of a group of people. There's Doris de Ville holding a savage-looking, silver-jawed mechanical litter picker. There's Mr Wetherill himself, hefting a musket in each hand. There's a frail-looking elderly lady wearing a wolf pelt and a spiked glove, and Mrs Giddimus brandishing an iron stake. There's Farmer Digby holding a harpoon gun, and Mr Banderfrith with a fencing foil. There's

Benton Furlock — both hands healthy, one of them gripping the handle of a curved knife. And in the middle there's the group's leader. David Nathaniel Thompson, caught mid-laugh. He's the only person in the photograph without a weapon. He's holding a sleeping baby girl: his daughter, Molly. At the bottom of the photograph, someone has written the name of the old gang of Howlfair citizens who'd once sworn to guard the secrets of the Gates of Hell:

The Guild of Asphodel

Meanwhile, in a crypt below Loonchance Manor, shadowy creatures descend from secret nooks and assemble in the middle of the chamber, firelight fluttering upon each vile fanged face.

Their left eyes no longer glow. The blue moon has passed.

They stare at the portrait of Lady Orgella, as though waiting for their mistress to confirm what Molly Thompson told them.

All at once they stagger backwards as the nightmare face begins to move.

NICK TOMLINSON is a former English, Drama and Special Needs teacher, academic learning mentor, singing waiter and admin clerk. He has performed in a sell-out show at the Edinburgh Fringe, accidentally camped on a military target range in West Africa and managed to pass his karate black belt grading despite choking on his gum shield. A lifelong bookworm, Nick has been writing stories since he was five. His adult novel, *Saint Valentine*, was published by Transworld. Nick lives with his wife, Jayne, on the Welsh/English border, near Hay-on-Wye.

-based advice, practical tips and exercises, this book
resource for the university and college sector. Not only is it
an invaluable self-help guide for students, those who support students
professionally or those studying to be mental health professionals should
also find it useful."

– *Steven Pryjmachuk, Professor of Mental Health
Nursing, The University of Manchester*

"Bridie, Sue and Phoebe are friendly and practical in their approach and
provide a wide range of questions and suggestions which will boost the
understanding, skills and confidence of any young adult living with anxiety."

– *Dr Pooky Knightsmith Mental Health Advisor,
Author Speaker & Educator Vice Chair - Children
and Young People's Mental Health Coalition*

by the same authors

My Anxiety Handbook
Getting Back on Track
Sue Knowles, Bridie Gallagher and Phoebe McEwen
Illustrated by Emmeline Pidgen
ISBN 978 1 78592 440 8
eISBN 978 1 78450 813 5

of related interest

You Can Change the World!
Everyday Teen Heroes Who Dare to Make a Difference
Margaret Rooke
Illustrated by Kara McHale
ISBN 978 1 78592 502 3
eISBN 978 1 78450 897 5

Anxiety is Really Strange
Steve Haines
Illustrated by Sophie Standing
ISBN 978 1 84819 389 5 (PB)
ISBN 978 1 84819 407 6 (HB)
eISBN 978 0 85701 345 3

The CBT Art Activity Book
100 illustrated handouts for creative therapeutic work
Jennifer Guest
ISBN 978 1 84905 665 6
eISBN 978 1 78450 168 6

THE ANXIETY SURVIVAL GUIDE

Getting through the Challenging Stuff

*Bridie Gallagher, Sue Knowles
and Phoebe McEwen*

Illustrated by Emmeline Pidgen

Jessica Kingsley *Publishers*
London and Philadelphia

First published in 2020
by Jessica Kingsley Publishers
73 Collier Street
London N1 9BE, UK
and
400 Market Street, Suite 400
Philadelphia, PA 19106, USA

www.jkp.com

Library of Congress Cataloging in Publication Data
A CIP catalog record for this book is available from the Library of Congress

British Library Cataloguing in Publication Data
A CIP catalogue record for this book is available from the British Library

ISBN 978 1 78592 641 9
eISBN 978 1 78592 642 6

Printed and bound in Great Britain

Contents

Part 3: Anxiety in AdultHood: Some Top Tips

Acknowledgements

Our biggest thank you goes to all of the young people who have in some way contributed to this book, through completing the survey on anxiety in social situations (included in this book) or courageously agreeing to write their story down for us.

Bridie would like to say a big thank you to her partner and children for making being an adult more fun than she ever expected. Also, huge thanks to her colleagues and the young people she works with, for reminding her what is worth worrying about and what needs to be let go of.

Sue would like to thank her long-suffering husband Ben, who puts up with all her book-related stresses, and her son Tom, for reading and commenting on endless chapter drafts (still for ice-cream). She would also like to acknowledge the support of her brilliant team at CMUK, who keep her feeling enthusiastic about her work.

Phoebe would like to thank her best friend Connor, for his unwavering love and support, her Mum, Dad and brother Liam, for helping her to navigate a tough few years and her Nana Pearson who, while not being here to read this, would be very proud.

A big thank you to our super-picky draft readers, Steve and Rach.

Thank you to Action for Children (especially Amanda, Lisa and Roma) and Llamau (Emma) for all your support, enthusiasm and for helping us to collate stories for the book.

Preface

This book is for young people who are struggling with all the changes and decisions that adulthood brings. All three of us know that the transition to adulthood can be both exciting and incredibly anxiety-provoking. We wanted to write a book that not only suggests strategies for managing anxiety, but also gives some expert advice to 18–25-year-olds to help them to navigate some of the major transitions and challenges that they face.

There has been significant media coverage and recent evidence that young people are struggling with loneliness and their mental health. At the same time the services that might connect people to others and support them when they are struggling are being reduced due to austerity. With this in mind, we provide some ideas for managing anxiety, based on clinical evidence that you might receive from a professional, alongside lots of stories and examples from "real" people who have been right where you are now. Some of those who contributed their stories used their own names and others chose to use a pseudonym.

Socialising, friendships, studying, moving away from home, going for interviews and stress at work are important tasks of adulthood so we have given some concrete advice about managing anxiety relating to these topics, including recovery stories and some expert tips from young people, a lecturer and course tutor, and a human resources (HR) manager. We also talk about managing uncertainty, calming your mind and self-care as these are skills that everyone needs and that are going to make a positive difference. We have seen (from our own experience and through our work) that they can be the buffer you need to protect against life's stresses and strains.

The only chapters that directly talk about what we call "problem anxiety" relate to panic attacks and obsessive compulsive disorder (OCD), but we have included a wide range of evidence-based, practical strategies in all of the chapters so that you can try out different approaches and see what fits for you.

We imagine that you will dip in and out of this book as the different chapters feel more or less relevant to you. The most important thing for us is that you know you're not alone with your stress and anxiety, and that struggling with anxiety is a part of many people's lives. It can be really tough and challenging but is not something to be ashamed of. We believe that if you can learn ways to tolerate uncertainty and anxiety and find the things that help you to feel calm and connected, then you really are a grown-up! We are all very happy to admit that we're still working on this.

Bridie, Sue and Phoebe

x

◇ Part 1 ◇

WHY ADULTHOOD CAN MAKE US ANXIOUS

Part 1 is an introduction to anxiety in adulthood and dealing with not knowing. Chapter 1 has thoughts and reflections on what is tough about adulthood (including stories from people who have been through it) and how different coping styles and ways of relating to other people might affect how you cope with the challenges of adulthood. In Chapter 2, we then think about some practical ways that you can cope with the inevitable "not knowing" when you are facing lots of changes and decisions.

◇ Chapter 1 ◇

What's So Hard About Being an Adult?

Learning to manage anxiety is a key skill that *all* adults need in order to be successful and feel well	It's very easy to get stuck in an anxious thinking pattern
You'll have lots of choices to make	One of the best protective factors is social support

So, we hope that you've chosen this book because you want to learn how to manage the challenges of adulthood and the anxieties that often come along with it. When we talk about entering adulthood, or "new" adults, we are usually talking about people aged 18–25 years, although Sue and Bridie are still trying to convince people that they fall into this group!

We wanted to write this book because, depending on where you live and exactly how old you are, you'll have lots of choices to make. These might be deciding whether to live at home or move out, to stay in education or to get a job, as well as decisions about romantic relationships and friendship groups. You'll also be facing some new responsibilities like paying bills, food shopping, or maybe caring for family members. For lots of people, this can be stressful and can cause a lot of anxiety.

Perhaps you're not ready to make decisions at the moment or perhaps you're just desperately trying to get through each day. Changes and feeling overwhelmed by life's demands are common triggers for problem anxiety and so, understandably, making the transition into adulthood can be a tricky time. People who, in the past, have felt confident and haven't struggled with anxiety before might begin to experience difficulties as the demands of adult life outstrip their ability to cope. Alternatively, you might have a history of anxiety and need some extra help to think about how to cope with the new challenges you are likely to face over the next few years.

What you will find in this book

You are likely to dip in and out of this book depending on where you are in your life and the things that are causing you to feel anxious or stressed out. This quick overview can help you to navigate around it and find what you need.

Part 1 is an introduction to anxiety in adulthood and dealing with not knowing. The chapter you are reading, right now, has thoughts and reflections on what is tough about adulthood (including stories from people who have been through it) and how different coping styles and ways of being with other people might affect how you cope with the challenges it presents. In Chapter 2, "Dealing With All The Stuff You Can't

Possibly Know", we then think about some practical ways that you can cope with the inevitable "not knowing" when you are facing lots of changes and decisions.

In Part 2, we go on to think through some of the stuff that might be more difficult if you suffer with anxiety, such as socialising, or that might be the cause of lots of stress and anxiety even if you are really confident, like job interviews and tricky work situations. We spoke to lots of young people as we wrote this book, and this confirmed what we already suspected: that one of the biggest challenges in early adulthood is making friends and socialising. So, we made this our focus for the first chapter in Part 2, "Getting Out and Socialising With Other Adults", where we explore social awkwardness and anxiety and talk through some top tips taken from the 18–25-year-olds who took part in our survey.

The next chapter, "What Can I Do With Anxious Thoughts?", also focuses on social situations; however, the ideas used here can help you to manage anxious thoughts about anything! We know that anxiety can interfere with your ability to study effectively and that studying as an adult is different from studying when you are at school. In Chapter 5, therefore, we think about how anxiety might impact on your learning and we give lots of practical strategies to help you study and revise, whether it is for college, university or professional qualifications. Included in this chapter, "I Can't Focus! How to Study With Anxiety", is advice from a lecturer and course tutor who has been supporting students for a number of years. Studying at university or college can often mean that people move out of home at 18, so Chapter 6 is a quick guide to transitions and endings more generally, and how to deal with them. It focuses on the specifics of leaving home and moving out – "What About Moving Out?".

One of the most anxiety-provoking things most people do is going for a job interview. In Chapter 7, "Surviving (and

Thriving) in Job Interviews", there are lots of tips for managing anxiety in an interview and also some advice from professionals who are on the other side of the table.

Now you may already have a job, but this does not mean that all the stress is over, so we also have Chapter 8, "Workplace Worries", to think about practical ways to manage stress and anxiety at work.

Part 3 aims to give some practical advice that relates directly to the problems that anxiety can cause and the skills that you need in order to make sure anxiety doesn't take over your life or stop you doing what you need to do.

Chapters 9, "A Quick Guide to Panic Attacks", and 10, "A Little Bit OCD", are introductions to these specific kinds of anxiety, offering some coping strategies but focusing on building understanding and reassuring you that you are not alone. While knowledge and reassurance can be helpful, we also point you to some good resources for more specific help and interventions if this is what's needed. We chose to include panic and OCD as sufferers felt that they are issues that may be more stigmatised or poorly understood.

Chapter 11, "How Do I Stay Calm and Healthy in a Stressful World?", covers a lot of practical information and advice, from getting a good night's sleep to improving the moment, and positive coping statements to thinking about the role of alcohol and drugs. We believe strongly that getting your self-care right is key to managing stress and anxiety and that we do not always learn the skills we need to stay calm and healthy at school or from adults around us growing up, so this is a chapter everyone should read.

Similarly, Chapter 12, "What Is This Mindfulness All About?", is helpful for anyone. There is increasing evidence that mindfulness – the ability to be present in the moment – is a skill that can help you stay calm and healthy and is especially useful when anxiety is taking over and making life difficult. Chapter 12 has lots of ideas for how you can introduce mindfulness into your daily life and how it can help to calm your mind. In Chapter 13, "Where Can I Get Some Extra Help?", we think about how you might talk to people about anxiety and other sources of support and advice.

Adulthood: the challenges

When we were writing a book for teenagers with anxiety (*My Anxiety Handbook: Getting Back on Track*) we realised that things can be especially difficult for people as they move from being a teenager to becoming an adult. As an adult, you might no longer have to worry about curfews or homework, but you are likely to be facing new responsibilities and situations and there will be an increased expectation from others (and maybe yourself) to cope alone. A recent survey carried out by the Samaritans[1] found that 40 per cent of 16–24-year-olds sometimes feel overwhelmed by their problems, but that over half feel there is significant stigma attached to talking about their feelings, so are more likely to pretend that they are coping in order to not be seen as "weird". A big survey about loneliness in the UK, done by the BBC,[2] also showed that 16–24-year-olds reported feeling lonely more frequently and with more intensity than any other age group. We know that the

---

1   Samaritans (2015) Talk to Us Survey. As cited at: www.samaritans.org/news/feeling-fresher-out-water-you-are-not-alone-say-samaritans.

2   BBC (2018) "All in the Mind" Loneliness Experiment. As cited at: www.bbc.co.uk/programmes/articles/2yzhfv4DvqVp5nZyxBD8G23/who-feels-lonely-the-results-of-the-world-s-largest-loneliness-study and as discussed in: https://thepsychologist.bps.org.uk/all-mind-shines-light-loneliness.

current generation of young people in the UK ("Millennials"), are going to be the first generation who are financially worse off than their parents. The media constantly highlights how stressful it is: young people pay high tuition fees, high rent costs and cannot afford to buy a house. The constant pressure of making comparisons with friends and celebrities through social media doesn't help either. The idea that one day you'll wake up and because you have reached some arbitrary milestone you're an adult is part of the problem. In the eyes of the law, someone magically becomes an adult on their 16th, 18th or 21st birthday, but actually *becoming* a grown-up takes quite a long time and a lot more effort than this idea gives us all credit for.

This book will help you to navigate through the transitions of adulthood while also learning how to manage the anxiety that comes with it. Learning to manage anxiety is a key skill that *all* adults need in order to be successful and feel well. Anxiety is likely to be a problem at some stage for lots of people, with around one in five adults having anxiety that causes them significant problems at some point in their lives.

Competing goals and responsibilities

As children and teenagers, we often long for the day when we are no longer beholden to the expectations of the adults around us, whether they be parents, carers or teachers. Adulthood sounds glorious, as we can "do whatever we like". But what do you like? What do you want to do in life? How do you keep friendships when your lives might suddenly look very different? Who are you going to live with and spend time with when you're not at work, college or university? What part do your parents and brothers/sisters play in your life if you no longer live together, or even if you do? These are big questions and the competing demands of earning money, pursuing career goals and often living independently or contributing more to the household can feel overwhelming. Just *having* lots of choices can lead to anxiety, never mind making decisions about them! As an adult, there are often fewer rules and people keeping you in check; as the expectation to "cope alone" increases, you can come to rely on less helpful ways to manage your anxiety – such as trying to ignore it, drinking alcohol or avoiding things that make you anxious.

Separation and loss

This might seem like a depressing heading; however, alongside the exciting challenges that adulthood presents, we also must manage separation and loss. The process of becoming an adult involves separating from our family and finding our own place in the world, and there's a greater focus on our friends and on our ability to manage within the wider community. Our childhood experiences of separation and loss are likely to have a significant impact on how we manage this and what coping strategies we use when things start to get tough and anxiety makes its presence felt. Separation from your parents and family might feel irrelevant to you at this point as you already feel independent and separate or, alternatively, perhaps you're shaking your head at the idea that you will ever be anything other than inseparable from your parent or carer. You might not have felt part of a family growing up as you were apart from your family, maybe within the care system, and it could be separation from other carers and supportive organisations that you're struggling with. It may be that you feel very little will change as you continue to rely solely on yourself as you always have or you continue to live with your family well into adult life.

You might have felt you didn't need anyone else, you've coped alone, and just "got on with life" in the face of difficult or distressing situations, putting any difficult feelings to one side and not acknowledging them. We might talk about your relationship style as being "avoidant". This doesn't mean that you avoid relationships or are isolated; it could be that you are outgoing and have lots of friends, but maybe don't share your feelings or allow other people to help you when times get tough. Instead, you might ignore difficult feelings and do lots of things, maybe throwing yourself into a project or activity. To others, you might seem as though you're always doing really well and are unaffected by difficult things, when actually, you're struggling to connect with others about your true thoughts and feelings. You might not trust that other people will "get it" or be able to help when you feel anxious, uncertain or upset. As an adult, if you have this approach to your relationships, you may seem to be doing well and coping fine, but then you hit a wall when you can no longer cope alone and need support.

It's likely that you haven't had to ask for support before and you might not know how to or feel uncomfortable doing so. It becomes normal to ignore or suppress feelings of anxiety and distress and after a while they can begin to burst out in unexpected ways; for example, getting angry with someone over small things or suddenly crying at a TV advert. We call this "bottle, bottle, bang!" These sudden outbursts might surprise you and reinforce the idea that you need to keep your emotions hidden because they're scary, unexpected or unacceptable. It can also mean you feel an obligation to create a "fake self" that you present to the world, while no one knows the real you. You might feel that this is OK to do because it feels safe and protects you from having your emotional expression judged by other people; however, this is a lonely place to be.

Learning how to reach out to others and build trusting relationships where you can share everything, even the "bad bits", can be key to managing anxiety and the difficult stuff that life throws at you. Sue knows that she has a tendency to be a bit avoidant at times, when she is feeling really stressed or anxious. She tends to try to cope alone and just get through it, but sometimes it can get too much – you can usually tell as she will be super grumpy! Over time, Sue has learned that the best thing for her to do at these times is to let someone close to her know that she's struggling, and then they can be there for her if she needs them.

Many adults are still in very close and loving relationships with their parents, talking to or seeing them daily and relying on them for comfort and reassurance. This closeness can be helpful and we always encourage people to seek support and connection when they are struggling with anxiety. However, as an adult, you might be put into situations where you need to manage your anxiety and relationships alone. If you haven't developed your own ways of coping with emotions and still tend to rely on your parents when times are tough, new "adult" situations can feel overwhelming and impossible. We sometimes talk about this as an "anxious" relationship style. People who have this style of relating only feel OK and able to cope when they are with another trusted person who they use to help them to cope and calm down, as they struggle to do this alone. Developing confidence in your own ability to manage your feelings and the challenges of adulthood will also help you to become more confident and able to cope alone, seeking support when it's needed, but not being over-reliant on the people around you.

Phoebe's story

On starting my A-levels for the third time, despite being a bona fide "adult" of 18, I came to the realisation that I was still very reliant on my close friends and family. In order to navigate the minor hiccups of everyday life, I depended on the constant reassurance of others. After years of struggling with my mental health, I didn't believe in my own ability to "cope" and avoided taking responsibility for my own emotions. Once I took ownership of my struggles and took off my metaphorical stabilisers, I discovered that even though it was difficult, I could weather the storm on my own.

Bereavement and loss

Sometimes as we reach adulthood and need some support and guidance, we feel the absence of a lost parent or grandparent more keenly, or, if we have not had trusting relationships with adults growing up, we can start to feel this loss too. At important points such as getting engaged, married or graduating, the grief may be just as painful as when you first lost your loved one. It may be that as a child or teenager you were not fully able to grieve for that person and then, at these later points, you become overwhelmed by feelings that you thought were under control.

Young people who have grown up in very stressful and difficult environments, where their emotional and/or physical needs have not been sensitively and consistently met by the adults around them, are often extremely resilient and strong, but may begin to grieve for their lack of parenting and find that their old coping strategies don't work so well for them as adults. It might be that you have ended a relationship with a parent who has been abusive or maybe others aren't responding to the way you communicate or behave in the same way, now that you are an "adult". Perhaps the system of support you were used to as a child, although imperfect, is now almost completely gone. Finding compassionate ways to manage anxiety alongside different ways to seek support and connection to other adults is often the key to becoming a secure and confident adult. This is what we aim to offer some help with throughout this book.

Acute and chronic stress: activating the threat system

Separation, loss and transitions are all things that can activate our "threat system". Reaching adulthood can be a difficult time because of these things and all the other challenges that we will discuss in this book. So, what happens to our brains and our bodies when we are under a lot of stress? How do our anxious thoughts, feelings and behaviour interact with each other?

In Chapter 9, we talk more about "panic" so we discuss the interpretation of your body's threat response in detail then, but we thought it would be helpful to introduce the impact of stress and anxiety on the way you think and feel early on in the book. When we detect any kind of threat (physical or emotional), our brain responds quickly in order to keep us safe. We call this our survival instinct. Imagine that you are walking across an empty car park late at night, you hear footsteps behind you, and a hand grabs your shoulder. What do you feel? Probably your heart beats faster, your body becomes tense, your breathing quickens, and adrenaline pumps around your body. What do you automatically do, or want to do, in that moment? Probably you either spin round ready to punch the person in the face, freeze on the spot, or run away as quickly as you can. What are you thinking of in that moment? Probably you are thinking very little, or it might seem as if your thoughts have disappeared.

You may have heard of your "fight, flight, freeze" response, which is the clever way that we have evolved to respond to danger. The threat brain is the oldest part of the brain, right at the base of your skull, and it sets off our fight, flight, freeze response using stress hormones. When the threat brain is activated, it bypasses or shuts down the most developed and social bit of our brain, the frontal cortex just behind our forehead. The frontal cortex is responsible for empathy, problem solving and language, so in a "threat" situation it makes sense that we simply shut this bit down. It wouldn't be very helpful to go through the pros and cons of each possible action if you are being stalked by a sabre-toothed tiger – you are basically dead by the time you have looked round to work out if he looks hungry. Your three simple choices are to fight off the predator, run as fast as you can (flight), or play dead (freeze). So, this is why, when you are feeling anxious, you often are less able to think clearly, focus or concentrate and see the wider picture. You may be suffering from the acute onset of anxiety and are battling your fight, flight, freeze response. When we are chronically stressed (over a long period of time) we can suffer from bouts of acute anxiety (anxiety that was a sudden onset and lasts for a short period of time, like panic) or alternatively we might feel exhausted and "switched off" from being on the lookout for danger all the time and worrying constantly.

Anxiety that has a sudden onset and lasts for a short period of time.

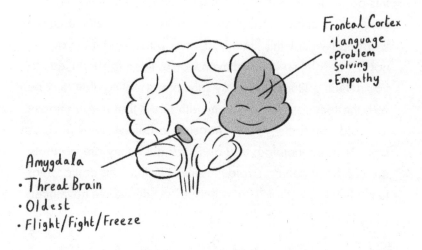

Frontal Cortex
• Language
• Problem Solving
• Empathy

Amygdala
• Threat Brain
• Oldest
• Flight/Fight/Freeze

It's very easy to get stuck in an anxious thinking pattern or for our brains to play tricks on us when we are anxious and stressed. Our brain needs to be tuned in to any possible threats when we are in danger (hypervigilance). This keeps us safe, but when this happens, we often feel on edge, unable to relax and enjoy things, and can see danger everywhere, worrying about every little thing. Your threat brain being active for a long period of time (chronic stress) might not make you feel as if you're about to die or pass out right then and there, as it does during a panic attack (see Chapter 9), but it could mean that you feel constantly exhausted from being hypervigilant and continual worrying. This stops you doing things that you usually enjoy, which is pretty miserable and can have longer term consequences for your health and wellbeing.

One of the problems with anxiety is that you might be experiencing a valid worry; for example, "I'm worried about my exam results". This worry will then trigger a threat response in your brain and body (the brain releases cortisol, increasing tension in your muscles and possibly causing stomach ache or shallow breathing), which does not help you deal with this particular threat. Then the horrible physical feelings and heightened emotion are interpreted as a sign that something is wrong (we call this "feel bad, think bad") and that you are not OK or safe, so you feel even worse. This might then lead to you avoiding situations to stay safe, or not feeling able to cope with the feelings. The problem with this is that if you choose to avoid situations, you're choosing to believe your anxious thoughts, and therefore you don't test out if they are accurate are not. So, if you do avoid the situation, then this can appear to confirm to you that "I cannot cope" or "this would have been dangerous/a disaster".

Alternatively, it might be that the strategies you have developed to manage these anxious feelings have now become unhelpful and are interfering in your life. Sometimes we need some down-time to be able to take care of ourselves and soothe our threat system; just watch out that you are not getting into a cycle of avoidance or overly relying on alcohol, substances or obsessive rituals to feel safe and more able to cope with everyday situations (see Chapters 10 and 11).

Phoebe's story

For over a year I avoided public transport because it made me anxious. I would wake up ridiculously early just to get to college at a time when my Dad could drop me off. I couldn't get anywhere independently. The longer I avoided public transport, the more of an issue it became until I was no longer worried about feeling anxious on the bus but was actually afraid of getting on the bus. As you can imagine, this wasn't very convenient for anyone, especially my Dad, who had by now become a personal taxi service. If, instead of avoiding the bus because it made me anxious, I had worked through the anxiety, I wouldn't have been kicking myself a year later when I finally forced myself onto a bus and wasn't eaten by a grizzly bear or stared at by angry-looking strangers.

How can this book help you to cope with anxiety in adulthood?

So, in early adulthood there is a time of change and transition where you need to be independent but also make new relationships and connections in a stressful world, coupled with a brain that still thinks you need protecting from predators rather than from social rejection and perceived "failure". This can lead to some really difficult thoughts and feelings and what we call "problem anxiety". In this book, we talk about some of the big transitions that young people face and offer some ideas about how to manage anxieties about these situations, using real-life examples from people who have found their own way through. These examples may act like a "guide" or mentor for you; however, we would also encourage you to reach out to people close to you and share your fears and worries so they can offer you support and advice. One of the best protective factors for young people who face stress and adversity is social support, and this can come from many places, but anxiety can sometimes make us feel that we are alone, not good enough, or unable to cope, and stop us from seeking support exactly when we need it most.

We also help you to identify your current coping strategies and beliefs so that you can take a step back and work out whether these ways of coping are helpful and effective for you. We provide you with alternative ways of coping so you can see which ones feel right for you. Universally, taking good care of yourself – eating well, getting enough sleep and doing regular exercise (see Chapter 11) – may seem like eye-rollingly obvious things to advise you to do, but they are often the things that we forget about or lose motivation for when we are struggling. They are "obvious" because they really help you to feel stronger and more able to cope. This book provides you with some evidence-based advice so that you can begin to develop your own ways of coping and have confidence when you face new situations. This might be moving out (Chapter 6), getting a job (Chapters 7 and 8), or studying as an adult (Chapter 5). We talk throughout the book about involving important people and talking to others about anxiety (Chapter 13) but we hope the ideas and strategies mean you can face adulthood with positivity and independence. We also have ideas about how to overcome social anxiety (Chapter 3) and tackling the anxious thoughts that can get in the way of developing new friendships and relationships (Chapter 4) for those of you who may have previously "gone it alone".

Amy's story

For the majority of my life, the concept of "mental health" was not something I was very aware of. I sympathised to an extent, but I didn't understand why some people seemed so ill-equipped to deal with stress and pressure. In hindsight, ignorance is bliss!

I had grown up around a family of high achievers and excelled both academically and creatively. My childhood dream of becoming an actor appeared to be coming true as, at the age of 18, I was offered a place at a top drama school on a year-long foundation course. Drama schools are vastly over-subscribed (less than 1% acceptance rate in some cases) and it often takes years of rigorous auditioning to be accepted. Gaining a place on a full three-year course finally seemed achievable. It looked as if another piece of my seemingly copybook life was falling into place, but during my second term my world was significantly rocked for the first time. In quick succession, my treasured first relationship ended in deceit and heartbreak, a dear friend lost his life in a tragic accident and my closest friendship fractured beyond repair. I was devastated, but, despite the cumulative trauma, at this point I was not unwell. I was thriving at drama school and, while I had some sort of outlet for my feelings, I could just about weather the emotional storm.

Unfortunately, despite significant recognition from other top schools when re-auditioning, I returned home facing the prospect of taking a year out. Home felt haunted by the past and I struggled for a sense of identity. I became indignant, overindulging in alcohol-fuelled nights with loose connections far too frequently.

Then the unimaginable happened. I received a late offer for a full three-year course from one of the most prestigious institutions in the country. It was a niche course and I doubted my suitability but, ultimately, I had no real reason to refuse. I thought it would save me. It nearly destroyed me. Within a few days of the course commencing, it was apparent my premonitions were valid. I began battling crippling anxiety, which presented itself as chronic insomnia. Whole nights were spent wide awake, heart and mind racing, only to spend the next day consumed by panic that it all would re-occur the next night. The methodology of the course was neither conducive nor logical; the delivery was quite frankly abusive and student voices were censored. We were subjected to scathing character assassinations and psychological torment to the extent that I stopped trusting my own intuition and reasoning. My self-value was decimated and, somewhat unsurprisingly, I sank into a deep depression. I did not speak out, however. Emotionally, I had invested everything in this opportunity so acknowledging its culpability in the demise of my mental health was inconceivable. Alcohol became my medication of choice; it conquered both the insomnia and the despair. The anxiety made me manic, preventing me from appearing "down", but I was compensating for numbness and beyond control.

I hit rock bottom on my 20th birthday. I had been prescribed sertraline (anti-depressant medication) which, unknowingly, triggered hallucinations and severe physical illness. My parents drove through the night to bring me home and so began my long journey of recovery.

Counselling helped me to excavate the layers of psychological rubble (such as determination, fear, ignorance) I had shielded myself with and gave me the courage to leave the school. However, despite the head-space talking afforded me, I still didn't know how to control my demons; in fact, they controlled me.

That is when I found my psychologist. We agreed that a relapse in my mental health scared me more than the original root causes so our sessions were pragmatic, focusing on the psychology of anxiety and depression. I learned that, at their root, mental illnesses are trying to protect us. They are our in-built, primal fire alarms so when "danger" is detected, they produce a high-definition response that prompts us to re-assess. Most importantly, I learned that mental illnesses lie. Just like burning toast and smoke alarms, sometimes there is no imminent threat, but until you know the difference you will continue to fall into the same trap. Balance and perspective are the victims of anxiety and depression, but they are vital to conquer them. My recovery started just over a year ago and, post-therapy, I feel liberated. For me, knowledge gave me the freedom to look forwards optimistically. The process isn't linear and there are still challenging days, but I have conviction in knowing they will pass. My passion for acting is intact and now I am much less fragile. I am working towards my aspirations again.

I am not exactly grateful for this episode, but I am thankful for the self-awareness and understanding it has given me. Thanks to the help I received, my struggles no longer define me but to deny them would be to deny my ability to overcome them and that is the part of myself I am most proud of.

Chapter 2

Dealing With All the Stuff You Can't Possibly Know

The idea of the unknown can be terrifying	Although your brain may search for certainty and predictability, you will feel a lot less anxious if you can learn to get used to "not knowing"
If you learn to survive when things go wrong, this will make you more "resilient"	Don't get caught up doing any of your "safety behaviours" but instead "allow" the anxiety to come and go

One of the most difficult things that adults face is the unknown. What's going to happen in their future? What big decisions will they be forced to make? All these things are out of their control. Humans tend to crave certainty; it can make us feel safe and secure, and can help us to prepare for what might happen. When we have some certainty and a sense of safety in our lives, we feel more able to go take risks and challenge ourselves. As children, we may have other people who sort out our plans, our routines and help life to feel quite predictable. Sometimes this might feel overbearing ("stop trying to control me!" Sue has screamed at her parents on many occasions), but as we get older we're suddenly left to make our own decisions, and big ones at that.

If we are lucky, we might have people around us (such as trusted adults) who can help us to make these decisions, but some people might not have anyone to talk to about these things and may suddenly find themselves in what feels like a position of great power, which can be scary and overwhelming. We wonder about the impact of having constant rolling news from multiple sources too. Constantly hearing about disasters, crime and corruption can make us feel as if terrible or unknown things are just around the corner, no matter how unlikely they are in our immediate environment. Political change, both in the UK and United States, and the conversations we are exposed to in the news and media can also make it feel as if nothing can be relied on and the future suddenly seems less certain. In this context, we can feel that we need to create certainty in our lives any way that we can.

When planning out our futures, we also may try to work out what is expected of us and when. We might have our own expectations (our hopes and dreams for our futures), but we also may feel the weight of the expectations of others such as family or friends, or society more generally. It's difficult when we compare ourselves with others. At times, it might feel as if everyone else has things sorted, and is leading a perfect life. Social media has a lot to answer for, as people often try to portray a happy existence or show a positive "highlight reel" of their lives, whereas this is often not a true reflection of life.

We've all seen it – the person who posts the most perfect holiday pictures of themselves lying on a sunbed next to the beach, with their girlfriend holding an expensive-looking cocktail. Then we bump into them around town, and they're screaming at their partner, looking tired and pale, buying things from the local discount store. Things are not always as they appear.

So, comparing yourself with others doesn't make sense. We don't know what's going on in the lives of other people or what they might be struggling with behind their Instagram filter, plus, we are all individuals so will do different things at different times, and that's OK.

This chapter looks at anxiety and uncertainty about the future, ways of tolerating uncertainty, and a process to support "wise" decision-making.

Choosing the right path: why this is so difficult

There are many reasons why people might struggle with making decisions, particularly big ones. It might be because they have never made many decisions of their own before and have relied on other people to do this; it might be because they have made a decision before that they perceive to be a bad one, and therefore have no confidence in their ability to make future decisions (e.g. choosing to stay in a negative relationship, which they now wish they had left earlier). The truth is that we all make all kinds of decisions at different stages in our lives, and some may be more successful than others, but we can never truly know how they will work out. People may also be afraid of failure – but keep reading this chapter to hear why learning to fail is actually a good thing! This uncertainty and not knowing can be terrifying. One of the reasons why people particularly struggle with making decisions is that when we choose a particular option, it may feel as if the other options suddenly disappear and fall away and are no longer available to us, which is known as "existential dread".

Tolerating uncertainty

The idea of the unknown can be terrifying. When life feels unpredictable, it can lead to us feeling unsafe and unsure.

To cope with these feelings, we often employ different strategies or "safety behaviours" in an attempt to try to reduce the uncertainty as much as possible. These can include the following:

- Trying to do everything by yourself (rather than allowing other people to take control of some things). For example, Sue has always had difficulty delegating things to others at work, as her anxiety can make her want to stay in full control of everything. However, with support from her manager, she is getting much better at relinquishing control.

- Repeatedly seeking reassurance from other people – constant checking in with people how things are going, if they are OK, rather than "trusting in the process" (or believing that things will go as planned).

- An extreme amount of planning/organising/over-preparing – think multiple lists, plans, charts, micro-managing everything and trying to keep things as predictable as possible. For example, Bridie admits to having two separate books of lists as well as her work diary and a home diary.

- Avoiding any situation where there could be some uncertainty – including new situations, situations where other people are in control and spontaneous situations which may already be familiar or previously practised but which are now happening unexpectedly. However, this avoidance could lead to life feeling a bit dull.

- Refusing to make decisions or even getting other people to make decisions for you.

- Trying to ignore the fact that you need to make a decision, by keeping busy doing other things.

- Double, triple and quadruple checking everything. For example, Phoebe checked her personal statement an extraordinary amount of times before letting her tutor see it.

Do you recognise yourself doing any of the above? These patterns, although they might feel helpful short term, are likely to get in the way of you learning to feel comfortable making future decisions (and realising that you actually are able to make decisions and feel OK about it), taking balanced risks and moving forwards. Sometimes we might think that we only managed to keep the worrying or anxiety-provoking situation feeling safe/OK because we did the things described above (which is why they are called "safety behaviours"). What these behaviours actually do is stop us from "testing out" whether we are able to cope with the uncertainty around making a decision and prevent us from facing the truth – that we just cannot know what is going to happen and do not have control over everything.

Although it might feel like it, you don't need certainty to be OK

Although your brain may search for certainty and predictability, you will feel a lot less anxious if you can learn to get used to "not knowing" and ride the understandable anxiety that this can sometimes provoke. We know that it's never possible to be fully certain about anything, and there is usually at least a 0.01 per cent chance that something could go "wrong", even if we feel quite sure about something. It might be worthwhile asking yourself what the pros and cons are of trying to achieve certainty "all of the time".

TRYING TO ACHIEVE CERTAINTY

Pros: If you could feel certain, it might help you to feel safer.

Cons: You can never be truly 100 per cent certain about anything. It takes up lots of time and effort and can be highly anxiety-provoking. It can get in the way of you moving forwards/doing things and can lead to avoidance.

ALLOWING UNCERTAINTY

Pros: If I can do this, then I can cope with almost anything.

Cons: This will be hard and scary at first.

Learning to make decisions and not worry too much if they are "right" and to tolerate not knowing or not having plans so we can be more spontaneous are important skills to have (and could allow for more fun!). It might be useful to think about times when you have been able to cope with uncertainty; how have you managed, what have you done? Or how have you seen other people coping with uncertainty? If there is someone you know who appears to cope with uncertainty and decision-making well, maybe ask them how they cope with it and what they do. Often the best people who can help us to cope with anxious thoughts are trusted people whom we know already, and we just need to ask them.

Learning to embrace uncertainty

There are four main points in learning to embrace uncertainty:

1. *Get to know yourself* – Recognise if you are craving certainty and how this affects you. What are your safety behaviours? What kind of patterns do you tend to get pulled into when you are feeling uncertain or have to make decisions? How do you feel in your body when you are feeling uncertain, and what do you tend to think? By knowing and understanding yourself, you can start to feel more in control of your thoughts and behaviour.

2. *Notice any urges but don't react* – Notice any urges that you might have to do any of your safety behaviours and allow them to come and go. We call this "riding the urges" (like riding the wave of emotions that we talk about in Chapter 12). Face the uncertainty without having to "do" anything.

3. *Learn a new narrative about uncertainty* – If you have some unhelpful thoughts about uncertainty (e.g. "I cannot cope if I don't have a plan/don't know what is going to happen/don't have control"), then it can be useful to have some more balanced statements that you can tell yourself to counteract these thoughts. You might want to focus on simple words or phrases such

as "let go" (of the need for certainty) or "accept" (the uncertainty). You might want to make up your own saying or mantra, or pick one of the ones below:

> "I am feeling worried/anxious, but everything is OK."

> "This feeling will pass – I can sit with these feelings for a while and they will eventually go."

> "I don't have to do anything right now, but just wait for this feeling to pass."

> "Not knowing is tough, but I can get through it."

4. *Stay in the present* – Try to stay in the present as much as possible and not get caught up with listening to your anxious thoughts about the future. One way to do this is to use mindfulness skills (see Chapter 12) such as mindful breathing or paying attention to your surroundings. Every time your mind wanders back to your anxious thoughts (which might happen a lot at first!), just gently bring your attention back to the present and your mindful activity.

Testing this out

A good way of testing these skills out is to expose yourself to situations that can be different, unpredictable or uncertain, or try making decisions where you are unsure what the outcome will be. This could include adding some spontaneous activities into your day, talking to someone new, changing your routine, asking your friend to plan a day for you both without you knowing what is going to happen, starting a new activity or group that you haven't done before, or making a decision about a film that you are going to watch with a family member. They can be as big or small as you want.

Make sure that you don't get caught up doing any of your "safety behaviours" but instead "allow" the anxiety to come and go and remind yourself that you can get through this. Challenge yourself and put yourself in situations that might feel a bit uncomfortable but which will allow you to learn that you can survive, for example choosing where you go out for a meal if you are with your friends. Start with something small-ish first, before moving on to decisions or situations that scare you, slowly building up your tolerance to that uncertainty.

It can also be useful to test out your anxious beliefs about uncertain situations. You could ask yourself:

- What am I actually scared of? What would be the worst possible outcome?

- How likely in percentage terms is it that this outcome will happen? (0 = not at all, 100 = definitely will happen)

- When I tested out this uncertain situation, what actually happened?

- Did I get stuck doing any of my safety behaviours?

- Did I manage to cope with the outcome, whatever it was?

Making balanced, "wise" decisions

In dialectical behavioural therapy (DBT), we talk about the concept of having three states of mind: your emotional mind, your rational mind and your wise mind.

Your emotional mind is when your emotions are completely in control, when you have no inhibitions at all. So, if you were "in" your emotional mind you might feel sad and then, quite quickly, start sobbing and wailing in the street. You might feel angry and immediately get the urge to hit someone. You might feel worried and your thoughts might spiral into "what if, what if". If you listened to your emotional mind, and responded to it, you might choose to curl up in a corner and never leave the house. It would not be nice to live fully in your emotional mind as there would be lots of extreme highs and extreme lows and it would probably feel quite out of control.

Your rational mind is more like a robot or computer. It looks at the facts, statistics and logic of situations and makes decisions based on these, such as assessing probabilities and risks from a more factual perspective, without taking into account your emotions. So, if you were to listen solely to your rational mind, life would probably be quite boring as it would not consider how you felt about a situation.

Your wise mind is a bit different. It sits in-between your emotional and rational minds and listens to both, then makes a decision based on the information it receives (both the facts and how you feel about the situation). For example, you might be trying to decide whether to get a job close to home so that you are still living near to your friends and family, or to search for a job further away which would allow you to progress in your chosen career more easily.

Your emotional mind might be saying – you need to stay very close to home. It's scary moving away from things that you know, and people that you care for. If you moved away, you might feel very lonely... What if you couldn't cope and you couldn't come home often?

Your rational mind might tell you – you should just pick the best job opportunity, wherever it is, so you can have the best career in the future. Logically, you are more likely to find a good job in a big city so you should move there, even if it is far away from your family and friends.

Your wise mind may find it hard to challenge the emotional mind in this instance as the fear of being far from home and alone is pretty strong. However, if you choose to listen to your wise mind it would probably say – you need to feel safe and be able to visit the people who you care about and who care about you, but you also need to take an opportunity and a risk because if it doesn't work out, it is not the end of the world. So, maybe look for a job that is an hour or two away from home, so even if you live close to work, you can still visit your friends and family at weekends.

So, one of the best ways to make decisions is to consider both how you feel and the facts of the situation. The three steps to achieving this would be:

- **Step 1: How do I emotionally feel about the situation? (emotional mind)**

  This is something that you might instinctively know, or something that you might need time to work out. One of the best ways to work out your feelings is to talk to someone you trust. Sometimes it can be useful just to speak to one person, or a couple of people, so that you don't feel overwhelmed by lots of different opinions.

Talking through your options with someone and thinking about how you feel about each potential choice might help you to start to understand how you feel. Another way could be to write down some of your feelings. You may suddenly get a strong response when doing the exercise in step 2 as to which option you want to choose or which you don't.

— **Step 2: What are the facts of the situation? (rational mind)**

One way to do this is to research different options and look at the pros and cons of each option. You might write down a list of facts/evidence for each option, then you can directly compare and contrast them. You also might want to talk to people who know more about each option, to get further information about what each might involve.

— **Step 3: Making a balanced decision (wise mind)**

So, if you were to take into account both your emotional mind's response and your rational mind's response to the situation, what would your wise mind think about it? What would a potentially balanced view be (considering both the facts and your emotions)?

Sometimes there is no clear right or wrong decision, and that's fine. We just need to make a "best guess" about which option to choose, and if this goes "wrong" then we can choose another option and start again. Another way to help you to make good decisions is to be aware of what your main values are, and what drives you day to day. Exercise 1 at the end of this book will help you to live a life that better fits with your values.

Failure is a good thing

Things are never going to be perfect, and it can be useful to learn to fail at things, for things to go wrong, for you to make "bad decisions" and to learn that you can survive them. If you learn to survive when things go wrong, this will make you more "resilient" (able to "bounce back") in the future when you may face other difficulties. It can be helpful to start new hobbies or activities that you may initially be "bad" at but have fun practising and learning. It can be such a big relief to not be perfect, and to not need to try to be perfect all of the time. You're rubbish at this thing and you have survived being rubbish at it; nothing bad happened! You need courage to allow yourself to fail and must remember that failure can also be motivating. Failure can lead you to push yourself further, as what's the worst that could happen? Well, I could fail again, but now I know that I can survive this.

◇ Part 2 ◇

THE CHALLENGES OF ADULTHOOD: A HOW-TO GUIDE

In Part 2, we think through some of the stuff that might be more difficult if you suffer with anxiety, such as socialising, or that might be the cause of lots of stress and anxiety even if you are really confident, like job interviews and work worries. We spoke to lots of people and this confirmed what we already suspected – that one of the biggest challenges in early adulthood is making friends and socialising, so we made this our focus for the first chapter in Part 2, "Getting Out and Socialising with Other Adults". Here we explore social awkwardness and anxiety and talk through some top tips taken from the 18–25-year-olds who took part in our survey.

Chapter 4 also focuses on social situations but the ideas used here can help you to manage anxious thoughts about anything! We know that anxiety can interfere with your ability to study effectively and that studying as an adult is different from studying when you are at school. In Chapter 5, therefore, we think about how anxiety might impact on your learning and we give lots of practical strategies to help you study and revise, whether it is for college, university or professional qualifications. Included in this chapter is advice from a lecturer and course tutor who has been supporting students for a number of years. Studying at university or college can often mean that people move out of home at 18, so Chapter 6 is a quick guide to transitions and endings more generally, and how to deal with them. It focuses on the specifics of leaving home and moving out.

One of the most anxiety-provoking things most people do is going for a job interview. In Chapter 7 we give lots of tips for managing anxiety in job interviews and also some advice from professionals who are on the other side of the table.

Now you may already have a job, but this does not mean that all the stress is over, so we also have a chapter on "Workplace Worries" to think about how to manage stress and anxiety at work.

Chapter 3

Getting Out and Socialising With Other Adults

Whether you're an introvert or an extrovert, it's important to have social relationships

It may feel horrible, but sometimes you need to force yourself to face something to realise there's no need to fear it

Social anxiety is a fear that other people are going to judge us negatively

One of the best ways to conquer anxiety is to learn more about it

As we become adults, we start to learn about who we are as social beings: are we a party-goer, someone who prefers to stay in and play board games with friends, or both? That's OK, everyone is different, and that's a good thing. Life would be very boring if we were all the same. You may have heard of the terms "introvert" and "extrovert". An introvert is someone who likes to spend time by themselves and is more reserved in social contexts, whereas an extrovert refers to someone who is seen as outgoing, engaging and energetic within their social environment. This doesn't mean that everyone with anxiety is an introvert. In fact, lots of people who may seem confident and extroverted may struggle with anxiety and worries underneath. For some, the more anxious they are, the more confident they seem. Sue, for example, is often told how confident she looks when doing a presentation in front of a large audience, but the truth is that she is shaking underneath.

In our survey outlined below, 61 per cent of young people saw themselves as an introvert or "a bit of an introvert"; however, only 34.5 per cent of young people stated that other people saw them as an introvert. This suggests that approximately a third of all people who responded to the survey felt like an introvert inside, but may have seemed more outgoing to others.

What we know is that whether you're an introvert or an extrovert, it's important to have social relationships. This is one thing that makes us human: our need to connect with others. So, if you wish things were different, if you would like to feel more comfortable in social situations, to make new friends more easily, or "survive" in a new environment with new people, then this chapter and Chapter 4 are for you. This chapter will outline the results of our survey of 18–25-year-olds and look at anxiety reactions in social situations. Chapter 4 will focus on how to cope with anxious thoughts that can get in the way of forming relationships.

Anxiety and social awkwardness

We thought it might be useful to do a survey of young people aged 18–25 (with and without problem anxiety), to find out how they feel in social situations and to see how common these anxious feelings are. A big thank you to the 41 people who completed the survey.

Over a third of people who responded to the survey considered themselves to have anxiety (or awkwardness) in social situations. Most felt that anxiety had prevented them from attending social situations at least a few times a year, and half acknowledged that they avoid social situations at least once per week. Only 35 per cent said that they would approach someone new to say "hello". We asked people what they would say, and these were some top tips that they gave.

TOP TIPS FOR STARTING A CONVERSATION WITH SOMEONE NEW

◇ Start by saying "Hello" or "Hi" or "You alright?" Ask how their day/evening is going.

◇ Make sure that your body language is welcoming, for example smiling and looking friendly.

◇ Introduce yourself and acknowledge that you haven't met before, for example, "Hi, I'm XX, I don't think we've met."

❖ Ask how they know everyone else in the situation/at the event, for example, "How do you know Alice?"

❖ Usually people tend to have general chit-chat until they can stumble on something where there is some mutual interest. Suggested topics of conversation include:

» What do they watch on TV? What kinds of music do they listen to? Which books – or sports, social media, art and fashion, games – do they like?

» What are they studying/what do they do as a job/what they are planning to do in the future?

» What are their hobbies and interests? What do they like doing?

» Where are they going on holiday? Where have they been on holiday?

» Where they're from, where they live, who they live with.

» Comment on their clothes, for example, "I like your shoes, where did you get them from?"

» Talk about the situation that you are in, for example talk about the comedy if you are at a comedy gig, or different films if you are at a cinema, or drinks of choice or where they are going later if you are at a bar.

» If all else fails, talk about the weather.

We asked which situations made people feel the most anxious, and the top four were:

- a gathering of people you don't know
- a new social environment (such as workplace/college)
- a person that you partially know approaching you in the street
- needing to ask someone you don't know for something.

However, several people stated that they feel anxious in familiar situations too, including meeting up with a friend (12%) or with a gathering of people that they know reasonably well (7%). The main ways that anxiety affected the people who responded to the survey were: becoming quiet and withdrawn, trying not to be noticed, avoiding talking to others unless needing to, waiting for an opportunity to leave, "freezing up", avoiding eye contact, stuttering, speaking quickly or in short sentences, fiddling with something such as their phone, clinging to someone close to them. One responder also spoke about how they would force themselves to get through the situation due to a fear of upsetting others:

> Someone had bought smoked mackerel just for me at a family gathering. So I put some on my plate but soon noticed it wasn't smoked mackerel, it was raw. I didn't want to seem rude and also I didn't know how to raise the point that it was raw. So, I ate the whole fish... I think I usually put myself through extremely uncomfortable situations to avoid awkward interactions, because me being uncomfortable would be better than making someone else feel bad or awkward themselves.

Other people also spoke about how they would "power through" or "sit through" the anxiety-provoking situation, however difficult that might have felt at the time. This included "faking a smile" and sticking with it, trying to act "normally" or acting like an extrovert, making jokes, taking a moment to have a deep breath (perhaps going to the toilet to do this), giving themselves a pep talk, and then returning to the social situation. Many people who responded were not sure how to cope with anxiety, but others gave the following ideas/advice for coping with social situations.

ADVICE FOR COPING WITH SOCIAL SITUATIONS

◆ Remember that you're not the first person to experience social anxiety, and you're not the last. Everyone has insecurities and you won't be the only person who feels anxious. They're only people, and they will be glad if you choose to speak to them.

◆ Any interaction has the possibility of creating new friendships or connections.

◆ If in the extremely unlikely event that someone you don't know is hostile towards you, the chance of ever seeing them again is rare and, in the end, it's not worth caring about someone like that.

◆ Fake it – we're all just idiots trying our best.

◆ Nobody will hold it against you if you mess up by accident. If you are honest, kind and open about mistakes people will be more likely to be understanding.

◆ Just try to stay calm and breathe.

◇ Leave if you need to – you're not a bad person for doing so.

◇ People don't judge you as much as you think.

◇ It can be helpful to think that you are someone who is confident and can speak to people easily, and then pretend that you are that person.

◇ Tell the people you are closest with not to "enable" you. For example, if you are too frightened to order your meal in a restaurant and ask them to, they should say no, because then you'll have to order it yourself. The more you do it, the easier it is.

◇ Awkward situations are only temporary. The more often you put yourself in situations that make you anxious, the more likely you are to improve your social skills and eventually overcome some degree of anxiety and awkwardness. The more you see yourself succeed in social situations, the more confidence you will gain.

◇ Even though it may feel horrible at the time, sometimes you need to force yourself to face something to realise that there's no need to fear it. It's a mini achievement each time you stick something out, and often you will learn that the longer you sit with the anxiety, the more the anxiety begins to reduce.

◇ Always approach things with a smile. It helps a lot and makes you feel happier. It's better to be brave than regret not doing something you want to, no matter what the outcome.

Social anxiety

So, what is "social anxiety" and why does it affect us so much? Well, the textbooks tell us that social anxiety is a fear that other people are going to judge us negatively in a social situation. That we will "fail" at being socially acceptable and will do something that is socially wrong, and other people will notice this and laugh at, make fun of, or criticise us for it. This will understandably lead us to feel rubbish about ourselves and worry that people are going to reject us, or not want to spend time with us anymore. If we are catastrophising, we might decide that we will be a social outcast and spend our lives living in the woods in a small hut never getting our hair cut... (although sometimes living in isolation might sound tempting!).

We can get worried about how the anxiety might show when we are in a social situation – the anxiety about being judged makes us feel even more likely to be judged! It can make our hands shake, our mouth dry up, our cheeks blush, our thoughts race, or our speech come out all jumbled. How will other people perceive us then? The fear is often that if people notice our anxious responses, then they might think that we are crazy, weak or stupid. For example, someone might be worried about carrying a tray of food across a room, due to a fear that their hands will shake as "everyone" will be looking at them.

What makes it worse

When we feel socially anxious we become focused on what others might think (see the next chapter for how your anxious mind can play tricks!) and on hiding our anxiety from others. Both can really get in the way of developing our social skills.

The thing is that trying not to appear anxious can make us seem odd or disinterested, so we might get exactly the strange look or rejection that we fear. Some common examples include clasping or sitting on our hands so that they don't shake, giving even more eye contact than usual (also known as staring) or completely avoiding eye contact, and over-preparing topics to talk about with people. These behaviours can appear strange and make it harder for us to just enjoy being with other people and listening to them (see "Behaviours that get in the way). Also, we are often so caught up in our own anxious bodily reactions and trying to appear "normal" that we have no idea how people are perceiving us. We might *feel* as if everyone is staring, but we don't know if this is the case. The truth is that no one may have noticed anything, and they are more likely to be focusing on themselves and how they might negotiate a social situation.

Behaviours that get in the way

To help us to cope with our anxious bodily reactions, we might find things that we can do that help us to feel calmer, which we refer to as "safety behaviours". Although the term "safety behaviours" sounds undoubtedly positive (who wouldn't want to be safe?), these behaviours can actually get in the way of you learning to cope with your anxiety.

There are three main problems with safety behaviours:

1. *They sometimes don't fit well with what you want to be doing.* For example, if your safety behaviour is to hold a bottle of water at all times to stop your hands shaking, what if there is no bottled water available, or if you leave it somewhere by accident? Or you finish it and someone offers to throw it away for you? If this is your way of feeling safe in this situation, in order to cope, you might have the urge to wrestle it back out of their hands.

2. *You might seem less friendly to other people.* For example, if your safety behaviour is to make sure that you give people lots of eye contact, you might end up seeming as if you are trying to stare them out. Or if you are trying not to talk in a jumbled way, this might lead to you not talking very much or appearing uptight, and other people might think that you are not interested.

3. *You might start to believe that you cannot cope without them.* You might think that your survival in social situations depends on you being able to do your safety behaviours, although this isn't the case (and you may be able to survive perfectly well without them). This can then reinforce your need to use them and increase your

dependency on them. For example, "I only managed to cope in that meeting because I had my stressball under the table. If I hadn't had it with me, I would have panicked and lost my train of thought. I need to take it into all of my meetings from now on."

Behavioural experiments

Now that you are starting to understand yourself in social situations a bit more, it will be easier to start to tackle your anxiety around them. One of the ways you can do this is to carry out what we call "behavioural experiments", which means that you test out your thoughts or worries about the social situation, without using your safety behaviours, to learn that you can survive the situation without having to "do" anything.

This may mean doing the opposite of your safety behaviours.

SAFETY BEHAVIOURS AND THEIR OPPOSITES

Safety behaviour: Withdraw from your friends

Opposite: Bring your attention to your friends and listen

Safety behaviour: Rehearse what you are going to say

Opposite: No rehearsal, just go straight in and say what comes into your head

Safety behaviour: Sit on your hands

Opposite: Don't sit on your hands, let them relax

Once you have done your experiment, it's time to reflect on whether what you thought was going to happen actually happened. Exercise 2 at the end of this book has a sheet that you can fill in to help you to plan and reflect on experiments to test out your safety behaviours. It can also be useful to get feedback from your friends, or even video the interaction to see what actually happens.

Learning about how social anxiety affects you

One of the best ways to conquer anxiety in social situations is to learn more about it and better understand it, as the more that you know it, the easier it will be to tackle and overcome. Try answering the next few questions about your own experiences of anxiety. Take your time over them, and maybe ask for help from a close friend or family member who knows you well.

- What are your fears about social situations? What do you worry about the most?

- What are your safety behaviours around social situations (anything that you do to hide your anxiety or avoid drawing attention to yourself)?

- What anxious thoughts do you have in preparation for, during or after social situations?

- Where do you feel anxiety in your body in social situations?

- Which of your anxious bodily reactions bothers you the most (or do you try to avoid)?

- If people noticed your anxious bodily reactions, what would that mean to you?

- How do you think other people perceive you in social situations?

- What is the evidence (for and against) this belief that other people might see you in that way?

- When you are in a social situation, what are you most aware of?

- When you use your safety behaviours, how might you look or behave then?

- If you didn't use your safety behaviours, what do you believe would happen?

- How do you know that would happen? Do you have any evidence of this?

- If you could be less self-conscious, would that help? How?

These questions are simply prompts to encourage self-reflection and awareness of your own thoughts, feelings and responses.

Liam's story

I was recently asked to play guitar at my parents' wedding. After agreeing to do this, I almost instantly felt a little anxious about it, but I soldiered on. When the day finally arrived, I was feeling somewhat tense, but alright. Then it was my time to play. I suddenly found it very hard to breathe, and as I started playing, I couldn't look up at the people watching out of fear. I was very aware of being unable to breathe, and for half the song I was just trying to hide this. Then as I kept playing I slowly started to regain control. I kept pushing on and I started to breathe, albeit with a very shaky breath, and I could feel myself calming down. I kept telling myself that I had this, and the only person judging me as much as I thought I was being judged was myself.

Chapter 4

What Can I Do With Anxious Thoughts?

We think about how anxious thoughts can impact on relationships	The more that you do something, the less anxiety-provoking it becomes	Lots of people find it helpful to find coping statements to carry with them

It can be useful to "catch" and note down our thoughts so that we can start to challenge them and identify more balanced ways of thinking

Anxious thoughts can be tough to deal with, like bullies who stop us from getting on with what we want and need to be doing. They can get in the way of us being ourselves and make us feel unable to make friends and start relationships. In this chapter, we think about how anxious thoughts can impact on relationships, but the ideas that we talk about can be applied to lots of anxious thoughts and to dealing with worries about many things.

Bob's story

I recently started a new educational course, so as you can imagine I was very anxious as there were several different new experiences I would be facing. First there was the issue of meeting people. I'm not exactly the most outgoing person, so this was naturally difficult for me to begin with. My fear is that people won't really like me, that I won't fit in. I initially avoided talking to people. I worried that they would be dismissive of me or mean to me if I tried to talk to them, because they wouldn't like me. For the first week or so, I managed to talk to one person who just so happened to be from my college. I had never spoken to them before, but after many times of awkwardly thinking, "Aaah, I don't want to annoy this person", I talked to them anyway and we fairly quickly became friends. From there I felt slightly more confident talking to more people, and that was enough to help me emerge from my little anxiety cocoon. I just go for it. I tend to say anything relevant to the situation that we're both in, so that we can both relate to it at least.

Getting used to it

There are lots of different ways to conquer anxious thoughts, which we will outline in this chapter; however, one of the simplest (but not particularly easiest) ways is to expose yourself to what scares you. As discussed in the previous chapter by many of those who completed our survey, one of the best ways to alleviate anxiety is to "power through" a social situation and learn that you *can* survive it. The idea is that the more that you do something, the less anxiety-provoking it becomes and you disprove your anxious thoughts with real-life evidence!

EXPOSURE TO FEARS

Albert Ellis (1913–2007), a famous American psychologist, had a fear of speaking to women. It's reported that Albert was 19 years old, when he decided to face his fear by talking to a hundred women over the period of a month in a local botanical garden. Although he didn't get a date, he stopped being fearful of talking to women. He was no longer scared of rejection as he had become "desensitized" to this. Albert ended up contributing to the development of several therapies including rational emotive behaviour therapy (REBT).

One way of getting over the fear of speaking to people is to speak to many of them, and a lot. The more you speak to people, the more your anxiety will reduce, and you will feel more confident and comfortable doing it. When we decide to expose ourselves to social situations, it can be useful to take small steps, choosing something quite small to try first, and then slowly working our way up the "exposure ladder" as our anxiety reduces. It's also important to clearly identify what you want to achieve, so that you know what you are working towards. You might want to decide on a nice reward for yourself for achieving each step, as this can be quite a challenging task to do. Below is an example of what an exposure ladder for "starting a conversation with someone new" might look like.

AIM: TO BE ABLE TO START A CONVERSATION WITH SOMEONE NEW AT WORK

Step 1: Smile briefly when I see someone at work who I haven't spoken to before.

Step 2: Say "Hi" to someone at work who I haven't spoken to before.

Step 3: Say "Hi [insert name]" to someone at work.

Step 4: Say "How has your weekend been?" to someone at work.

This exposure ladder is likely to look quite different for different people, as it depends on what you find the scariest and most anxiety-provoking task, and then what steps you have to take to complete it, and what they might feel like for you. The idea is to do each step as many times as needed (so that your anxiety reduces to a more manageable level) before moving on to the next step. You might choose to rate your anxiety each time you try a step (we recommend rating it on a 0–100% scale) and decide that you'll only move on to the next step when your anxiety reduces to, say, 35 per cent. So, it might take several days, weeks or months to get through the ladder, and that's OK.

There is more information about exposure ladders, and the challenges completing these, in our previous book: *My Anxiety Handbook: Getting Back on Track.*

Dealing with your thoughts

When we're feeling anxious, this impacts on the way that we view the world; we're more likely to think that things are going to go wrong and that we will be unable to cope. It is as if we have an anxious filter on life, or we are constantly hearing horror music in the background. Within relationships, we may worry that the other person doesn't like us, is going to make fun of us, is going to reject us or not want to spend time with us anymore (among lots of other worries).

Thinking shortcuts

It's important to remember that when we feel anxious, we think in an anxious way (also known as "emotional reasoning") and although these anxious thoughts are not facts, we can often treat them as though they are *true* just because they feel "right". Our brain has evolved a lot of helpful shortcuts so we can think smart, not hard, and make sense of the complex social world that we live in. The problem is that these shortcuts can be hijacked very effectively by our anxiety to make us "anxious thinkers" rather than "smart thinkers". The ten "errors" outlined below are to help you spot when the shortcuts are being hijacked by your anxiety and are becoming unhelpful.

1. *Catastrophising* – This is when we think about something that worries us and we keep going with "what if" until we reach a total catastrophe.

CATASTROPHISING

Experience	Worst-case scenario
Coughs	I have TB
Boss calls your name	I'm going to be sacked
Friend doesn't reply to a text immediately	They have fallen out with me/they have been in a horrible accident
Someone in the street smiles at you	She's laughing at my hair/nose/outfit... aaahhhh!
Boyfriend smiles at someone	They fancy someone else/are cheating on me

2. *Jumping to conclusions* – This is when we use a small amount of information to make a judgement and we come down on the side of caution. For example, if we see that our girlfriend has messaged another man, we might immediately jump to thinking that they are cheating on us, rather than speaking to them about this and seeing what is really going on.

3. *Taking things personally* – When we are doing well, we usually blame the universe for the bad things that happen and take personal credit for when good things happen. It helps us to stay healthy and happy. However, anxious thinking means that we can start to blame ourselves for things that have very little or nothing to do with us. For example, if a friend has to cancel a trip to the cinema, you might think that this is because they don't want to spend time with you or that you embarrass them.

4. *Negative filtering* – This happens when we ignore all the good stuff that has happened and focus on the bad things. For example, you might become preoccupied with something that you said to your boyfriend earlier that day that you felt he might have taken badly, while ignoring the fact that he did not seem bothered by it and spent the rest of the day with you. The negative filter can mean that we make a judgement about the whole day and ourselves based on only a small amount of negative information and this focus makes us feel horrible. Our brains are tuning in to the negative to keep us safe, but it really ruins our day.

5. *Overgeneralising* – A lot like the negative filter, this means we use one event or piece of information about something specific to make a global judgement. For example, I didn't get invited to the party on Saturday, so everybody hates me.

6. *Overestimating* – We overestimate the likelihood that bad things will happen (e.g. if I go to that course, no one will speak to me). We could call this "better to be safe than sorry" reasoning. It makes us more cautious, which if the world is dangerous could be considered helpful, but when it's just our anxious brain tricking us, it can make life difficult.

7. *Mind-reading* – Being a human is all about relating to other humans. We are designed and programmed to want to be known and to know other people. However, this important and pretty wonderful bit of being a human can mean that we (wrongly) think we can read people's minds and because we are thinking

negatively, we assume they can too. We can then misinterpret intentions and behaviour in a way that is unhelpful. For example, if a person is looking at you on a bus you might think, "They are judging me, they think I look weird", when you have absolutely no idea what they are actually thinking. They could be admiring your shoes or coat or they could simply be staring straight through you worrying about what other people on the bus are thinking of them. This kind of anxious mind-reading makes us feel awful and has no basis in reality.

8. *Fortune-telling* – Just like relating to other people, working out what might happen next is also what makes us the dominant species on earth. It allows us to solve problems and be creative and inventive. The problem can be that when we are feeling anxious and believe we already know what the future holds, we can begin thinking that we don't need to try things out. Why would you go and talk to that interesting-looking person if you already know that they are going to hate you?

9. *Labelling* – We need to have quick ways of making sense of the world around us so that we can make decisions efficiently and effectively. If we can assess a situation and quickly give it a label, then this can help us quickly make sense of what is going on in order to choose the best option: "I am safe" or "This isn't OK". When we are having a difficult experience, we label it or ourselves. For example, you forget to call a friend on their birthday and you think, "I am a useless friend" or even more generally, "I am useless".

10. *Black and white thinking* – Just like labelling, categorising things as either "brilliant" or "terrible" is a good way to make quick decisions and reason efficiently when there's lots of information available. It takes time to think about and analyse the complexities of people and situations and we don't always have lots of time, especially when we are anxious. If we rely on this kind of thinking, then we can get into trouble. An example of this might be, "She is good at talking to people and I'm no good at talking to people" rather than recognising that there are grey areas, or that talking to other people is a complex skill. A more complex or grey way of thinking about this could be, "I am good at talking to people one to one but find it harder in a large group".

Do you recognise yourself perhaps using any of these shortcuts? If yes, it might be useful to make a note of these (or use a highlighter to mark them in this book) so that you can start to notice if you are falling into any of these traps and you can then begin to challenge your thinking.

Catching your thoughts

Now that we know ways in which anxiety can "hijack" our thinking, it can be useful to "catch" and note down our thoughts so that we can start to challenge them and identify more balanced ways of thinking. You might feel that your thoughts are a never-ending stream of anxiety, and it can be difficult to catch them at first. The most important anxious thoughts to be able to recognise and challenge are usually global statements about you as a person (I am...) or others (Everyone...). We sometimes call these "hot thoughts" because they are an immediate emotional response that we believe intensely, and our anxious feelings make them seem "right" or true. These thoughts can be so intense that we try to avoid or ignore them. It may be useful to write down the situations that make you feel particularly anxious, and the thoughts that you tend to have at these times. You might choose to write these down in a thought diary or notebook, or even on your phone. You can then use some simple questions to help you to work out which shortcuts your anxious mind might be using. Then rather than simply accepting your thoughts as true, you can challenge them to see if they stand up to scrutiny.

Challenging your thoughts

Once you have caught your anxious thoughts, it is a good idea to take time to sit down and try and make sense of your ways of thinking and challenge these thoughts. For example, if you messaged your friend half an hour ago asking if she wanted to meet you later on, you can see that she has viewed the message, but she hasn't replied yet. You might start to worry and think, "She's ignoring me. She's seen the message and is choosing not to respond. She is pulling away from me like everyone does. She hates me too." So, your "hot thought" in that situation would be that "Everyone hates me".

The next step would be to look carefully at that thought and ask yourself, "How much do I believe this?" In that moment, you might believe that thought quite strongly (say, 90%). You need to answer this question in the moment so that you don't forget how you were feeling at the time, so you ideally will need this as a column in your thought record or a prompt in your diary.

Next, you need to be a detective and look for all the evidence for and against the thought. If you're struggling, it sometimes helps to imagine what a friend might say, or to think what you might say to them if they were thinking this way. Most of us are much kinder to our friends than we are to ourselves. One way to help you to do this, is to use the "compassionate other" task in Exercise 4 at the end of this book.

CATCHING AND CHALLENGING THOUGHTS IN YOUR NOTEBOOK OR DIARY

◇ Write down the exact thought in quotation marks and give a short explanation of the context.

   I thought "Everyone is laughing at me" as I walked into the room.

◇ Rate how much you believe it (in that moment).

   90 per cent.

◇ Rate how anxious you feel (and how this anxiety feels in your body).

   I felt very anxious, about 8/10. I suddenly felt dizzy and light-headed.

◇ Then think about the evidence.

   For: A few people were looking in my direction.

Against: They were probably just looking as I had opened the door. They could have started laughing before I entered.

My best friend would say, "You are just feeling anxious; you always think that people are laughing at you when they are not. They have no reason to laugh at you. You need to take a deep breath and find a friendly face."

◇ Spot any possible anxious shortcuts.

I am jumping to conclusions because I don't have enough information. I'm taking things personally by assuming they are laughing about me.

◇ Rate how much you believe the thought now

40 per cent.

◇ Rate how anxious you feel.

I don't feel too bad now, about 4/10.

◇ What would a more balanced thought be?

"Although that felt horrible, it doesn't mean that they were laughing at me. I can manage this."

There is a template for a thought-challenging sheet in Exercise 3 at the end of this book. As you get more practice at looking for evidence and seeing the biases in your thinking, it becomes automatic and you will no longer need to record this on a sheet or in a diary. You'll be less likely to just trust your anxious thoughts and will begin to recognise that a lot of the time you are thinking negatively because you feel anxious, not because things truly are bad. Having said that, it isn't always the case that challenging a thought makes you feel less anxious as sometimes it might set you off catastrophising, especially if you are alone and still feeling very anxious. It can be hard at first but don't let this put you off. Changing the way you think isn't an easy thing to do and it will take time and practice. If you think this sounds helpful and can commit to this way of approaching your thoughts, we know it can break the anxious cycle, so you will feel more in control when your anxious thoughts try to lead you down an unhelpful track.

Finding the evidence

We might remember times when we do or have done things badly, and it can feel as if these are imprinted on our brain, but, often, we might forget when we do or have done things well. Like a magnet, these thoughts "stick" to our existing beliefs while those that don't fit are repelled and forgotten. We might also think of anxiety as a security guard who only "lets in" the information that agrees with our anxious thoughts or evidence that other people are scary and judgemental and that we are not very good at social situations. So, someone looks at us and we think that they looked at us in a funny way because they don't like us, and the security guard welcomes this information into our brain. Our friend doesn't call when they were meant to, and the security guard welcomes this too (it fits with what is on the guard's "list"). However, any evidence to the contrary – that people are wanting to spend time with us, or we can sometimes be good or cope in social situations – is turned away and not "let in" by the guard. It's as if it never existed! We end up with biased evidence that supports our biased thoughts.

One way to get away from this a little is to start to collect the contrary evidence. Maybe have a little notebook or use your phone and write down every time someone shows you any positive attention (they smile, choose to speak to you, ask you to go out somewhere), or when you've actually had an "OK time" in a social situation (say, had a good conversation with someone). You can then use this evidence to help to challenge any anxious thoughts when they arise and give yourself a more balanced perspective.

Counteracting the negative thinking

When we feel bad, we think bad thoughts. We can start to talk to ourselves in a negative way, criticise ourselves and point out mistakes or flaws. This can be a damaging habit to develop. We do this more and are more critical when we've had other people saying horrible things to us, providing us with external "evidence". These negative voices can end up being the voices that we use to talk to ourselves much of the time. Then, when we make a mistake, instead of recognising that we all make mistakes and that they are part of life, we might say, "Well of course I messed up, I am a mess!" or even worse, when we start to feel anxious say, "Look at me, I'm pathetic, I can't cope with anything!" due to the influence of the now negative, internal voices. To counteract this "negative self-talk", we don't always need to catch our thoughts and challenge them. Lots of people find it helpful to find coping statements to carry with them. To find your own coping statements, you might look at the suggestions below, or quotes from the internet, song lyrics, things that people close to you have said, some of the top tips from the anxiety survey (see Chapter 3), or you might look to religious texts for inspiration. You can refer to them when things are difficult and you become aware that the voice in your head is being critical. It becomes easier and more natural as you practise and they are there ready to jump to the front of your mind and divert you from the negative self-talk.

COPING STATEMENTS

◇ "Just because I am anxious doesn't mean I cannot manage this situation just fine."

◇ "This feeling will pass."

◇ "It's natural to feel like this. I didn't choose, or want this feeling, but I'm stuck with it for a while until it passes. I can just cope the best that I can."

◇ "I have got through this before, I will get through it again."

- ❖ "It's OK not to be OK."

- ❖ "Anxiety makes me feel horrible, but it won't do me any harm."

- ❖ "I am not my thoughts."

- ❖ "I don't have to give these anxious thoughts love and attention. I am going to be kind to myself instead."

Chapter 5

I Can't Focus! How to Study With Anxiety

For lots of people, anxiety makes being organised difficult	Getting the environment right is important and having clear, realistic goals will help you to plan and organise
Scary events become less and less of a challenge as we face them	We aim to give you some understanding of how anxiety can impact on your thinking, learning and planning

Going to college or university or pursuing professional qualifications can be anxiety-provoking for many reasons. Taking on a new role and learning new things can be exciting and refreshing but can create lots of uncertainty and pressures too. If you already suffer with problem anxiety, then studying in a more independent way while managing all the other pressures we talk about in the book (financial and social) can feel overwhelming and get in the way of achieving what you might be capable of. In this chapter, we aim to give you some understanding of how anxiety can impact on your thinking, learning and planning, and we provide tips so you can study as effectively and independently as possible. If you are about to move away to college or university, you might also want to look at the next chapter, which is about moving away from home and how to manage endings and transitions.

Studying in the adult world

There is a stereotype of "lazy" students sleeping in until lunchtime, watching daytime TV, then falling into the bar to drink cheap booze (please note, none of the authors fulfilled this stereotype...much...well hardly at all...maybe just a tiny bit in the first year). Lots of you will understandably have expected it to be the time of your lives, filled with parties and excitement, but we know that students nowadays report high levels of stress and worry and this tells us that most students take their studies seriously and, sadly, can be going through some difficult times. This is often with little support as they are living away from their family and other support systems. The pressure to be "having the time of your life" can make it even harder to accept feeling anxious and to let others know you're struggling. If you're hiding under your duvet watching reruns of *The Inbetweeners* to avoid your anxiety and *it seems as if* all your friends are out doing new things and enjoying themselves, then this can make you feel doubly miserable and as if you have somehow failed. Bridie spent a lot of time watching "real crime" programmes in her pyjamas when her course mates were at the students' union, so she knows a bit about how this feels.

For many adults, the need to balance working to earn money, alongside studying, or if you are undertaking professional qualifications then working and doing a lot of study in your own time, means you have to be super organised and motivated. Lots of people become tired and stressed out and wonder why they are putting themselves through it! The cost of education can also be stressful and can contribute to added pressure to achieve and do well. As the cost of higher education has increased, students expect more from their university or college but they also feel under greater pressure to "make it count" as they see enormous student loans mounting up.

Avoiding avoidance

When we feel anxious and stressed, a common coping strategy is to avoid whatever we see as causing the anxiety. In the short term, we feel much better, but with studying this most often means we avoid doing the work (or even thinking about the work), then it piles up and we end up with loads of tasks and deadlines to meet. This then creates more stress and anxiety and can lead to bigger problems if we start to fall behind. Recent research has also found that when students compare themselves with others and over-estimate the amount of studying that other people might be doing (worrying that other people are doing more than them), this can lead to them feeling unprepared for exams, and feeling anxiety and self-doubt, which then leads them to perform less well. It's normal to feel pressure and a little stress when we have deadlines and assignments, but for some people this feels unbearable and they get caught up in anxious thinking and avoidance that then stops them achieving their academic goals. We need to treat this anxiety like we do all challenges...take it slowly but always have a go, set short-term, realistic goals, and take good care of ourselves while we are doing it.

There may be lots of distractions in your student life, such as going out with friends and joining different clubs and societies. For people who have been anxious during their teens, college, university or studying can be where they find their place and make friends who "get them". If this is you, then *congratulations*, we are very happy for you. Just a teeny tiny note of caution – all that anxiety can come flooding back if you are not getting on with the studying part! It's important to think about self-care (Chapter 11) and finding a balance between socialising, time for you and being able to complete your studies, so you're healthy as well as achieving your academic goals and objectives.

Anxiety and getting organised

One way that people can learn to cope with their anxiety is to become very controlled or controlling. If this is you then you probably have lots of lists, clear timetables and study plans, and accompanying high (maybe even unrealistic) expectations of yourself. For you, anxiety becomes unmanageable when you become overwhelmed by the demands of your studies and your coping strategies become ineffective. You might start to feel you've lost control or you don't feel you are achieving if things don't go exactly as you had hoped and planned. Group working is often key to studying as an adult and this can be hard if you are used to doing everything in a particular way, being in control, or have a need for everything to be "perfect". Being able to recognise when your coping strategies are actually causing a problem can be important. If this sounds like you then "getting organised" isn't the problem, but it will be learning to let go and manage the feelings it brings up when you are not able to control everything and get the best grades all of the time. It's OK to not be OK, and even to (shock, horror) not meet your own high expectations, to get a poor grade or ask for an extension occasionally. Learning that the world will not end, that we can cope with the awful feelings that come alongside feeling like a failure, is a key skill in overcoming anxiety and developing resilience. Being organised and working to a plan is helpful, so we're definitely not saying throw away the lists and timetables, just maybe think about the other ways you can manage your high expectations and anxiety.

If this doesn't sound like you then we get it. For lots of people, anxiety makes being organised difficult. Anxiety can significantly interfere with the part of the brain responsible for "executive function" and hence the processes that help us to set goals and plan the sequences of steps to get there. Basically, this is why you can't find your glasses or lose your parking ticket/car keys when you are going to an interview or an appointment that you feel worried about. Your planning brain doesn't work so well when you are feeling anxious or stressed even if the goals seem simple – for example, to drive there without crashing, to park the car and get into the building without falling up the steps. These might be easy tasks when you are going around to a friend's for a catch-up but not so much when you are desperate to get a new job or a place on a competitive course. Executive functioning is also important for effective independent studying. Maybe your anxiety has meant that this has always been a struggle for you, or alternatively it may be that previously at school and college there was a lot of structure and support around to help you. Structure can help when anxiety is overwhelming and things feel chaotic;

however, as an adult, there is often less support or people just feel less able to ask for help.

Self-talk and "mindset"

One of the things that can really get in the way of being able to sit down and study can be the way we talk to ourselves about our abilities. We know that anxious young people have more negative "self-talk" and they are more likely to put themselves down and say negative things to themselves.[1] These negative messages to ourselves can impact motivation and engagement, increasing the likelihood of avoidance. Do you recognise this as something you do? Looking at Chapter 4 and dealing with anxious thoughts could be helpful, and Chapter 12 also talks about using mindful strategies to cope with negative thoughts.

Carol Dweck[2] in the US has written a lot about "growth mindset" and the idea that rather than thinking about ourselves as having things we are good or bad at and this being fixed, for example, "I am just not good at maths" or "I am just not academic", we can think about ourselves as being on a learning journey, needing to practise more and not having those skills yet.

Noticing how you talk to yourself and think about your abilities when you are approaching studying can be important in preventing avoidance and managing motivation. How helpful is it to tell yourself how bad you are at something just as you are about to start or when things begin to get tough?

---

1   Sood, E.D. and Kendall, P.C. (2007) "Assessing anxious self-talk in youth: The negative affectivity self-statement questionnaire – anxiety scale." *Cognitive Therapy and Research*, 31 (5), 603–618. doi:10.1007/s10608-006-9043-8.
2   Dweck, C.S. (2017) *Mindset: Changing the Way You Think to Fulfil Your Potential.* London: Robinson.

Try to keep some positive messages in your diary/organiser or on your wall, for example, "I am working hard and I am getting there".

Goal-setting and prioritising

You may only have one assignment to complete but lots of other responsibilities to manage (paid work, caring for others, cooking and housework) or you may feel that other things are taken care of but you have multiple assignments and deadlines to manage. Getting the environment right is important and having clear, realistic goals will help you to plan and organise while making sure you are getting enough time to take care of yourself.

The Pomodoro technique (all resources freely available online) is a way of managing tasks and deadlines while ensuring that you take adequate breaks, which aims to make you more productive. It means breaking your day up into short chunks of time (40 minutes), listing all the tasks that you need to complete that day, then making good guesses about how many chunks that might take. It also makes helpful suggestions about ways to prioritise your tasks, so you can make sure you meet deadlines. One suggestion that helped Bridie when she was studying was to never read or respond to emails first thing in the morning – you can basically waste half your day replying to emails if you're not careful. This can, however, be a nice way to finish off your study session when you are starting to feel a bit tired and are losing motivation. Don't waste your morning brilliance on tasks that require less brain power or concentration.

Writing a colour-coded list of tasks

Maybe you don't feel the need for such a regimented approach to your study time, but it can be helpful to have a clear list of deadlines and assignments and to make it clear what your priorities are. Bridie likes a traffic light approach: red for the things that you need to get done this week or even today; orange for the things that need to be done in the coming two weeks or will take a long time to complete; green for things that need to be planned but not completed. Obviously, you can change this to magenta, teal and aqua according to your pen selection.

Make a study haven

One thing that can be important in helping you to be able to focus and concentrate on studying, is to have somewhere that feels safe, calm and away from distractions that can help you to study. If you live with other students, then agreeing how you can support each other can be helpful.

TOP TIPS FOR CREATING A STUDY HAVEN

✧ Choose a space as distraction free as possible, ideally not where your kids/brothers/sisters/ friends are going to be asking you to wipe their bottom/take the dog out/help them move furniture/persuade you to go out. It can also be helpful to keep your phone out of sight.

◇ If you prefer to study with music on, or relaxing sounds (whatever works for you), consider creating a study playlist with relaxing or motivating music or sounds.

◇ Make sure that you feel comfortable, but not so comfortable that you will be sleepy. Sitting up straight might help with this and prevent backache. Posture is important, especially when using laptops, as we tend to slump forwards.

◇ Try to get the temperature right – not too hot, not too cold.

◇ Stay out of bed! It's for sleeping.

◇ If you're lucky enough to have a desk, make sure that it's fairly tidy and uncluttered (maybe tidy it at the end of each study period?). If you don't have this, then find a space in the house where you can study, for example a kitchen table.

◇ If you need things to help you study (or just like buying stationery), such as post-it notes, highlighters, dictionaries and flash cards, try to buy these in advance of your study session and make sure that they are close by when you need them.

◇ Consider getting some snacks and drinks ready for your study session. This way, you won't get too hungry and can treat yourself regularly.

Anxiety and learning/studying

So, once you have written your lists, prioritised your tasks according to deadlines, allocated the time, and set up your study haven, you have to actually do the work.

One of the difficulties with anxiety is how it interferes with attention and concentration, as when you feel anxious, it's common to have racing thoughts and find it difficult to focus. Before we can start to get our brains in gear and do our studying, we need to calm down and feel OK. Doing some simple breathing exercises can be helpful (see box below), as is making sure the environment is as calm and as conducive to studying as possible (your study haven). One person might feel safest and calmest sitting in a busy cafe and another may prefer to be at home in a familiar environment.

Sometimes when we are struggling to concentrate it can be helpful to do short bursts of studying in different environments, for example spend 40 minutes in your haven then walk to the cafe and do 40 minutes with a coffee, then walk to the library and do 40 minutes there. If Bridie has some serious studying to do, then she likes to take her laptop to the library and find a quiet corner where no one can see her and it's totally silent. Phoebe tends to gather all her studying supplies and take refuge in the silent study room of her college library and Sue tends to work best on long-distance train journeys, or when she gets into the office super early before everyone else. Everyone will have different preferences about where they feel safest and most able to focus. Some of us do better in one study location and others will need to chop and change to help maintain concentration.

Break it up

Taking regular breaks is important. We don't want to ruin our "flow" when we are working hard and are focused, but making sure you are getting up, drinking plenty of fluids and eating healthy snacks (and an occasional salty or sugary treat) is going to mean you can stay the distance rather than falling asleep at your desk or storming off in a rage. Studying somewhere where you can see trees or even get out and go for a walk can be helpful. Having a nap can also make you more productive, but only if it's less than 30 minutes and is before 3pm so it doesn't interfere with bedtime (depending on your bedtime – maybe 3am works well for you!).

Use your technology

Phones and apps are great, from simply setting reminders on your phone so that you know when each 40 minutes has passed and what task you should be working on (maybe even add a little word of encouragement or a joke to your reminder to keep you going) to more sophisticated apps for study. Your phone can be great for listening to or recording lectures or lessons if you struggle to attend or write good notes, and many courses now have resources and lectures online so you can pause and rewind. There are now lots of apps that can help you to remember when you should be taking a break, what topic you should be studying next, and even reading any text aloud to you so you can lie back and visualise it, if this helps you to remember and make sense of the information. There are apps to help you prioritise your "to do" list and even share it with your study group or partner where appropriate. Some can even block you accessing apps until your study period is over.

CLEANSING BREATH

✧ Sit or lie down comfortably.

✧ Close your eyes or choose a spot in the room on which to focus your gaze gently.

✧ Place one or both of your hands on your stomach.

✧ Breathe in slowly and notice your stomach rise with your breath. Then slowly breathe out, again noticing your stomach fall.

✧ Notice the pace of your breathing and gently allow it to be slower and deeper, until it feels comforting and soothing.

✧ Everyone has a slightly different breathing pattern that feels soothing to them, so play about with yours a little until you find one that helps you to feel relaxed.

Exercise

Research has shown clearly that 30 minutes of exercise four or five days a week helps to improve executive function and our ability to focus. Something like yoga can be especially helpful as it helps you to focus on your body and calmly accept your thoughts. Again, make sure you are setting time aside in your study timetable and having realistic goals, for example just starting with a brisk walk if you are not currently doing much physical activity. You do not want to create another anxiety!

Sipping a sugary (but not too sugary) drink

We need some energy to keep us going so having some apple juice that we can sip (not gulp down) can keep glucose levels adequate to keep our brains powered. Cola and other high sugar drinks can be too much, but a small drink of fresh juice that you drink slowly throughout the session can be helpful (and something sweet can be grounding and calming too).

TOP TIPS FOR EXAM STUDY/REVISION

Studying for an exam is much like any other studying but people can feel more stressed so there are a few strategies you can also try:

◇ Use lots of visuals: flash cards, post-it notes, mind maps (there are apps for this too). Be creative and don't make long lists or use lots of prose as this can be hard to maintain focus on. Sue likes to write her study notes onto "posters" and stick them onto the walls in her home so that she can read them as she walks past. Bridie likes little colour-coded cards that she can carry with her and flick through.

◇ Don't "cram" the night before. Avoid avoidance. Make sure that you spread your studying over the week before the exam, doing an hour (or two lots of 40 minutes) a night rather than four hours the night before.

◇ Be active in your learning. If you are passively reading notes, then you are more likely to find your worries or negative thoughts are creeping in and getting in the way. Research shows that making and taking practice tests is much better than passively reading. You can do this by going through your notes, talking to your classmates, looking over old quizzes or class questions, and talking to your tutor. You are likely to find it easier to maintain concentration and learn while you are actively constructing the test and thinking through what you need to know or to answer, than passively reading notes. Phoebe was very nervous about her English exams so kept pestering her teachers for extra assignments. Even though she was worried she might be annoying them, the teachers were happy to see someone keen to learn and the feedback she received helped her to improve her confidence and do well in her end-of-year exams.

◇ Do a quick bedtime review. Make a bullet point list of the main things you have learned in your study session, then review them before bed. This doesn't mean study before bed, just read your main learning points so they are fresh in your mind.

Advice from a university lecturer and course tutor: Dr Sally Little

Starting at college or university is a time of big change and upheaval. Whether you are moving away from home for the first time or not, meeting new people, making friends and developing new life skills in addition to the pressures of a completely new style of independent, self-directed learning can be daunting for even the most confident of people. It is very common and completely normal to feel anxious when starting at university or college and to experience periods of anxiety throughout your studies, particularly during stressful times, whether these are personal or academic (such as relationship issues and family life or assessment deadlines and presentations).

Many students who suffer from anxiety at college or university have dealt with these issues since childhood; they know their triggers and have ways of coping and behavioural strategies that help them manage. However, it is very important not to internalise these feelings and try to deal with them on your own. As a lecturer and course tutor, I urge my students to ask for help and seek support if they are struggling. A lecturer or student support officer can put specialist support in place and make alternative arrangements for examinations and other assessments. However, it can also be really helpful to have somebody to talk to (such as a pastoral tutor, a housemate or friend) who is not part of the academic department. They could potentially be easier to talk to about these issues.

Student anxiety is very common and, because of this, many colleges and universities have excellent mental health support and counselling services. Make sure you select a college or university based in part on what provisions it has in place for student support in addition to whether you find the lecturers friendly and approachable, and the class sizes and the student-to-staff ratio acceptable. Small class sizes, low student-to-staff ratios, and friendly and approachable lecturers generally mean closer relationships and greater one-to-one support. For example, I know the names of all of my students by the end of the first term of the first year and I am the first port of call for many of them if they are struggling and need support.

For some students, just the prospect of having to sit down and start a piece of work can trigger anxiety which can affect confidence and concentration. In this situation, you may find that freewriting may help. This is when you continuously write for a set period of time without regard to spelling or grammar. You may not end up using any of the text you have written, but it is a great way to generate thoughts, break down those mental barriers and start putting words down. It can also help to split the assessment up into sections so you can work on these independently, putting all of the sections together and formatting these at the end. This can make the piece of work appear more manageable.

Successfully completing your course and getting your degree can, at times, seem like a daunting task. Try to keep your mind on completing one particular task at a time, because often as soon as thought turns to the bigger objective (i.e. getting your degree), anxiety can kick in, which makes it impossible to do the smaller tasks.

At college or university, you will be out of your comfort zone for some activities and you will find some parts of your studies hard. However, by experiencing new and different situations and surviving them, you can learn how to manage your anxiety. Scary events become less and less of a challenge as we face them. The first time you stand in front of a group of people to deliver a presentation is terrifying, but you get used to it and it gets easier each time. So, expect challenges, but realise that it is part of growing and gaining confidence and skills.

◇ Chapter 6 ◇

What About Moving Out?

Transitions are exciting beginnings, but they can also be scary or uncomfortable endings	Moving into our own place is one of the biggest transitions that adulthood can throw at us
People often report that a lack of structure and routine contributes to stress when they leave home	Let people know that you are struggling with the idea of moving away

This chapter may be skipped by lots of people as we know that it's becoming more difficult to move out of the family home, with rental and house prices making it unaffordable for many. But moving into our own place is one of the biggest transitions that adulthood can throw at us, whether it's moving into a flat down the road, going further afield to live in student housing or maybe even going to study or work abroad. We have some top tips for managing this transition (tips that can be applied to lots of other big changes you might experience too).

Don't avoid and ignore

Transitions are exciting beginnings, but they can also be scary or uncomfortable endings, which can mean dealing with separation and loss (see Chapter 1). Learning to manage transitions and especially endings is an important life skill. At school and college there are often proms or leavers' balls which are important ways to mark an ending, say goodbye, and help us to move on to the next phase of our lives. As you reach adulthood, you might notice that lots of people try to avoid having to say goodbye to others, for example if someone has a party as they are leaving their job, one or two of their colleagues might suddenly develop a headache or have to rush home to complete an important task that just can't wait. You may also notice people don't show up for their last shift or day at work to avoid saying goodbye. Bridie recently changed jobs and desperately wanted to avoid her leaving lunch, but she didn't, proving she is now officially a well-adjusted grown-up. She didn't hate the experience either.

Some people do anything to avoid goodbyes and so stay in the same job or friendship group for ages rather than go through a transition and make a new start. It feels so much safer to stick with what you know. If you learn your own way to acknowledge and manage the pain of endings and the anxiety of new beginnings, then you have a skill that will be important and useful throughout your life.

Prepare yourself

We don't always have the luxury of preparing for transitions. Some changes in our lives happen unexpectedly and we therefore must deal with the consequences while also dealing with the shock. When moving away from home, we usually have plenty of time to prepare, so it can be helpful to make the most of it. If we are feeling anxious, then it can be tempting to bury our heads in the sand and pretend that it isn't happening, leaving everything to the last minute. The desire to ignore things is normal and understandable, but rarely helpful, meaning that you can end up with lots to do at the last minute. Sitting down and making a list of all the practical tasks and working out when and how you can complete them (or get others to help you to do them) means less stress.

Moving away may feel overwhelming because of the practical differences, for example having to take care of your own home and pay bills, maybe in a new town or city; or it may be losing the emotional support from your current home life that you are worried about. When people move away for work or study it often triggers a feeling that everything is going to change. It can mean making new friends, a different structure to your day, less contact with family, and endings in your current job or school/college. We suggest you do everything you can to prepare yourself for these changes, first by making practical preparations (e.g. sorting out accommodation) and then by finding out as much as you can about where you are going and, if it's close enough, visiting. It's a good idea not just to check out where you'll be working and living, but also to explore places where you will do your food shopping and where you might register with a GP, and to do as many practical things as you can to help you feel prepared and so that the area feels familiar.

Ed's story

At the age of 18, I moved into my own property to live independently, but unfortunately, I was not equipped emotionally or practically. I grew bored within the confines of the flat and I was lonely, did not go out, did not know how to use public transport, and had no one to go to at times of distress, resulting in a severe decline in my mental health. I didn't feel as if I had anyone, and I no longer had people living with me. I cut everyone off. Due to this and the emotional difficulties I experienced, I accumulated quite a lot of debt. I found it hard to go out to places like supermarkets as it made me anxious when people talked to me, asked how my day was, or even made eye contact. I used the self-service checkout when I could to avoid interaction with people.

I eventually accepted some help and got my debt sorted. I engaged with an organisation which taught me some new skills such as how to deal with my anxieties and how to deal with my emotions, so they were easier to tolerate. My support worker set me small tasks like going to a staffed till in my local supermarket, and she referred me for a volunteering role within the organisation, which put me in lots of social situations. This was hard at first but is now easier. I find that I can make eye contact quite a bit more now but it's still uncomfortable.

I still suffer with anxiety and have days when I don't want to talk to anyone, but these are less frequent. If a day is too much I can sometimes reach out to professionals and tell them how I am feeling. I am less inclined to hide away and I do now try and keep myself busy. I am aware of my feelings and what makes me anxious, so I try and do things to lift my mood or try and put myself into situations that provoke my anxiety, so I can prove to myself that I am capable.

Sharing concerns

It's often a good idea to talk to the important people in your life about all the potential changes taking place and to identify any worries and possible problems so that you can start to manage them. If you feel unsupported then there are organisations that you can reach out to (see Chapter 13 for contacts and ideas about talking to people about worries).

Structure and routine

When we are going through a change, we can lose our usual, familiar daily routines, and this lack of structure and neglecting our routines can make us feel even more out of control when things get stressful. It's not helpful to ignore the basics of getting a good night's sleep and eating a balanced diet at these times (see Chapter 11). Simple things like keeping your meal and bedtimes regular, and as close to your "normal" routine as possible, is a good start and helps you to take care of yourself. It's important that you continue making time for yourself and the things that make you feel calm and relaxed, whether this is listening to music, calling someone you love, or going for a walk.

You might be looking forward to leaving behind the old routines that were imposed in your old home and that you may consider childish. In this case, it's worth spending some time thinking about what you want your new routine to look like and to make sure that you include things that will help you to relax and stay calm, and develop some consistency. People often report that a lack of structure and routine contributes to stress when they leave home.

Make your peace

When you are leaving people behind it may seem easiest to let any differences be forgotten. Avoidance is often tempting when the alternative can be a difficult conversation; however, if something has upset you or you feel that you might have upset someone else, it's important to make your peace and try to correct any misunderstandings before your separation. It might be an uncomfortable conversation, but if you can face it rather than taking it with you, you can move out or move on knowing that you did everything that you could to make it a good ending with no unresolved issues. It can be helpful to think of this as "exposure" to a feared situation and an opportunity to test out your predictions about what you think might happen. It will also help you to learn how well you can cope, even when things don't go the way you would like. Also, if you have a propensity to be anxious and dwell on past events, using these as "evidence" that you are a bad person, then resolving any issues will also help to neutralise this and enable you to see things that have happened in a more positive way.

Harry's story

The fear that I feel is real and takes over. Change is a huge barrier or hurdle for me. Moving to new schools, meeting a new stream of people, leaving people I have just got used to. I never wanted to live on my own and my anxiety increased when I started living independently. A few years later, I transitioned to university. Nine days before I had to leave to start my degree, my head was so messed up I started to cry and get angry with everyone around me. I felt stressed and could not breathe. I think it was anxiety. At times like this, I cannot breathe and my heart gets faster. I don't eat very well at all, and my thoughts are all over the place. I don't normally cry, but when I get anxious, I cry lots and lots. This was the case, especially before starting university. I told everyone that I was not going to university. They all just said the same thing, "You are going. You will do great. It's so exciting." But they don't understand, I cannot feel the excitement, I just feel scared. At these times, I feel like I want to be on my own. I don't want to speak to anyone or be sociable, although I did let one person in, as I like her.

Everyone else is excited, but they don't have to go to university themselves, so they don't understand. I didn't want to do anything. I wanted to give everything up so that I didn't have to worry. I felt funny. I felt separated from everything and everybody. I had to learn to cope with it all and everything that came with it. I suffered quite badly mentally and didn't think I was going to carry on with university at all. But thankfully, I spoke to a few of my family and friends and had a little weekend away, and they told me not to quit and that they would help me find a house to live in or something. Luckily, a new room was offered to me, quite different from what I was in before but I took it so I could get away.

I have had to use various different anxiety techniques and have also gone for long walks to clear my head and to get away from everything for a while; this helped me immensely. I still get good and bad days. Being busy and having a focus helps a lot. However, there are always new people to meet, new situations and challenges to experience, moving homes, starting degrees and so on. I still get extremely anxious and worried that I will not be successful. I have to work hard to remind myself to take it one step at a time.

Say your goodbyes

We don't just mean shouting "See ya!" as you walk out the front door. Saying goodbye and having a good ending is important in making a transition successful. Goodbyes can be sad and difficult, but they can also be a time of celebration. It's a chance to let people know that they are important to you and to take meaning from the end of a chapter in your life. If it's hard to tell someone face to face what they have meant to you or how they have helped and encouraged you up to this point, then writing a note or a card can be another way to let them know. Make sure that you plan your goodbyes with people or there's a danger that they may not happen. It might be that you plan a big party with lots of important people, or it might just be a quick coffee or walking home together. As we discussed earlier, endings can feel really difficult, but they are also an important part of moving forwards. Take photos with your loved ones before you go (you can display these in your new home/accommodation) and make sure you offer ways of keeping in touch. Plan your first return visit or if you are going a long way then think about a reunion. Sometimes goodbyes are a personal process that is more about feeling OK with the ending than communicating with others. Be creative, revisit your favourite places, take photographs, make a collage or start a journal.

Seek support

Let people know that you are struggling with the idea of moving away (this can be as well as feeling excited). Don't assume that they know how you feel (remember mind-reading as one of your anxiety thinking traps from Chapter 4!). We all need other people to help us when we are struggling. Some members of your family might feel sad that you are leaving home and others might be envious and think you're lucky to be going, especially younger siblings! Having honest conversations and sharing your worries can make problem-solving easier as well as soothing or neutralising your anxiety and helping you to feel more connected to the people you are leaving behind. If you're not someone who often asks for help then you might need to think about how you can do this and what you might say. If your close family are struggling with you leaving and you feel you cannot seek support from them, think about who else you feel comfortable talking to and use their support.

Give yourself some time

It's completely normal to feel anxious and unsettled (as well as excited) when we are approaching something new, and moving out is a big change and a new start for everyone. It's normal to feel sad when we are saying our goodbyes, even if we know we will see people again soon. Be kind to yourself. Be aware of being self-critical and use the ideas from Chapters 11 and 12 to help you to be mindful, relax and soothe yourself through this potentially quite difficult time.

TOP TIPS FOR MANAGING TRANSITIONS

⬦ Be prepared! Face your worries head on and where possible make yourself familiar with what is to come.

⬦ Talk to people you trust about how you are feeling.

⬦ Keep your daily routines as "normal" as you can.

⬦ Say your goodbyes and heal old hurts wherever possible.

⬦ Be kind to yourself.

Ellen's story

After receiving my offer to study at university I was ecstatic; years of hard work had led up to this moment, and I had high expectations for what the future was to hold. I had friends who were already at university who were constantly being tagged in social media photos of them having an amazing time – I wanted the same for myself, nothing less. I eagerly bought my freshers' wristband for my college and after buying all the necessities needed to survive at university I was off.

Nothing could have prepared me for the anxiety that swept over me during freshers' week. I was away from home living with 20 strangers (all on one floor!) who all seemed to be getting on with each other so much better than they were with me. My thought processes went into overdrive, resulting in me spending a lot of time by myself in my room; at one point, I felt I needed to go to the hospital because the physical symptoms that accompanied my anxiety were that bad. I felt let down, as if I was missing out on "the best week of my life", as so many people told me it would be.

I had worked so hard and overcome so many barriers to get my place at university, so why was this such a challenge for me? It was so new, and I felt out of my depth – I knew I needed help. The first thing I did was tell my family and friends from home how I was feeling and seek out support from them. Many of my friends told me they themselves had felt similarly during their first few weeks at university (to an extent), giving me the push I needed to leave my room and continue to try and make friends with my flatmates. As it turns out, my flatmates felt the same… I confided in one of them on a night out, which led to a sort of domino effect of several other people saying they too weren't having an amazing time and they were missing home.

On the one hand it was reassuring to know that I wasn't the only one experiencing negative emotions during freshers' week; but on the other, why isn't this talked about more? More emphasis needs to be put on the fact that freshers' week isn't everyone's cup of tea and often you will experience some degree of negative emotion in your first few weeks at university. So much pressure is put on young people who are beginning a new chapter of life to make the most of it, and it sometimes felt as if I wasn't allowed to be experiencing anxiety. However, it really is OK to not be OK. After finding out I wasn't the only one in the same position, my feelings of isolation and anxious thought processes calmed down massively, and I slowly began to enjoy my time at university.

I'm going into my final year at university now, having had a well-rounded university experience despite my shaky start. My key piece of advice for anyone starting university would be to remember that there are people who care about you and will support you back home – don't forget it! Keep in contact with them regularly if you feel up to it, even if you aren't struggling. Also remember that if you're struggling to make friends with the people you're living with, there will definitely be a group of people out there for you, whether it be course friends or people you meet through societies – university is a big place, take advantage of it! Do not let anxiety define who you are, learn to manage it and never be afraid to seek help if you're struggling to cope.

Chapter 7

Surviving (and Thriving) in Job Interviews

It's completely normal to be anxious before an interview	Try to remember that the people who are interviewing you are interested in finding out more about you
Dress smartly – first impressions matter!	A good company will spend the time telling you why you should join the company

Over the next few years, you will probably have lots of interviews, as you settle into a job or an educational course. It's completely normal to be anxious before an interview – even those people who perform really well get nervous. Typical worries that people have include fears about:

- being judged or seen as "not good enough"

- doing something silly in the interview

- not being able to speak or forgetting what to say

- failure/rejection

- perfectionism (if I can't answer the best that I can, I will fail).

This chapter outlines a few key tips for going to an interview and how to manage your anxiety through this process.

1. *Look after yourself* – Throughout this book, we talk about the importance of looking after yourself generally (especially in Chapter 11), but this is particularly important when you are going through a stressful experience such as an interview. If you're able to get a good night's sleep the night before and have a decent breakfast in the morning (or a few snacks if you are struggling to stomach food), then this is some of the best preparation that you can do for an interview. It will mean that your body and brain will be in good working order to help you get through it. Maybe try to help your body to relax, have an early night, a stress-relieving bubble bath or go for a walk or run.

2. *Wear something that you feel comfortable in* – It's generally a good idea to look smart (depending on what kind of interview you are going to), but also it can be best to find an outfit that you feel comfortable wearing, maybe something that you have worn before. If you can get this ready, ironed and put out the night before, this may help you to feel calmer and more prepared. The more comfortable you feel, the more confident you're likely to appear to the interviewers too. Bridie once wore new pretty shoes with rather big heels to an interview, and only realised once she got there that she couldn't walk in them. This meant that she almost fell over (having

to grab onto the door) as she walked into the room, and then cringed with pain when walking out.

3. *Remember that it's JUST an interview* – Often people put so much pressure on the actual interview that they start to believe it's their only chance of success. This is completely untrue. It's just one interview, of the likely hundreds of interviews that you will go to in your life. Try to remember that the people who are interviewing you are interested in finding out more about you. You can use this time to tell them about your work, what interests you, things that you are proud of. They just want to see if you are a good fit with the role and team.

4. *Remember that the interviewers are just people (even if they don't look like it)* – So, you've just walked into the interview room, and there are four people staring straight at you in their perfect suits and beautiful shoes. You feel a sweaty, shaky mess. Although we often have worrying thoughts about the interviewers, they are often just as anxious as we are, or sometimes even more anxious. In our minds they might be monsters, but they are actually human beings. They will understand your anxiety, as they have been there too. If you need to take a minute to think of your answer or want a question to be repeated, they will get that.

5. *Let your enthusiasm shine through* – If it's a job that you really want, then let the interviewers know that. You might choose to study their website first, find out about their own interests (we are *not* suggesting that you stalk them on social media, but it might be worth finding out about their areas of work and work-related interests). Tell them why you want the job, and why you are interested in working for their company. Also, one of the best ways to connect with people is to be interested in them. So, try to listen to what the interviewers are saying and be attentive.

6. *It's OK to ask for clarification* – The chances are that the interviewers are not trying to catch you out. If they are, do you want the job anyway? So, it's OK to ask for clarification on questions or to ask for information about the team and what the job would involve.

7. *Take a breath* – You can take a minute to ground your-self. Have a pause or take a breath or two to feel better.

Or take a drink of water before answering a question (there is usually one available, or if not, it's fine to ask for one). Feel your body against the chair, your feet on the floor. Pay attention to your breath – make sure that you are still breathing (sometimes when feeling anxious we can forget to breathe), and that your breathing is slow and calm. Relax your shoulders, making sure that they are not tense, and this will open up your body, helping you feel calmer and appear more confident.

8. *Practise, but not too much* – Imagery and exposure can also be useful. This could include having a mock interview with a friend (it's often far scarier doing this with someone you know, which means that you will be fine in the interview!), imagining yourself answering interview questions, or practising in front of a mirror. One thing that is important is to not over-prepare. It's often much better to have a few key points for answers, rather than a full script prepared which can sound unnatural or might not quite answer the interviewer's actual question (if it's slightly different from what you had prepared). You will stand out more if you answer by reflecting and thinking on the spot.

9. *It's all about good fit* – Interviewing is a two-way process. The interviewers will be thinking about whether you are a good fit for their position and team, but it's also important for you to think about whether this is the right job or course for you. It's good to ask a question about the role or team, both to show interest and to find out more, and to see whether you're happy with what they would be potentially offering you.

10. *Treat yourself afterwards* – It's always nice to have something to look forward to, so planning a treat for after the interview might help you to focus. Such as, I've only got to think about this for another hour, then I can go see my friend/eat that chocolate cake/play football/watch my favourite film or TV show.

Tips from professionals

Sue asked a director of a small healthcare company and an HR manager about their views of interviewing people who may be anxious, and these were their responses.

What do you look for when interviewing for a member of staff?

Director: Primarily openness (openness to themselves – recognising their own strengths and the things they need to work on), openness to others (the ability to communicate well, show some vulnerability – the ability to say what they don't know) and willingness to share appropriately, and openness to learning (a desire to learn/understand more about themselves, others and their work). Most "job skills" or tasks can be taught relatively quickly with appropriate guidance, but social and communication skills, and understanding of people and openness are much more difficult and a more lengthy process to develop. Other important elements are honesty, integrity, a strong work ethic. We also look for what we don't want. We don't want falseness, over-confidence or arrogance.

HR manager: We look for a number of things. The criteria are personal attributes such as being warm, friendly, making eye contact; qualifications relevant to the role; skills and knowledge and ability to answer questions; team fit; motivation, reason for the role.

If someone came into an interview looking anxious, what would you think?

Director: I would think that's pretty normal, to be honest. I would view it as unusual not to be anxious – and it would mean that you didn't particularly want the job, as if you're not anxious about getting it, you probably don't think it's important enough. I would rather have someone presenting as anxious than seeming over-confident. I would hope that as the interview went on, they would start to relax.

HR manager: I would expect a level of nerves from candidates. I don't think anything negative; in fact, I interviewed today and realised that although the man was in his thirties, he had only had two jobs and while it was difficult to get information out of the man, I put some of this down to his nerves. We realised he was nervous and inexperienced in interview techniques. We are seeing him for a second interview next week.

Have you ever personally been anxious in an interview situation before?

Director: Yes, many times. In fact, I think every time. The more I want the job, the more anxious I tend to get. In terms of affecting me – I tend to feel sick when I'm anxious and my thinking gets more confused, making me less clear to others. Some of the other things are dry mouth and sweaty palms! More positively, I think that getting anxious tells me how important it is and helps me to perform better, as long as it doesn't take over. I'm aware of this now, so would try to retain a bit of perspective beforehand, maybe do some relaxation exercises and concentrate on my breathing. I'd often speak to people I trust beforehand to get some positive messages from them to boost my confidence! I'd make sure I did some preparation, although I'm wary of over-preparing as that can get me more anxious. The biggest thing I do, however, that seems to be most successful, is to acknowledge that I'm anxious to the interviewers, right after introducing myself. I say something like, "I'm a bit anxious about this interview, probably because I'm keen to get the job!" Most people will then try to make you feel more comfortable.

HR manager: I am always nervous because I am bothered about the job and my career progression and I think that it is OK to be nervous. I find that my mouth gets dry and my heart beats faster. To overcome this, I remind myself that it's OK to feel nervous and I take some deep breaths. I try to say to myself, "Feel comfortable being uncomfortable".

Any tips that you would give to someone going for an interview?

Director: Be yourself, genuinely – someone trying to be false is always pretty easy to see through. Prepare well, do some research on the company and what they do – an internet search is often useful! *But,* don't over-prepare – what will be, will be. Dress smartly – first impressions matter! Always show that you're keen to get the job – people who talk passionately about what they do always stand out. Be willing to say what you can do, but also what you don't know. Be curious (it shows initiative); make sure you ask some questions of the role, if given a chance.

HR manager: Give yourself time to get there; better to be super early than five minutes late. If you get the chance, do a dummy run and find out where the offices are. Practise what you're going to say, practise by saying it out loud and practise a few times.

Companies will usually ask the following questions:

- Tell me when you worked in a team.

- Tell me when you worked under pressure.

- Tell me when you dealt with a difficult customer.

- Tell me something that you are proud of.

- What is the best part of your current job?

- What is the least enjoyable part?

- What are your career plans?

- What was it about this job that interested you enough to apply?

- What do you know about the company?

Make sure you know your curriculum vitae (CV)/résumé well, which sounds daft, but you need to familiarise yourself with it. Remember to learn as much as you can about the company so that you can ask some good questions at the end of the interview, such as:

- How big is the team?

- Where is the company headed?

- How many people are you interviewing for this job?

- When might I hear back from you?

- What do you like most about working here?

- What is the best thing about the company?

- And a brave question is: How do you think I did today?

If you practise what you will say then you won't go blank when they ask those questions.

Any tips that you would give to someone going for an interview who is feeling anxious?

Director: Anxiety is normal. Acknowledge your anxiety with the panel. Retain perspective – remember the interviewers are just people, not monsters; they have their own lives, fears and worries just like everyone else – and they have all been interviewed themselves.

HR manager: Give yourself time so that you aren't late and put yourself under unnecessary pressure. Remember they are human like you. Practise your words – out loud. Find out about the company and have a few questions ready. Remember that nerves are OK. Remember that it's not a one-way street, and the company is there to sell the job to you. A good company will spend the time telling you why you should join the company. And finally, use every interview as a learning opportunity. The more experience you get, the easier it will become. So treat every interview as a chance to practise your skills rather than as a black or white, pass or fail.

Chapter 8

Workplace Worries

Often if we are feeling anxious at home, then this can spill into our working life	The more you practise winging it, the easier the situation will become and the less anxious you will feel
Establish a good work–life balance – switch work phones/ emails off as soon as you finish	Feeling comfortable around people at work will help to lessen your anxiety

One thing that we know about anxiety, and mental health in general, is that it can impact on both home and work life. Often if we are feeling anxious at home, then this can spill into our working life. Equally, stress or anxiety at work can lead to us feeling anxious, exhausted or burned out at home. It can lead to difficulties "switching off" from work (particularly when we receive emails and texts outside working hours), difficulties sleeping, not eating properly, lots of rumination (going over things in your head), and sometimes even taking it out on those around us. Within work, it can lead to difficulties doing our job, not being able to think, panicking under pressure, emotional outbursts (crying, anger) and even panic attacks. See also Chapter 5 for information about how anxiety can affect the brain and make it far more difficult to work or think logically.

The most important thing to say in this chapter is that often anxiety can be a sign that something is wrong in your environment (especially if it's only present at work). So, the most useful thing to do is to work out why you are feeling anxious.

Consider if the cause might be the environment – working too many hours, too high a workload, not feeling competent in your job, not having had relevant training, being bullied or harassed, not having anywhere safe to raise your concerns. Or is it related to how you are coping generally, for example not feeling good about yourself, lacking confidence, not feeling confident to raise your concerns or ask for support?

Often it might be a combination of both. What we don't want to do is to treat your anxiety if your anxiety is actually trying to be helpful and alert you to something that is wrong – for example, if it's trying to communicate that you should not be bullied anymore, or that you are working too much. In these examples, it's more important to stop the bullying, or get a better work–life balance. Once you have a good understanding of the anxiety, then you will have a better idea of what to do about it.

This chapter will therefore focus on strategies and skills that you can use when you are struggling with anxiety at work.

Skills to help to manage anxiety-provoking work situations

Being open and honest

When Sue first started her doctorate course, she was told a story by a colleague. This colleague said that on the first day of one of the regional doctorate courses, the tutors get all of the new students into a room together and say, "We've made an admin error. Unfortunately, one of you failed our entry requirements and isn't eligible for the course and will need to leave immediately." Although this story is probably just hearsay, how do you think that the students would have felt in that moment? Most of them probably would have started to panic, avoided eye contact, and assumed that it was them who was not meant to be there – that horrible moment of shame! We call this "imposter syndrome".

We can often feel like an imposter, that our bosses have made a mistake employing us; that when they find out that we don't have the skills we need to do the job, they will sack us; that they are going to see that we are no good and don't fit in. This feeling of being an imposter can feel overwhelming, and can lead us to:

- do everything we can to be the best employee

- take on more work/avoid saying "no"

- *never* ask for help or advice for fear that this could be seen as a weakness or something that we should know already

- try to hide our "failures" or pretend that we can do things that we can't

- pretend to our managers that everything is fine when it's not

- end up feeling incompetent, useless and worried about our jobs, our futures and life in general.

However, what we generally find out once we've been in our jobs for a while is that pretty much everyone feels the same, especially at first. Even senior managers will be put into situations at times where they feel completely out of their depth, that everyone around them knows far more than them, that they don't fit in and so on. So, the more that you can be open and honest about what you can and cannot do, the more support will be put in place to help you to "learn your craft". It can be useful to have these open discussions with your manager early on in your job role, at review times such as appraisals, or you can talk to them more generally about this at any point. Although these discussions may lead you to initially feel quite vulnerable, this openness should lead to clear communication pathways and understanding between you and your manager where they can support you to achieve and progress and avoid misunderstandings in the future.

Winging it

What we (the authors of this book) have learned is that most people are to some extent "winging it". "Winging it" is one of our favourite phrases (Sue even has a small pin badge with this on). It's the idea of going into a situation and "just having a go", using the skills that you have to do the best that you can in a situation. It doesn't have to be perfect – it can be messy – but it's just putting yourself out there and having a go. The idea is that you can feel the anxiety but decide to do the task despite it. The more you practise winging it, the easier the situation will become and the less anxious you will feel.

Being interested in your colleagues

Work can be a lonely place unless you build some relationships with the people around you, as you are going to be spending so much time around them. One of the best ways to do this is to show an interest in them and their lives inside and outside work. Maybe ask what they did at the weekend, who they live with, what their interests are, how long they have been working in the role, what they have learned about the company and what their hopes are for the future. Sharing a little bit of yourself (e.g. your interests) will also help people to feel connected to you. Feeling comfortable around people at work will help to lessen your anxiety generally within the work environment.

Clarification and communication

Have you ever had a conversation with your manager about what exactly their expectations are of you? This can be helpful to clarify what they want you to do, and how they want you to work, and it can sometimes alleviate anxiety. If you are ever asked to do a task, or a project, and you're not sure when/where/how/what, the best thing to do is to check what exactly is expected and how they want you to report back. Having these systems and processes in place can protect against future miscommunication. People have different communication style preferences, so maybe find out what works best for your manager and try to find some common ground.

For example, Sue can often find it difficult to answer direct complex questions about her work, and much prefers to be given some time (a few minutes) before giving a fuller answer. So, her manager will often let her know a little in advance if there is a particular topic that he wants to discuss. This helps Sue to feel more confident in her answers, but also makes her much clearer and to the point (which her manager likes).

Being assertive

Assertiveness is a useful skill to have across a range of settings and includes being able to express your point of view. In dialectical behavioural therapy, there is a skill that you can learn that can help you to be assertive and "get someone to do what you want them to". This skill is named DEAR MAN, and consists of:

D – Describe the situation in a factual manner.

E – Express how you feel about the situation, for example I feel…

A – Assert your position and state clearly what you want.

R – Reinforce what will happen if the person does what you are asking them to (what will be in it for them).

M – (Be) Mindful about what you are asking for and try to stick to talking about this without going off on a tangent. Be a bit of a "broken record" if you need to be.

A – Appear confident throughout, keeping good eye contact, open body language (shoulders back) and speaking clearly.

N – Negotiate and try to find a solution that is suitable. But also remember that you can agree to disagree and end a conversation if needed.

DEAR MAN can be a useful skill to have and to use across a range of scenarios where you need to be assertive, ask for something, or say no to something. It can be helpful when planning what you are going to say or writing an email to someone. For example, you might use it to let your boss know that your workload is getting too much.

USING "DEAR MAN" IN AN EMAIL

Hi Andrew

Since Andrea has left the team, I have been picking up her workload, but this has meant that I am struggling to get all of my work done by the end of the week *(describe)*. I am feeling quite overwhelmed by the amount of work that I am trying to do and feel that I am falling behind *(express)*. Please can we look at my workplan next week and see where I can reduce my workload, and if someone else in the team is able to pick up some of the additional work *(assert)*? If we can reduce my workload to a manageable amount, I should be able to get all of my future reports in on time *(reinforce)*.

If you are happy with this plan, should I liaise with your secretary to book a time for us to meet next week *(mindful)*?

Best wishes
Sue

Looking after yourself

One of the best ways to lessen your anxiety and improve your general health (both physical and mental) is to focus on looking after yourself. Try some of the following ideas:

- *Have a break* – Make sure that you are using your annual leave and actually taking time off work. This break or pause can be beneficial for your wellbeing, and hopefully you will return to work feeling refreshed.

It can be helpful to book this time off in advance so that you have something to look forward to. When you take time off, we recommend that you have time to relax and also do fun things (rather than spending it all doing boring things like getting your car serviced or jobs round the house that you have been putting off).

- *Regulate* – If you do a stressful job, or are going from one stressful meeting to another, think about how to help yourself emotionally regulate (feel calmer) during the day. This might include making yourself a hot drink, keeping snacks in your desk drawer, having a walk round the office, going to speak to a friend, or doing a breathing exercise or some mindfulness between meetings.

- *Make sure that you have a proper lunch* – Not at your desk! Spend time with colleagues or do something nice. Maybe go for a walk or go to a shop. Clear your head.

- *Establish a good work–life balance* – Switch work phones/emails off as soon as you finish. Do not take your laptop home. Be able to "switch off" and not think about work. If you are friends with your work colleagues, maybe have an agreement not to speak about work when you see them socially (or for only five minutes to debrief).

Seeking additional support at work

As we have discussed throughout the book, it can also be useful to seek some additional support. At work, this might be letting your boss know that you have been worried about something in particular or that you have been feeling a little anxious. Or, your work might have some good links to occupational health or psychology services that you can access. For example, Sue has previously worked one day a week in a company where she provided wellbeing support to staff.

TIPS FOR TALKING TO YOUR BOSS ABOUT ANXIETY

◇ **Choose who to talk to** – whether it's your boss or HR manager, or the work wellbeing service.

◇ **Arrange an informal meeting** – at a place and time where you are unlikely to be disturbed.

◇ **Consider confidentiality** – you might want to discuss confidentiality with them, so that you can agree what they would need to share and with whom.

◇ **Prepare** – think about what you want them to know. It's up to you what you share with them, but it might help them to understand you a bit better.

◇ **Make suggestions** – (if you have any) about how they, or your work generally, can help. This might include, for example, allowing you to shadow someone who has done the job before, being able to take brief breaks if feeling particularly anxious, or maybe having regular check-ins with them about your workload.

Chapter 13 also has suggestions of how to talk to people about your anxiety. If your job is causing you lots of stress and despite all attempts, things are not changing, then you might choose to leave and this is OK. It's always important first and foremost to look after your mental health.

Oliver's story

The feeling of anxiety has been with me for many years. This started from being self-employed but it was magnified when I went and worked in a large company. I had become a small cog in a very large machine and this was incredibly alien to me. When I look at my life I realise I am very lucky. Inside, however, I am crippled by fear, which has driven my anxiety so high that I decided to seek help. My anxiety is mainly associated with work. I was in a supermarket on a Saturday morning and was so anxious about my job that I had to run to the toilet and be physically sick. At that point I realised something had to change in my life.

I was fortunate enough that through my work (I appreciate the irony) I was able to reach out and speak to a professional therapist. I had never done this and find it very hard to talk about my emotions, so it was going into the unknown and was very uncomfortable. When I started the process, I felt I had no right to be there, why was I special enough to have this help? I imagined everyone suffered the same; most people hate their jobs, so why should I get help? I realised this mindset was a symptom of the problem. I feared what people thought of me, feared that my issues would be dismissed as attention-seeking, feared I was wasting a professional's time. What I was doing was just seeing the worst in all situations, catastrophising. I would imagine worst-case scenarios, and believe them to be true. This would go from worrying about what people thought of me, to not upsetting people, but the worst thought was about losing my job. What would I do if I lost my job? That was my biggest fear. It then descended into losing our home and pretty much everything going down the toilet. But I learned that all these worries and fears and the anxiety caused by them can be combatted, maybe not beaten, but made easier to deal with.

I quickly learned through a process of examining previous situations and the feeling generated by them that if I looked at the actual outcome, it wasn't as bad as I had imagined it being. By keeping a journal about these situations, I had evidence that if something happened that was similar, I had already got through it and the feelings I was having were not true and I could get past them. From this, I could reduce the fear and the anxiety caused by the situation. By writing these moments down I could literally go back to them and reiterate to myself that it would be OK. If I looked at it subjectively, most of the things that happened at work were not the end of the world. They felt like it at the time, as I couldn't breathe and started shaking, sweating and catastrophising.

Try to put it into context – most things can be sorted. You just need to slow your breathing down, take two minutes and calm yourself down. Many times, I just go to the toilet and do long slow breaths; I take some deodorant in with me so that I don't think I'm sweating and people will look at me! That works for me. Don't be afraid to admit you need to walk away and compose yourself. I would sit there and it would just get worse and worse until I literally could not type on the keyboard.

I had never meditated before but I would say this has been the most important thing I have taken from all the help in the last three months. Get up ten minutes earlier and do an internet search for morning meditation. Is it the answer to anxiety? No, but it allows you to be in the moment to relax before the day starts. It has allowed me to be calm in the mornings and made me realise that these things won't matter in the long term.

I still am a long way from where I want to be. For me, work has become the driving factor in my life, it's what controls my emotions. It affects my family life and if I changed jobs I imagine the same feelings would still exist. However, if I look at what I have in my life, I am able to chip away at this. Gratitude allows you to appreciate the now and not always change the next thing which you perceive will make you happy. When I spoke to a professional, he told me that my feelings are very common. It was consoling to know that it's not just me, there are so many people like this. Talking about it and not being embarrassed is the first way to help alleviate the feelings you have.

◇ Part 3 ◇

ANXIETY IN ADULTHOOD: SOME TOP TIPS

Part 3 aims to give some practical advice that relates directly to the problems that anxiety can cause and the skills you need in order to make sure anxiety doesn't take over your life or stop you doing what you need to do. We talk about panic attacks and obsessions and compulsions, then think about self-care, mindfulness, and getting extra help and support. We chose to include panic and OCD as sufferers felt that they are issues that may be stigmatised or poorly understood. Chapters 9 and 10 are introductions to panic and OCD that offer some coping strategies but focus on building understanding and reassurance that you are not alone. We know that this can be helpful, but we also point you to some good resources for more specific help and interventions if this is what's needed.

Chapter 11 is about taking care of yourself and covers a lot of practical suggestions for staying calm and healthy, from getting a good night's sleep to improving the moment and reducing unhelpful coping strategies like alcohol and drugs.

Getting the basics right is key to managing stress and anxiety but we don't always learn the skills we need to stay calm and healthy at school or from adults around us as we are growing up, so this is a chapter everyone should read.

Similarly, mindfulness and being present in the moment are skills that can help you stay calm and healthy and are especially important and useful when you have lots of transitions or when anxiety is taking over and making life difficult. Chapter 12 has lots of ideas for how you can introduce mindfulness into your daily life and how it can help to calm your mind.

The final chapter explores how you might talk to people about anxiety and where you can go to get extra help.

Chapter 9

A Quick Guide to Panic Attacks

When we have a panic attack, it can feel like the worst thing in the world	It's *just anxiety*, however horrible and scary it feels
A way to get through a panic attack is to take control of, and alter, our bodily sensations	Facing your fear can help you to feel some freedom over it

Panic attacks are a pretty common phenomenon and affect around 23 per cent of people during their lifetime. When we have a panic attack, it can feel like the worst thing in the world. We can feel ourselves struggling to breathe, sweating profusely, feeling tense, choking, shaking, dizzy, with a racing heart, feeling that things around us aren't real, and we may have chest pain. This can make us think: "I'm going to die! This feeling will never end! I can't breathe!" Then our survival instinct kicks in. This can make us feel even more tense, panicking as we try to get more oxygen (leading to us hyperventilating) and feeling even dizzier – which then leads us to feeling even more anxious and panicking more! We call this the "anxiety trap".

One of the problems with panic attacks is that we don't always know that we're having them. Although sometimes they might happen in a scary or difficult situation, at other times they seem to come out of nowhere. We might suddenly feel faint, have breathing difficulties or think that we're having a heart attack – which will make us feel even more worried that there is something seriously wrong. Lots of people won't know that what they are experiencing is anxiety and will end up going for medical tests, which come back with no medical cause.

Once we've had a couple of panic attacks, we can then become hyper-alert to our bodily sensations. We become a bit like a meerkat, always on the lookout for danger. However, because we're always on the lookout, we might start to see danger where there is none. For example, we could notice that our chest is a bit tight and think that this means that there is something wrong or we are going to have another panic attack (which could make us start to panic before it even happens). More vicious cycles! However, our chest tightness might just mean that we have a slight cold and there isn't anything really wrong. We can think about this as a smoke alarm that is faulty and overly sensitive. Helpfully, it will let us know when there's a fire in the building but unhelpfully, it might also let us know when there's burnt toast and make us evacuate (or turn on the sprinklers!) when there's no need to.

When we have a panic attack, we often misinterpret our bodily sensations as meaning something that they don't. For example:

- Tightness in my chest – "I'm having a heart attack! I'm going to die!"

- Breathlessness – "I'm suffocating! I can't breathe! I'm having an asthma attack!"

- Throat feeling tight – "I'm choking!"

- Feeling dizzy – "I'm going to faint!"

- Feeling numb (e.g. in legs or arms) – "There's something seriously wrong with me."

- Wobbly legs – "I'm going to fall!"

These anxious bodily sensations feel uncomfortable, incredibly scary and even painful. However, despite how they feel, science tells us that they are actually quite safe and will eventually go away on their own. We might try to cope with these bodily sensations by doing things like trying to take deeper breaths; however, this can lead to us hyperventilating and feeling dizzy, which can make us feel even worse and even more panicky. There's also a danger that we might start to avoid things (such as situations, objects or people), and think that we're only managing to survive because we are avoiding these things. This reinforces the idea that avoiding an activity, place or person is a positive thing and that something bad would happen if we didn't. For example, avoiding driving a car because you feel panicky and think, "I could pass out", yet when we are panicking, our blood pressure is actually high, so we are very unlikely to pass out! But you might subsequently believe that you need to continue to avoid cars in order to avoid something bad happening or just to avoid the horrible panicky feeling.

While it's difficult, it's probable that if you face the situation (or thing that makes you anxious), you will learn that you are able to survive despite the panic, and that although it feels truly awful, nothing bad happens. Facing your fear can help you to feel some freedom over it. Some mean psychologists ask their clients to induce a panic attack in public so they not only see that they don't die, pass out or choke but also get evidence that most people either don't notice their panic or just show mild concern.

If you have panic attacks and want to get some help with them, the first thing to rule out is that they're not being caused by something else, such as having too much caffeine (strong coffee or energy drinks) or using drugs (including legal highs), as these can cause similar bodily sensations. Before you do anything, make sure you monitor and, if necessary, reduce your intake slowly; many people find this has a positive effect.

Why do we start having panic attacks?

There are many different reasons why anxiety might turn into a panic attack. We've usually built up anxious feelings about something and we may be anticipating disaster, we might be worrying about worrying, or thinking our worry can make us go mad or is out of control (which in turn makes us more anxious). Sometimes we just have a virus that sets off new bodily sensations that get misinterpreted, ending up in a cycle of anxious thinking and avoidance.

Anxiety x anxiety = lots of anxiety!

We talked a little in Chapter 1 about how our body has evolved to deal with a threat, so it can be ready for fight, flight or freeze. So, it's important to know that wobbly legs are because our blood is flowing rapidly to our arms and legs to prepare us to get ready to run and also to protect our vital organs from any harm. Our increased breathing and heart rate is also so that we are ready to fight or run. Our body is getting ready to deal with a threat, but we're not always sure what the threat is so it's hard to understand what the feelings in our bodies mean. It makes sense that our anxious thoughts go into overdrive, making the whole thing so much worse. When we feel bad, we know that we think bad thoughts, often about negative things like death or embarrassing ourselves in front of others.

What can we do about it?

The important thing to remember when having a panic attack is that it won't kill us, even if it feels harmful at the time, and that it *will* pass. It's *just anxiety*, however horrible and scary it feels, and anxiety is something that we can learn to accept and manage.

Ride the waves

One of the main approaches to coping with panic attacks is to allow them to happen and let ourselves learn that we *can* get through them and that everything will be OK. This is sometimes known as "riding the waves" of an emotion. Knowing that it will soon run out of fuel if we don't try to fight it can be very helpful. It can also be useful to spend some time facing up to smaller situations that are likely to cause us some anxiety, and then build up to facing bigger ones (see Chapter 12 for more on using mindfulness to ride the waves of emotion). Sometimes people like to imagine their panic like a wave, and notice the waves passing and becoming smaller and smaller as they go out to sea.

Take control of bodily sensations

Another way to get through a panic attack is to take control of, and alter, our bodily sensations.

- *Anchor yourself* – This is also called "grounding". To start with, sit or stand somewhere next to a strong, stable or steady surface, for example stand or sit with your back to a wall or take your shoes off and feel the floor under your feet (imagine your feet being "rooted" in the ground). Or sit or lie on something that will let you sink into it, like a beanbag or comfy duvet. You might like to use a weighted blanket, as many people find the pressure soothing and calming. Another way to ground yourself is by using "extreme" sensory items, such as sucking an extremely sour sweet, as a way to take your mind off the anxiety and shift your focus.

- *Cool yourself* – It's likely that when you have anxious bodily sensations, your temperature will rise. Run your hands under cold water or splash your face, or perhaps have a cold drink or an ice lolly. You might want to have some ice ready in a ziplock bag which you can take out of the freezer, and then hold the bag in your hands or gently put it on your face.

- *Breathe* – Slow down your breathing (although you might have the urge to take lots of fast breaths, slowing your breathing down will help). You might want to put your hand/s on your chest so that you can feel your chest rise and fall with each breath. You can also count each breath in and out (e.g. a count of five on the in-breath, and seven on the out-breath, then start to slow this down even further).

- *Relax your muscles* – When we feel anxious, our muscles become tense. Take time to notice any tension in your body, and gently let your body relax. Good places to check for tension are the shoulders, hands, face and legs. You could also do some progressive muscular relaxation (see Chapter 11).

- *Connect* – Having someone with you who can remain calm will really help, especially if they can talk you through this plan. Having someone you know will support you, such as a close friend or family member, can also make you feel more in control of your panic attacks when they occur.

– *Use a word* – You may have a word or phrase that you can say to yourself that will remind you of a feeling of stillness or calmness or remind you that everything is going to be OK. It could remind you of a safe place, a good memory or a person, or it can be useful to remind yourself, "This feeling will pass. I have felt like this before and the anxiety will soon run out of fuel."

How to use this in everyday life

Although you might read this chapter and think, "Yeah, yeah, I can do this", one of the hardest bits is putting it into practice. The more anxious we are, the less able we are to think clearly. So, when we're anxious because we're having a panic attack, it's likely that we will find it difficult to remember what we can do to help ourselves feel better. Here are some of the suggestions we've heard over the years:

– Type up the main steps onto a small piece of paper the size of a debit card, then laminate it and carry it around in your bag or pocket so that you can pull it out and use it to prompt you when you need it. You might want to personalise the phrases based on what works for you, for example:

  * Stand next to a wall

  * Ask my friend to come with me

  * Take a big breath

* Have an ice-cold drink

* I can get through this – it will pass.

If you wear a lanyard to work, you could pop it in the back of this for easy access.

– Put some prompts or reminders on your phone.

– Put a picture or words on the background of your phone which will prompt you.

– Use a breathing or relaxation app to help to guide you to slow down your breathing or relax your muscles.

– Tell your plan to people you are close to (and who are likely to be around you at times when you are panicking) and ask them to talk you through it.

Practise, practise, practise

There is an analogy about a swimming pool that always comes to mind – you wouldn't (we hope!) learn to swim by jumping straight into the deep end without armbands or water wings because you would be likely to drown. You would start at the shallow end with your inflatables and practise swimming first, and slowly build up your confidence before tackling the deeper waters. It's a similar thing with the coping strategies that we discuss in this book. Rather than attempting them for the first time when you're having a full-blown panic attack, perhaps try them out when you're feeling calm or just a little bit anxious, and then work your way up, using them as needed.

Charlie's story

I was a bit of an anxious kid. Things were not always easy in my house when I was growing up, but I had lots of friends, I did well at school, and I always felt able to cope. I worked (a bit too) hard at university and did really well in my degree. I started my teacher training when I was in my early twenties and I am not sure anything prepares you for the level of scrutiny that teacher training entails. I think (and I have been teaching a while now) that teacher training is pretty stressful even for the most confident people, mostly because of the constant observations and feedback. For the first time in my life, I experienced a kind of chest-crushing anxiety. I got through that year but it made me realise that anxiety can be a really crippling and unpleasant thing to experience.

My first panic attack came when I was working as a qualified teacher. I was hot, the classroom was stuffy and the kids were being difficult. Suddenly, I could not breathe, I felt paralysed, my face was burning and I felt totally unable to speak or move. I got out of the room quickly, splashed my face with water and took some deep breaths. I made it back into the lesson but I don't remember much of it. I had survived but I was really worried that it would happen again, especially when I was being observed or when I was talking in front of the class.

I started to feel more anxious and to notice when I was getting a bit nervous or hot. I had panic attacks in the classroom on two more occasions but I was having to leave and go to the toilet regularly to try and make sure I didn't have more. I was managing day to day but started to struggle with sleeping and be anxious about when it might happen again. One was so bad that I really felt that my heart was going to stop, my chest was so tight and painful. I went to A&E and they were really nice and did heart traces and chest x-rays and said they were confident everything was fine and they thought it was probably anxiety.

I felt really embarrassed. I was out a lot with friends and they had no idea how much I was struggling. I was fine when I was out having a drink but I was dreading the classroom and started to wonder if I had gone into the wrong job.

Things got immediately better when I told a friend. They said something like "Oh that sounds really shit, you should talk to … [my mentor] about it; this must happen all the time". Then when I talked to my mentor he was really understanding and suggested that I go to see my GP.

All the GP really did was to give me some information about panic attacks in a leaflet and tell me that he could refer me to a mental health support group for anxiety but I actually never needed to go. Empathy and some information was enough. I did have a couple more times when I felt as if it was going to happen again but I practised some really simple breathing techniques and told myself "This will pass, you are doing fine" and they became embarrassing flushes rather than full-blown panic attacks. Sometimes now I get the feeling of rising panic when I have to talk in front of lots of people but I can manage and I know that even if it was to turn into a full-blown panic attack it would be OK. Unpleasant, but OK!

◈ Chapter 10 ◈

"A Little Bit OCD"

We talk about what OCD is and some ways you can help yourself if you feel that you are struggling	Intrusive thoughts are a problem for people with OCD because of the way they understand and respond to them
Going to your GP and getting a referral to a therapist is always a positive way to start the journey of recovery	You shouldn't feel ashamed and you shouldn't blame yourself

In addition to the experiences of anxiety that we have already talked about, some of us also struggle with obsessions and compulsions. Although many of the people reading this book may not have experienced these, we thought it was important to introduce them, think about their impact and consider how you might get some support if you think you are struggling with obsessional thoughts or compulsive behaviours.

People with obsessions and compulsions commonly notice that their thoughts and behaviours get much more problematic when there are significant changes in their lives, such as starting college or university, moving away from home or entering their first serious relationship. So, it makes sense that moving into adulthood may well be a trigger for significant anxiety and more problematic obsessions and compulsions. OCD can sometimes be misunderstood by the media and general public, who may trivialise the disorder, adding to the stigma or stopping people understanding their problems and seeking help. In this chapter, we talk about what OCD is, some ways you can help yourself if you feel that you are struggling and where you might go for additional help.

What is OCD?

OCD stands for obsessive compulsive disorder (not exactly a catchy name) and can be very debilitating for those who suffer from it. People with OCD often experience what are commonly referred to as "intrusive thoughts", although everybody experiences these thoughts to some extent. Intrusive thoughts can range from feeling as though you might push a random stranger in front of a car to suddenly imagining yourself stripping off naked in an inappropriate location. Although you don't *want* these thoughts, they pop up anyway and we know that they actually pop up more often and with more intensity when you try to push them away. Some clever psychologists ages ago worked out that if you ask people not to think about something, such as a white bear, then they actually think about white bears a lot more. This is because their brain is monitoring their achievement of the goal "do not think about white bears" so it has to think about white bears every so often to check if you have achieved the goal.[1]

In a survey of 298 students who did not have a diagnosed mental health problem, it was revealed that while people might not talk about them, intrusive thoughts are really common. Every kind of intrusive thought you can think of, from hurting people to thinking inappropriate sexual thoughts, was included and it turns out that these thoughts pop into people's heads all the time. For instance, 64 per cent of women and 56 per cent of men interviewed said they had recently thought about running their car off the road, while 18 per cent of women and 48 per cent of men said they had recently thought about hurting strangers.[2] Looking at the evidence, it appears that these thoughts aren't as "weird" as we might think and that people who experience them aren't "bad" people. Intrusive thoughts are normal experiences and we can learn to view them that way. They become a problem if we start to think that they mean something about us or about what might happen in the future.

Intrusive thoughts are a problem for people with OCD because of the way they understand and respond to them. While many people may have a troublesome thought and be able to ignore it, people who struggle with obsessions and compulsions feel that they cannot ignore such thoughts. These thoughts can seem more meaningful if we have had difficult experiences related to the thoughts and images (e.g. if we have been assaulted or sexually abused) or if our upbringing or religious beliefs have led us to believe that we must always think good thoughts to be a good person.

---

1   Wegner, D.M., Schneider, D.J., Carter, S.R. and White, T.L. (1987) "Paradoxical effects of thought suppression." *Attitudes and Social Cognition*, 53(1), 5–13.

2   Purdon, C. and Clark, D. (1993) "Obsessive intrusive thoughts in nonclinical subjects: Part 1 Content and relation with depressive, anxious and obsessional symptoms." *Behaviour, Research and Therapy*, 31, 713–720. doi:10.1016/0005-7967(93)90001-B.

Another way of understanding why you might get stuck is to do with how you process your thoughts. If you think of your thoughts like a conveyor belt in your local supermarket then most people watch the items pass along the conveyor belt and pay only a little attention to each one before moving on. For people with OCD, it often feels as if the conveyor belt is full to the brim with thoughts and is also travelling at full speed. Once they've started to look at a thought, they may feel that they can't move on no matter how uncomfortable the thought is making them feel. Understandably, this can be very distressing, especially if the thought includes images or thoughts of bad things happening to a loved one or themselves, or indicates they are not a good person by their own standards and values.

Even if the idea of the conveyor belt doesn't fit for you, it can be helpful to understand that when obsessions and compulsions become a problem it is often because it is very difficult to let thoughts go and the person is getting caught up in them and giving them a lot of meaning, when most people would be able to dismiss them more easily. Lots of the ideas in this book can be helpful for stopping you getting too caught up in thoughts, so please keep reading!

Now, the obsessions often like to buddy-up with "compulsions", which are mental or behavioural rituals you feel you *have to do* in order to prevent something awful from happening or to prevent uncomfortable and scary thoughts or images. Compulsions can make life very difficult and they are different for everybody. For some, it might be washing your hands to try and neutralise a fear of contracting or giving a loved one a deadly disease, while for others it might be worrying that if you don't turn a light switch on and off a set number of times, something terrible will happen. No matter how the rituals manifest themselves, compulsions often make sufferers feel as though they are going "crazy" and can be very hard for other people to understand. They can also get to a stage where they have a big impact on everyday life. Some people struggle to get out of the house because they need to complete all of the rituals first.

But why?

This is usually the part where a bespectacled gentleman asks you to lie on a couch and talk about your childhood. Although this is an incredibly clichéd picture, there is, as always, some truth in the idea that who we are, and the ways that we learn to cope with things, are impacted by our early life experiences.

Although the causes of OCD are different for everybody, there's almost always some kind of underlying stressor that means the person needs their obsessions and compulsions to cope and feel safe. For some, it can be difficult memories from the past but for others, it might be a specific fear or insecurity. Once you are stuck in the cycle of needing to "neutralise" your intrusive thoughts with rituals, it can be very hard to take the leap and break the cycle. It can also be hard to reflect and discover where your obsessions and compulsions might come from, but for many (not all), this can be the key to taking back some control over them.

Escaping the spiral – positive ways to manage symptoms

There are a lot of different therapies out there and often they have impenetrable acronyms like "CBT" (cognitive behavioural therapy) or "CAT" (cognitive analytic therapy) which can be confusing and off-putting. Going to your GP and getting a referral to a therapist is always a positive way to start the journey of recovery. Once you meet with a therapist or psychologist, you can discuss what approaches they feel you would benefit from the most. Each therapy takes a slightly different approach to try to help you and it's always best to discuss your priorities and goals with your therapist and what you hope to achieve. Mental health and OCD-specific charities often run support groups for people experiencing OCD symptoms, and some people find these groups supportive and helpful. In addition to therapy, there are also some medications that can help alleviate some of the symptoms of anxiety, with the idea being that the person can then feel more able to access therapies. These are available on prescription from GPs and psychiatrists. It's always good to have an open discussion with your healthcare provider about what path you might take and the best ways to aid your recovery, whether these involve medications or not.

And, as always, there are things you can do yourself to alleviate the frustration and anxiety related to OCD. The key is to try as many as you can and then work with what gives you positive results. Some people find that exercise is a good way to get rid of mounting energy, while others find activities that keep their hands busy, like crafts or playing an instrument, helpful too (see Chapter 11 for more information on self-care).

There are also small ways you can challenge your thoughts yourself. Writing down the evidence you have for supporting a thought and questioning if whether what you are thinking is factual or just an opinion can be a helpful activity (see Chapter 4 for a more detailed explanation). Confronting these thoughts head on in this way can sometimes be too daunting, so mindfulness can be another way of learning to be in the present moment and not getting caught up in your thoughts (see Chapter 12). Working with your OCD may be something you need support doing, so other distracting tasks such as light exercise, crafts or taking a walk may help to alleviate some of the anxiety until you can talk to a therapist, psychologist or other supporting influence in your life. There are also lots of self-help books you could buy or borrow from your local library with helpful tips to challenge the condition at home; for example, *Overcoming Obsessive Compulsive Disorder* by David Veale and Rob Wilson.

Managing the stigma

The media might think that they're being helpful when they feature characters with OCD in soap opera storylines but often they are perpetuating common myths surrounding the diagnosis. We've also noticed that it's not uncommon for people to casually refer to themselves as having OCD when this isn't the case. For instance, someone wanting their desk, house or wardrobe to look neat may say they have OCD or that they're "a bit OCD" when their behaviours are a bit extreme but essentially within healthy and normal limits. When you are suffering and hear people trivialising your condition so openly, it's quite normal to feel angry or irritated. It's helpful to remember that the person you are talking to doesn't have a full understanding of what distressing obsessions and compulsions feel like. While for sufferers, these experiences are often disabling and impact on their life, people who have never had them only know what they've seen in the media and are probably accustomed to people casually referring to their tidiness as OCD. It's hard not to get angry (and even be rude), but usually it's ignorance rather than malice that is behind these thoughtless comments and attitudes.

If you feel yourself becoming upset or irritated by people's lack of understanding, rather than being rude (we would never advocate that!) you could perhaps try to gently educate them about what OCD is, how it affects or has affected you, and where they can access more information about it. You could even hand them this chapter of the book.

Phoebe's story

Contributing to this chapter was very important to me as I've experienced OCD symptoms for as long as I can remember and was formally diagnosed aged 15. Now aged 19, I have been through many different forms of therapy, including CFT (compassion-focused therapy), CBT and most recently EMDR (eye movement desensitisation and reprocessing). After years of trying to manage my symptoms, I'm finally in a place where I am functioning well and doing what I want to do in life.

At the height of my OCD, I could barely walk across a room without having to carry out numerous rituals and I didn't have the mental space to read or even watch TV, which was very frustrating. My OCD meant that when doing everyday activities, such as walking up the stairs or picking up a cup, I would become what I and my family called "stuck". I would feel frozen in place, terrified by the thoughts in my head which told me that not tapping an item numerous times, counting aloud, or looking and blinking at objects would cause a terrible tragedy. I had to keep doing the ritual until it "felt right", which might have been seven times on a good day or 20 on a bad one. These difficult feelings and rituals led to me using some very negative coping mechanisms, which therapy helped me to substitute with positive, healthy ones (such as knitting).

My OCD was related to traumatic memories and in order for me to recover, I had to address these. My therapist used EMDR (a type of trauma therapy) to help me process these memories and although this was very difficult, having just completed the course I can say that it was definitely worth it. Although my OCD will most likely always be there, therapy has empowered me to know I *can* have control over it. I now have the skills to manage my symptoms and get on with my life.

Until a few years ago, I was very secretive about my OCD and would go to great lengths to hide it. When people noticed it, I would lie or hide myself away, which made me feel very isolated and alone. As a young child, people had mocked my behaviours and I felt very ashamed. Once I opened up, I realised that lots of other people felt like me and that although there were some people who didn't understand, there were lots who tried their best to understand and support me. I was closed off for a long time but having OCD doesn't mean you have to go it alone. Friends, family and services are there for you and can help you make it through, even when you're certain you can't. You shouldn't feel ashamed and you shouldn't blame yourself but above all, you should remember that, with help, you can and *will* be able to manage your symptoms. I used to think I would never be in control of my OCD but now I know I can be. I also never thought I would be as independent as I am now, and I *definitely* never thought I would be getting ready to apply to university this year! But this is my new reality; recovery is possible.

Chapter 11

How Do I Stay Calm and Healthy in a Stressful World?

No two people are alike in what makes them feel awesome and more in control	Developing your own self-care plan and actually having a copy written down can be helpful
If you haven't got the basics sorted then all the other stuff is not going to work	We know for sure that anxiety and sleep are closely linked

Coping with anxiety – the basics

When you're having a hard time, it can feel dismissive or insulting if someone asks you about your sleep, your diet, or how much caffeine you are drinking, especially when you are in a crisis or feeling anxious all the time. We often find that people feel that distress and big transitions require complex solutions. The truth is, if you haven't got the basics sorted then all the other stuff is not going to work. Sometimes, getting the basics sorted means you don't need to do anything else!

Whether you are struggling with workload stress, exam revision or a difficult relationship, the first thing to check is, "Am I taking care of myself?" This means:

– getting enough sleep

– eating three meals a day with lots of fruit and vegetables

– getting active three times a week (at least a walk!)

– not drinking too much caffeine

– not relying on alcohol or other substances to cope with stress.

Once you have worked through this list then you can think about some of the other ideas and techniques we talk about in the book. We think a little about some positive coping strategies in the second part of this chapter.

Sleep

Getting a good night's sleep is easy for some and seems impossible for others. We know for sure that anxiety and sleep are closely linked. If you are feeling anxious it's hard to sleep, but also not sleeping and being tired can increase your physical stress response and anxiety.

It might take a bit of time, it isn't always a quick fix but try these six top tips and you should start to see a difference:

1. *Make your bedroom a sleep sanctuary* – Make sure your room isn't too hot or too cold, get blackout blinds or, failing that, wear a sleep mask, and make sure your room has soft blankets and cushions and photos of good times and people you love. Changing your sheets regularly isn't usually a priority for people who are super stressed out and anxious but having clean, nice-smelling bedding can make all the difference.

2. *Get a good routine* – This is boring but true. Consistent bedtimes and waking times are important. This gets your body used to a pattern, so it's ready for sleep when you go to bed. Although it can be tempting to take a nap during the day, particularly if you haven't slept much the night before, it's best not to. If you take naps in the day, this can further disrupt your sleeping patterns at night. Even if you had a bad night's sleep and are feeling super tired, it's important that you try your best to keep your daytime activities the same as you had planned. It's also better to only try to sleep when you feel tired or sleepy, rather than spending too much time awake in bed. If you haven't been able to get to sleep after about 20 minutes or more, get up and do something calming or boring until you feel tired, then return to bed and try again (but if you can't fall asleep after about 20 minutes, then get up again...).

3. *Know what to avoid* – Often the things that people think are helping them to relax for bed or get them off to sleep are actually stimulants; rather than helping us to get relaxed and ready for bed, they can lead to us being more awake, alert and hyperactive. The usual suspects are caffeine, cigarettes and alcohol. It's best to avoid

these for *at least* four hours before going to bed. Energy drinks should also be avoided full stop, as although they may make you feel less tired at the time, they also prevent you from being able to sleep when you need to. Exercise is great for improving sleep but try to do this earlier in the evening, and a snack before bed is helpful, but not a big meal. Before bed, it's best to do calming activities, rather than those that make you feel more alert.

4. *Minimise distractions* – If you use your bed as a place to watch TV, eat or work on your laptop, then your body will not learn the bed–sleep connection. Try to just use your bed for sleep. We know this is hard if you live in a busy family or house share and bed is your only space, but having a small desk to sit at so you are not in bed while working or on your computer is helpful. One of the biggest things that stops most people (including us!) from sleeping is looking at our phones. It can be so tempting to just check something on the internet, or see why it beeped, but this will bring your mind straight out of your sleep routine and back into the everyday world. Recent research has also told us that spending more time looking at screens on devices disrupts sleep because the blue light behind the screen makes our brains think it's daytime. We don't always follow our own advice but wherever possible, plug your phone in to charge in a different room (ideally downstairs) so you can't be distracted by buzzing or flashing lights. If you use your phone as an alarm, buy an inexpensive alarm clock!

5. *Deal with anxious thoughts* – Writing things down and putting them away, focused distraction (try counting

back in sevens from 999 rather than counting sheep) or even writing what's bothering you on loo roll and flushing it away are ways to interrupt your worries and stop you ruminating before bed. We all know night-time is the worst for dark thoughts so finding a way to put them away until daylight (where they always feel less terrible) is a good plan! See Chapter 12 for mindful ways of dealing with anxious thoughts.

6. *Relax* – Relaxing your body can help you to feel calmer and less anxious, and slow you down ready to fall asleep. You might choose to do a breathing or relaxation exercise, or just gently and mindfully let go of any tension in your body. Doing a progressive muscular relaxation exercise (slowly tensing and relaxing each group of muscles from your head down to your toes) can be a good way to release some of the tension. Some people enjoy bubble baths or showers as part of their night-time routine. Having a warm, milky drink before going to bed can also help people to fall sleep, but it's important to make sure that it hasn't got caffeine in it! Oils and other smells can also soothe and relax; a common bedtime scent is lavender, but you can use whatever smell is soothing to you.

Food and mood

Often anxiety makes people feel a little sick and their stomach is unsettled so they eat less than they might normally do or even stop eating entirely. Some people like the resulting weight loss so don't worry too much about this, but having low blood sugar isn't good for your mood, making you feel light-headed, possibly causing headaches and even increasing anxious bodily symptoms. Others might use food to "stuff down" anxious feelings and so they eat more than they would like, and often food that isn't great nutritionally.

Eating little and often can help with the queasy anxious stomach, and drinking lots of water with fruit and vegetable snacks is great for making sure you are hydrated and healthy. It can feel unimportant next to your feelings of dread but eating regularly and healthily will make a real difference to how you feel. Just make sure you are not being hard on yourself if you have a bad day and eat some salty or sugary snacks. We are all allowed a treat (or to make a rubbish choice) but berating ourselves rarely makes us behave better next time; it just makes us feel even more terrible.

Exercise and activity

The link between better mental health and exercise is becoming clearer all the time, with more evidence supporting the effectiveness of exercise and activity on mental health. Doing things with other people (team sports or joining a running club, for example) can make it easier to form social connections without too much pressure while also getting those endorphins going. If you don't want to socialise, then just getting out for a walk and paying attention to what is going on around you, mindfully walking through the park and noticing all the sounds, sights, sensations and smells, can help you to focus on the present moment and also give you some health benefits (see Chapter 12 for more mindfulness exercises).

Positive coping

You may have already developed some ways of managing anxiety that work for you. For some, it's rock climbing, for others, it's yoga. No two people are alike in what makes them feel awesome and more in control. Sadly, when we feel rubbish we sometimes stop doing the things that make us feel good. We know that avoidance is often a go-to coping strategy; this can be behavioural avoidance (get out of there) or "cognitive" avoidance (not thinking about it or trying to ignore thoughts and feelings). Alternatively, you might get upset and angry about the things that feel stressful or threatening, leading to conflict and feeling tense and angry. This is not a mysterious process, think fight or flight! Developing your positive coping strategies alongside good self-care is key to managing anxiety and getting through difficult transitions. Some positive strategies that we know do work are detailed below.

Recognising and managing emotions

The key to building resilience and coping with anxiety and other difficult feelings is first to recognise what's going on in your body (where you feel the feeling) and what thoughts might be accompanying the feelings. We're often focused on external causes of our feelings and don't pay attention to what is going on in our bodies or what we are thinking. We simply respond to the feeling that we are having; for example, you start to feel anxious when you are out at a social event, so you assume there is a threat, thinking maybe "people don't want me here" and so you get out of there quickly. The first step to managing emotions is to notice what is going on in our bodies as well as our surroundings and taking a few moments before we respond or react. Practising mindfulness can be very helpful for this (see Chapter 12) as can keeping a diary where you record your thoughts, feelings and bodily sensations.

Tolerating uncertainty

Not knowing is hard. Often as children we are protected from uncertainty by our parents; adults tell us "white lies" to make things seem less scary. As we get older, we realise there are a lot of situations where we have to just wait and see. We can drive ourselves crazy trying to control things that we have no control over (such as if we get sick or whether we passed the exam we took yesterday). Being able to accept that there are things we cannot know or control is hard but this is key to managing anxiety – this was covered in more detail in Chapter 2. It's OK to not be OK and to struggle with not knowing, but it is more helpful to take care of ourselves and try to improve the moment rather than trying to control our environment or other people.

Tolerating distress

We might want (and even expect) to be happy all the time but that is rarely how life works out. Being human means dealing with loss, grief and suffering and it's hard but it's also part of how we grow, learn about ourselves and connect with other people who are suffering.

Sometimes, life is just difficult and if we can accept whatever feelings this brings up for us ("this made me feel sad/guilty/ashamed/angry") then we can start to manage those emotions and make that difficult time more bearable. These are not situations we can problem solve, they are things we just have to get through and "cope with". Often, anxiety becomes a problem because a person feels that they "should not" feel things and therefore spends a lot of time thinking about what happened and how they or others messed up. Then they end up in a spiral of negative thoughts, feeling more and more terrible. Alternatively, they just ignore the feeling and pretend it's not there.

The best way to move on from the feeling is to experience it, accept it (not suppress it) and then find something that makes you feel calm, or energised, or just OK.

Take some time

It's OK to go to ground and eat ice-cream in bed, watching your favourite movies and sobbing for a while. If you are physically unwell you take care of yourself; if you take a real emotional knock then do the same thing. Some workplaces are now encouraging duvet days to help staff with their mental health. Just make sure you are not actually increasing your anxiety by *avoiding*.

Positive activities

Writing a huge list of all the things that you like to do can be helpful to prompt you when you have just failed an exam, missed out on a promotion, or said goodbye to a friend and you might find it hard to come up with a helpful activity.

Write down things you love to do and things you would love to try, from going bowling to walking through crunchy leaves; feeding the ducks with a tiny person to watching a horror film. Write them all down and pin them somewhere you can see. If you are struggling, there is a list of examples in Exercise 5 at the end of this book.

Coping statements

There are lots of memes on the internet or things that you can follow to help you replace anxious thoughts with something more helpful when you are struggling. Some people might have their own "mantra" that they repeat and find comforting. For example, one young woman told Bridie that she repeats, "Every day in every way I am getting stronger" over and over and the rhythm as well as the words are soothing; she taps her legs or times her steps to match the mantra. We have provided a list of positive coping statements in Chapter 4 to help you if you are finding it hard to come up with them, but have fun finding your own.

Acts of kindness

Doing something nice for someone else, even something as small as paying them a compliment, can have benefits for you too. Bake someone a cake, get a beautiful photo printed and frame it for them, offer to help someone you know who is in need of help to clean their house or do their shopping. Volunteering over a longer period of time could also help to develop confidence and to experience positive feelings.

Reward yourself

Many of the strategies that we talk about in this book can be quite challenging and can take a lot of courage and effort so it is important to recognise when you have worked hard at something or tried to overcome some of your anxiety (whatever the outcome has been). You can do this in many ways. You might want to just write it down, tell someone close to you, or reward yourself by doing something nice like watching your favourite film or having a nice dessert. Sue has also previously made some stickers for clients when they have worked towards achieving something – this might be something to do with their anxiety (e.g. I talked to someone new), looking after themselves (e.g. I thought compassionately about myself) or doing adult stuff (e.g. I made a big decision). Celebrating our achievements can help us to focus on some of the positives, rather than getting stuck in our anxious thinking.

Risky coping strategies

In adulthood, you often have access to coping strategies that may not have been available (or acceptable) in your earlier life. Trying smoking, alcohol and using substances can be part of teens experimenting and taking on "adult" behaviours. As an adult, you won't have quite the same restrictions and using alcohol or other substances may be considered normal in your peer group.

Drugs (including caffeine and over-the-counter medications) and alcohol can have a huge detrimental impact on your level of anxiety and your ability to cope with difficult thoughts and feelings. It's socially acceptable for adults to have a drink in order to cope with the tough stuff and we know that this is having a huge impact on the physical health of adults.[1] What is less well researched and talked about is the impact of using substances on our mental health. Drinking alcohol may make it easier to

---

1   World Health Organization (2018) *Global status report on alcohol and health.* Retrieved from www.who.int/substance_abuse/publications/global_alcohol_report/en.

socialise on a Saturday night because you feel a little more relaxed and less inhibited; however, your lowered inhibitions may mean you behave in ways that make you feel embarrassed and don't want to see people. The depressive effect of alcohol lasts long after the perceived positive effects of relaxation and lowered inhibitions, so together this can make for a very unpleasant Sunday. Drinking can also be used to help to calm anxious thoughts at night and make it easier to sleep; however, again, the quality of sleep is often poor and you don't feel fully rested, so anxiety levels are higher the next day.

There are too many substances available for us to discuss the impact of them all here; however, questions to consider when you are thinking about whether your use of any substance or coping strategy is unhelpful include:

- Am I using this substance every time I need to manage a feeling?

- Am I using this substance when I should be doing/need to do other things (like going to work or studying)?

- Is using this substance worrying the people who care about me?

- Is it stopping me from doing normal day-to-day activities (e.g. am I too hungover to get to lectures/ work)?

Sometimes, we come to rely on using drugs or alcohol because we have just not developed other ways to cope with anxiety and difficult thoughts. The problem can be that substances are "quick fixes" with lots of longer-term pitfalls, so when we try an alternative we don't get the same immediate "hit" and resolution to the feeling. This might be when you need some support to work out what function substances have and how you can find more healthy and helpful ways to manage anxiety. See Chapter 13 for sources of support for substance use, or talk to your GP.

Self-injurious behaviour

Sometimes, when people feel overwhelmed with anxiety they harm themselves, often by cutting, scratching or burning. This can be to manage the feeling or communicate to others how they are feeling. Self-harm is too big a topic to cover here and instead we will focus on it in a future book; however, trying to find healthy and helpful ways of managing your anxiety like the ones outlined in this book can reduce the need for self-harm, as can reaching out to others and letting them know that you are feeling anxious and need support.

If your self-harm is making you worried or you are having thoughts of ending your life, it's important that you get help and support as soon as possible. We recommend that you initially talk to someone close to you, your GP or a charity such as the Samaritans (see Chapter 13 for further information). If you are having serious thoughts of ending your life, or have plans to do this, it is important that you go to your GP or straight to an A&E department, where you will be assessed and offered support.

Making a self-care plan

Developing your own self-care plan and actually having a copy written down can be helpful. We have a downloadable template (Exercise 6) available from www.jkp.com/catalogue/book/9781785926419. But you can also sit down and do it right now.

Write down the checklist first. Am I...

- getting enough sleep

- eating three meals a day with lots of fruit and vegetables

- getting active three times a week

- not drinking too much caffeine

- not relying on alcohol or other substances to cope with stress?

And then include in your plan actions to make sure that you are going to do all the above but also ask yourself:

1. What are the warning signs that I need to pay a bit more attention to looking after myself?

2. What things can I do to improve the moment and make it easier to tolerate difficult emotions?

3. What can I ask other people to do to help and support me?

◇ Chapter 12 ◇

What Is This Mindfulness All About?

Mindfulness is a technique that helps us to focus our minds, calm our thoughts and be more aware of what we are experiencing	With mindfulness, it can be useful to give yourself some little prompts to use it
One of the most common mindfulness exercises is mindful breathing	Any thoughts that pass in your head should be acknowledged and accepted, but not thought about or acted on

Sometimes our heads might feel full – our thoughts are spinning around, we can't focus, we feel overwhelmed. When we're feeling like this, the idea of catching our thoughts and challenging them (as discussed in Chapter 4) can feel impossible.

Often people feel as if they:

just

        want

            it

                all

                    to

                            STOP.

We can get so caught up with what is happening in our minds (wondering, reflecting, analysing, planning and so on) that we can almost miss what is happening in the present moment. Mindfulness is a technique that helps us to focus our minds, calm our thoughts and be more aware of what we are experiencing. Just take a minute right now. Take your focus out of your mind and into the world around you. Notice:

- Where are you right now?

- What can you smell (have a good sniff)?

- What can you hear (listen to sounds near, far, all around you)?

- What can you see (shapes, colours, objects, textures)?

- What can you feel (physically)?

- What can you taste?

- How do you feel right now?

Taking a few minutes just to *be* in the present moment, to take your focus out of your mind and into your body and environment, can allow you to *pause*. When you pause, it can give you a break from all the "noise" in your mind and help you to feel calmer. If you can start to add some "pauses" into your daily routine, you might find that this helps to improve your wellbeing.

We have so much to do and think about in everyday life that we can easily miss the little things. We do things without thinking about them, as if we are half-asleep. For example, we can wolf down a bag of chocolates without thinking about what they taste or smell like. We can drive home with our focus so caught up in our minds that we do not notice what we pass on the way. We can walk down the street with our minds focused on what we're having for tea, or an argument we have had at work, rather than noticing the breeze on our skin or the crunch of the leaves under our feet. This is called "being on auto-pilot".

Mindfulness is about being able to choose where to focus your mind – whether you focus it on your thoughts, your body, a task that you are doing, the environment around you, or the present moment. This first exercise helps us to focus on an object using most of our senses.

Exercise: Mindfulness of eating or drinking

Sue likes to do this exercise with chocolate (any chocolate – she likes chocolate), but Phoebe prefers tea (being mindful during the process of making the tea too – the warmness of the cup, the smell and taste, and the time taken to "just be" and look after yourself. Plus, it's easy to incorporate into your day). Anything is fine – just whatever you enjoy that will help you to focus your mind.

Hold the chocolate between your thumb and fingers. Bring your attention to the chocolate, looking at it carefully as if you have never seen it before. What can you see? What colours can you see? Is it dark or light? Look at the texture – is it smooth or rough? What shapes can you see? Are the edges smooth or rough? Then lift the chocolate to your nose and smell it for a while. What smells do you notice? Is it strong? Sweet? Does it remind you of anything? Feel the chocolate in your fingers. What can you feel? Is it solid or starting to melt? Does it feel rough or smooth? Notice the weight. Is it warm or cool? Try to be aware of any thoughts you might have about the chocolate, noticing any thoughts or feelings of like or dislike. Bring the chocolate to your lips and notice any changes in your body. Put the chocolate in your mouth and let it start to melt on your tongue. How does this feel? What do you notice? What does it taste like? Does the taste change or stay the same? Eat the chocolate.

What did you notice during this exercise? Was it different from what you expected? Did you notice anything about the chocolate that you hadn't noticed before?

If you don't want to do this task with food or drink, you can also choose to mindfully observe other objects instead (just don't eat them). You could use: pebbles, candles, pieces of material (rough, fluffy, smooth), body lotion. You can choose to focus on just one of your senses, such as sight. Imagine that you have taken a photo of the scene in front of you – what can you see? Notice colours, shapes, any darkness/light, shadows, textures, patterns, anything that particularly draws your attention from the scene. You can also bring awareness to activities: doing something that you would typically do but bringing a new level of awareness to it, for example walking around a bookshop, brushing your teeth.

Exercise: Mindfulness of sounds

Another exercise which can be useful to have "on the go" is mindfulness of sounds. You can use this exercise anywhere. Just choose a time when you're unlikely to be distracted.

When you're ready, just gently bring your attention to the sounds around you. The sounds that are near and the sounds that are far away; the sounds above you, to the side, below you, behind you and in front of you. Notice sounds as they come and go. Try not to label them, but just notice what they sound like – the loudness, pitch, tone. Don't try to do anything with the sounds. You don't need to search for them. Just allow them to come and go as they will.

You are never too old for bubbles

There are also loads of other mindful activities that you can use which will help to focus your mind. Here are some of our favourites:

-   Blowing bubbles – focusing on the shapes, the process of blowing the bubbles, the colours, the wish to pop them. Blowing bubbles can also help to slow down your breathing.

-   Doing something that makes you concentrate – such as an art task, something creative, sewing, building something, playing an instrument.

-   Finding an object that's personal to you (e.g. a pebble, some jewellery). Carry it with you and mindfully observe it at times when you are feeling anxious.

- Mindfully having a shower. When you're in the shower, bring your attention to the sensation of the water on your skin. How does it feel? Looking at the water, what can you see? You could think about the temperature – is it hot or cold? Notice the smell of any soaps you are using.

- When you're having a (bubble) bath, let your body relax and sink down into the bath, feeling heavy. How does your body feel? Watch the water and bubbles – what can you see? Colours? Shapes? Smells?

- When you are having unhelpful thoughts, bring your attention to an object (such as a picture, pen, photo). Mindfully look at the object – what can you see and how does it feel? When your mind wanders, gently bring your attention back to the object.

So you want me to meditate?

Not necessarily. Doing some short mindfulness meditations can be useful to practise mindfulness, as a way to build up your skills. However, lots of people use mindfulness techniques in everyday life. One of the most common mindfulness exercises is mindful breathing. This can particularly help with anxiety, as it helps to slow your breathing and calm it down.

Exercise: Mindful breathing

Get into a comfortable position lying on your back or sitting. If you are sitting, keep your back straight and let your shoulders slowly drop. Make sure that you feel comfortable.

Feel your eyelids become heavy and gently close your eyes if it feels comfortable. If not, lightly rest your gaze on a point in the room and retain a soft focus.

Bring your attention to your breathing, breathing in slowly... and out slowly

Now bring your attention to your stomach, feeling it rise gently as you breathe in and fall as you breathe out.

Keep the focus on your breathing, being with each in-breath and with each out-breath.

Now bring your attention to your nose. Feel the cold air rushing through your nostrils when you breathe in, and the warm air rushing out through your mouth when you breathe out. If you find it hard to focus, maybe swap things around, breathing in through your mouth and out through your nose.

Every time you notice that your mind has wandered off the breath, notice what it was that took you away. Then gently and compassionately bring your attention back to the feeling of the breath coming in and out of your body. Don't judge the thought or yourself, just let it be.

If your mind wanders away from the breath many times, then your job is simply to gently bring your attention back to the breath every time.

Practise this exercise daily. See how it feels to spend some time each day just being with your breath without having to do anything.

When you are feeling anxious, take five mindful breaths and bring your attention to your breathing. Every time your mind wanders to an unhelpful thought, gently bring your attention back to your breathing.

Dealing with anxious thoughts

We can think about thoughts as just noise. What we know is that we can have all kinds of anxious thoughts, but it doesn't mean that they will happen, that they matter or that we will act on them. One of the most important things to remember is that thoughts are *not* facts. They are *just* thoughts. During this act of mindfulness, any thoughts that pass in your head should be acknowledged and accepted, but not thought about or acted on (allow them to drift in and out of your mind). Bring yourself back to the present moment gently; try not to be hard on yourself. Don't judge your thoughts as "good" or "bad" – they just "are". We can then learn to respond in a more helpful way to what is happening around us.

Leaves in a stream

Lots of people have told us they find it helpful to imagine their thoughts floating on leaves down a stream and this is a common mindfulness exercise we use in therapy. You can choose what you want to do for your own imagery or decide not to use it at all. Other examples include imagining lying down in a field and watching clouds (thoughts) be blown past you – some big, some small, some grey, some lingering. Or, imagining bubbles floating away. Other people may find it useful to write their thoughts down on paper, scrunching it up and throwing the paper away (noticing the thoughts as they arise in your mind, labelling them by writing them down, and letting them go). This technique could be useful particularly at bedtime when you might choose to write thoughts down and put them away (maybe in a drawer), then you can leave them until the morning, let them go, and allow your mind to rest. It also might help if you are feeling overwhelmed with too many thoughts!

When mindfulness isn't helpful

Mindfulness isn't for everyone. As with every therapeutic technique, mindfulness will be helpful for some people but not others. General mindfulness is not recommended for people who have post-traumatic stress disorder (although an amended version of mindfulness can be useful for people with these difficulties). If you try mindfulness out and find that it's not helpful for you, or makes things worse, the best advice is just to stop. Then, if you want to look into it further, see a professional who has had training in both mindfulness and mental health.

I can't focus!

This is a common difficulty when trying to practise mindfulness. We become so caught up in trying to do it in the right way, that we can become frustrated with ourselves.

Mindfulness is a bit like training a puppy to stay. When you first tell the puppy to stay, it will jump about the place, lick your face and ignore your commands. But after you have practised with the puppy, it will eventually learn to stay (most of the time, unless a cat walks past). Minds are similar. At first, when you try to do mindfulness, it's likely that your mind will keep being distracted and will struggle to stay on the task – this is OK and completely normal. After practising the exercises lots of times, your mind will slowly learn to stay on the task more (although it will still wander at times – this happens to everyone).

Mindfulness of anxious feelings in the body – riding the waves

In a similar way to managing anxious thoughts, we can learn to notice, allow and accept anxious feelings in the body. Some people call this "riding the waves" of anxious feelings (we talked about this in Chapter 9). We know that anxious feelings start to run out of fuel if we wait long enough, so we can accept them and wait for them to pass. When we experience these feelings, it can be useful to explore them in a mindful way. Step back and observe the feelings as you experience them in your body. Where can you feel them (in your arms, face, heart area, legs)? What are the sensations like? How intense are the sensations? What shape are they? Do they come and go or stay the same? Stay curious and investigate what you are experiencing. Then it can be useful to take a few deep breaths and allow the sensations to "just be". Don't fight against them, or struggle with them, just allow them and wait for them to pass. Remind yourself that these are normal, bodily reactions and make peace with them.

This mindfulness of feelings can be difficult, particularly at first. But when you have managed to ride the wave of anxious feelings once or twice, and have watched them eventually stop, it can build up your confidence to be able to ride the wave again.

Remembering to be mindful

Sometimes, even with the best intentions, we can forget to practise the skills that we learn. With mindfulness, it can be useful to give yourself some little prompts to use it. For example, Sue has a fitness watch which reminds her at ten to the hour that she has not done enough steps (almost every hour – she is lazy!). So, she takes that opportunity as a prompt to take three mindful breaths. This helps her to have pauses in her day. Bridie has started to do ten minutes of yoga every morning where she focuses on her breathing and her body and sets herself up for the day. Mindfulness apps can also be really helpful. A common one is *Headspace*, which will set you reminders to practise and provides guided mindfulness exercises and short video guides.

A final mindful exercise is the body scan. This can particularly help you to relax your mind in the mornings or evenings. It may need a little more practice though. You can take as long as you wish to do this exercise. Some people like to set an alarm (you can even use mindfulness bells) to end the exercise, so that their thoughts are not focused on what they are doing next.

Exercise: Body scan

Find a time and space where you are unlikely to be disturbed, where you can relax. Either sit down (keeping a straight back) or lie down on the floor. Relax into the chair, floor or cushion. Feel yourself sinking down, your arms getting heavy, your legs sinking down into the chair or floor. Let your shoulders relax. Feel your eyelids become heavy and gently close your eyes, if you feel comfortable doing this, or just allow your eyes to gently focus on a point in the room.

Start by bringing your attention to your breathing. Breathing in...and out... Notice the rise and fall of your chest as you do so. Then, when you are ready, imagine a spotlight shining on a part of your body, helping you to bring your attention and focus to that area. First, notice the spotlight move to your legs and feet. Notice any tension in your legs and feet, and as you breathe out, feel the tension releasing out of your body, down through your legs, your ankles, your feet and down through the ground.

When you are ready, notice the spotlight move to the trunk of your body – your shoulders, your back, your stomach and your hips. Notice any tension in these areas, then as you breathe out, feel the tension releasing out of your body, down through the trunk of your body, your legs, feet and down through the ground.

Then notice the spotlight move to your shoulders, arms, and hands. Notice any tension, and then as you breathe out, feel the tension releasing out of your body, down through your arms, through the trunk of your body, down through your legs and feet and down through the ground.

Finally, notice the spotlight move to your head, face and neck. Notice any tension in these areas, and then as you breathe out, feel the tension releasing out of your body, down through your shoulders, the trunk of your body, through your legs and feet and down through the ground.

When you are ready, gently bring your attention back to your breathing. Feel the spotlight bringing a focus to the whole body. As you breathe in, notice any areas of tension, and as you breathe out, let it release and feel the tension flowing out of your body.

When you feel ready, wiggle your toes, and gently come back to the room, ready and refreshed to carry on with your day.

Chapter 13

Where Can I Get Some Extra Help?

One in four people suffer from a mental health problem at some point in their lives	Sometimes allowing yourself to be vulnerable can promote courage, confidence and self-acceptance
It's important to identify the person you would like to talk to	Mental health is just as important as physical health

Although there are lots of tips and ideas about how to manage your anxiety included within this book, we would *always* recommend that you let someone know how you are feeling so that they can support you with it too. This chapter looks at why it can be difficult to ask for help, ways to do this, and what additional help might be available to you.

The vulnerability vice

Letting people know that you're struggling and asking for support isn't easy, and discussing your insecurities and feelings can make you feel vulnerable. Nearly everyone experiences discomfort and worry when they open up to others, and it's completely natural to be concerned about how people might react and to be hesitant about "letting people in". While acknowledging how difficult this can be, it's important to remember the benefits of reaching out for support and getting some extra help. Sometimes allowing yourself to be vulnerable can promote courage, confidence and self-acceptance. Letting someone know how you're feeling and being met with acceptance and love can also help to reinforce the idea that having these issues isn't a personal flaw or weakness and shouldn't make people view you differently.

It might seem counter-intuitive to tackle anxiety by creating more of it but making people aware of your difficulties means that your friends and family can support you and assist you to access any further help you may need, including therapies and medication.

But how do I do it?

Before you start thinking about exactly what you want to say, it's important to identify the person you would like to talk to. It should be someone whom you feel comfortable around and can trust. This could be a close friend, family member, work colleague or a healthcare professional (such as a GP).

Once you know who you'd like to talk to, you can start drafting ideas of what you do (and don't) want to discuss with them. At this point, it might be helpful to write them down so that you can refer to them later. For example, you might want to let the person know that you suffer from panic attacks or that you are struggling with anxious thoughts and feelings. You don't have to tell anyone more than you are comfortable doing and you don't have to tell them everything at once. It's important to remember that *you* have the control to tell them what *you* want to, when it feels right for *you*. There are no obligations when opening up to others.

While you're planning who you want to talk to and what you would like to say, it's a good idea to think of ways in which your loved one could help you. For instance, knowing you can call them if you're having a particularly anxious day or being able to bounce ideas off them when problem-solving might be helpful. Similarly, you might not be sure what support you want or need, and that's OK too. Together, you will be able to think of strategies to help you cope and test them out to see if they work.

Sadly, sometimes people aren't as helpful as we'd like them to be. Occasionally, people try to "solve the problem" rather than listening to your worries and validating your feelings; this can be a difficult (and infuriating) experience but it's a manageable one! Opening up about your anxiety can sometimes be met by some unhelpful comments such as, "You just need to relax", "You haven't got anything to worry about" or even "Stop worrying". There is a whole plethora of remarks that can make you feel dismissed or misunderstood.

While this is difficult, it's important to remember that somebody having an unhelpful reaction to your anxiety doesn't mean your feelings and struggles aren't valid. Lots of people struggle to talk about or connect with difficult thoughts and feelings, so they struggle to be helpful to those in distress. Sometimes, you might have caught somebody "off guard", and in the moment they were unsure of how to react. This doesn't mean they don't care and can often mean that they are worried about worsening the situation and want to think carefully about their response. If it feels difficult for your loved one to understand, a good way to move forwards is to be clear about the things that they can do to help. It might be being there to listen, coming with you to the GP, getting into a new activity with you, or just being on the end of the phone when you need a welcome distraction from your anxiety.

While some people might struggle with talking about and supporting you with your anxiety and worries, you can be sure that there will be others who will be happy to offer you support and compassion. Remember, this is mostly about them and their ability to talk about and manage their own feelings and anxieties rather than a reflection on you or a judgement of your character. If your first attempts aren't successful, try someone new or approach a mental health professional.

The shame game

The media and society more widely are working on mental health awareness and you will see a lot more mention of mental health around you, but there's still quite a way to go! Often mental health issues still evoke feelings of shame and embarrassment in the person experiencing or labelled with them. Having anxiety or another mental health problem is incredibly common and definitely not a sign of weakness or anyone's fault. Just like you wouldn't blame someone with the flu for being sick, you can't blame yourself for having your own struggles. Life can be difficult and we all have times when it feels overwhelming and we need help to cope – even if we cannot always see that this is the case.

Sometimes it feels as though society has created a divide between physical health issues and mental health issues, and this can make you feel as if mental health isn't "real" or "important". *This isn't the case.* Mental health is just as important as physical health. Minds can become unwell, just like bodies can, and they need looking after too.

One in four people suffer from a mental health problem at some point in their lives, so it's time we moved away from making people feel ashamed and not taking mental health seriously. There are lots of charities with helpful websites which offer information about anxiety, and some have links to stories from people experiencing similar difficulties (many of these websites are listed at the end of this chapter).

Reminding yourself that you are not alone can help to alleviate feelings of shame and allow you to move towards recovery. We hope that all the stories people have shared in this book can help you to see that you are not alone and that things can and do get easier.

Talking to professionals

Talking to friends and family can feel daunting but sometimes speaking to your GP or other health professionals presents its own challenges. Often, the clinical setting of a doctor's surgery or therapist's office can feel scary and overwhelming. If you can, it could be helpful to take someone along with you, such as a trusted friend or family member, to support you throughout the appointment (and remember the stuff that goes out of your head when you feel stressed and anxious). While this can give you the confidence to go and see someone, you might need to let the person know beforehand how much input you want them to have in the actual appointment. For instance, you might want to explain your feelings yourself and not be "spoken for". Typically, a doctor will ask you some questions about how you're feeling and how long you have been feeling that way. Sometimes, they will give you a few questionnaires to fill in so that they can get a better idea of what your individual problems are and how they can help you.

Your doctor may suggest you see a counsellor, attend therapy or consider taking medication to help with some of your problems. If you are unsure of any of the things they are discussing, it's always OK to ask. There are also some handy websites such as HeadMeds, which offer information about different medications and therapies, so you can get a better understanding of which treatment options are available and how they work.

If you feel that a professional isn't taking your anxiety seriously, don't worry too much. You can always book an appointment with another doctor. Some GPs and doctors specialise in mental health problems, which can make you feel more confident about going to see them.

David's story

I had always considered myself to be a robust person, a person who could take on any challenge and who doesn't let things bother them. However, much to my surprise at the time, I suffered a one-year period of anxiety that affected my emotional and physical health.

Anxiety became a problem for me when I was living away from home in another country with my partner. I was homesick at the time and I spent a lot of time worrying about my future. I had the option to emigrate and live in Canada, but found the prospect of leaving my home and family extremely overwhelming. I was very concerned about making such a big decision to emigrate, which would change the course of my life, without having a clear idea of what I might do for work and how I would support myself in the long term. I also felt incredibly isolated living in Toronto. I had made some friends through my partner, but didn't have anyone who "got me" or knew who I was. The cultural difference was also something that I found difficult – the sense of humour was different, the history and outlook of people were different. The people I met didn't seem to recognise my history or view of the world and it made me feel a lack of connection to the place and people.

What was also significant was that I found it very difficult to talk to anyone about how I was feeling. My partner's family put a lot of pressure on me to stay and this made it difficult to share with them how I was feeling. Friends and family assumed I was having such a wonderful time living in Canada that they didn't ask how I was doing. I also found it difficult to admit I was struggling, because I viewed myself as someone who could handle anything, therefore it challenged my view of myself to admit I was not doing so well.

This resulted in a pattern of over-thinking and ruminating over what I should do, which in turn made my experience seem even more overwhelming as it was all I was focusing on. I began to isolate myself from others, I couldn't sleep, I developed eczema and psoriasis, my mind raced constantly, I felt nervous and anxious around people and rarely enjoyed anything. These experiences lasted for around a year, where I "just got on with it" and hoped things might change. Things came to a head at work, when I quit and walked out of my bar job after a very minor disagreement with my manager over a customer's bill. I had finally had enough and could not cope any longer – the "bucket was full", so to speak. (I still haven't seen that manager since!)

I had to take a long, hard look at myself and recognise that I needed support. I called my parents and told them how I was feeling and had a good cry on Skype, which actually made me feel amazing at the time! It felt like an entire year's worth of anxiety just came flooding out in that conversation and it was such a release that I could physically feel my body relax. I was honest with my partner, told her how I felt, and we made some plans for the future to return to the UK so I could pursue my career. I discussed everything that was going on for me with some of my closest friends, who had no idea I was struggling. These conversations with friends provided me with the advice and support that actually made my situation and the decisions I had to make feel much less overwhelming. I also started to run. This was a major factor in supporting my anxiety, as running provided an instant release from feeling anxious and created a calm over my mind, reduced my tendency to over-think and also made me feel tired and relaxed at night, which helped me drift off to sleep.

What I have realised more than anything from this period is that it's so important to share concerns and ask for support at times when I feel worried or anxious. I realise that over-thinking and ruminating on problems on my own only makes the problems feel even bigger. Sharing my worries was so important for me to gain some control over my anxiety and provided the clarity I needed to make decisions for my future and my wellbeing. I also realise that wherever I am, whatever I do, I need connection with people, I need to feel as if I belong and there are many ways I can achieve this. Staying in touch with the people who matter to you, joining a sports team or another social activity and pursuing hobbies that give you a sense of enjoyment and purpose are things I will keep doing in the future. One day I will return to Canada, but I am now armed with the knowledge of things that I can do to support my move and support me!

Helplines and contacts

YoungMinds Crisis Messenger Service (UK only) – supports young people up to the age of 25 years when they are experiencing a crisis and need support. The service is open 24/7 and they try to get back to you within five minutes with a trained volunteer. To access this service, send a text message to 85258: www.youngminds.org.uk

Samaritans: free helpline: 116 123 or jo@samaritans.org or the Next Generation Text Service (for people who are hard of hearing): www.samaritans.org

Information about anxiety

Anxiety UK: www.anxietyuk.org.uk/about-anxiety/young-people-and-anxiety

HeadMeds (information about medication): www.headmeds.org.uk/conditions/6-anxiety

Information about education/exam stress

Pomodoro Technique: https://francescocirillo.com/pages/pomodoro-technique

Student Minds Charity: info@studentminds.org.uk or www.studentminds.org.uk

Information about substance misuse

Alcoholics Anonymous helpline: 0800 9177 650

FRANK: www.talktofrank.com

Mind: www.mind.org.uk

Study Apps

Mind mapping apps

www.Lucidchart.com

www.mindjet.com

www.mural.com

www.mindnode.com

Recording app with lots of features

www.voicedream.com

A pen that records what you write

www.Livescribe.com

To do lists

Many pomdoro apps available online

www.getfinish.com

www.Wunderlist.com

Bibliography

Barnes. C.M. and Drake, C.L. (2015) "Prioritizing sleep health: Public health policy recommendations." *Perspectives on Psychological Science*, 10, 6, 733–737. doi:10.1177/1745691615598509.

Chaskalson, M. (2014) *Mindfulness in Eight Weeks*. London: Harper Thorsons.

Coan, J.A., Schaefer, H.S. and Davidson, R.J. (2006) "Lending a hand: Social regulation of the neural response to threat." *Psychological Medicine*, 17, 12, 1032–1039. doi:10.1111/j.1467-9280.2006.01832.x.

Dweck, C.S. (2017) *Mindset: Changing the Way You Think to Fulfil Your Potential.* London: Robinson.

Hirshkowitz, M., Whiton, K., Albert, S.M., Alessi, C. et al. (2015) "National Sleep Foundation's sleep time duration recommendations: Methodology and results summary." *Sleep Health*, 1, 40–43. doi: 10.1016/j.sleh.2014.12.010.

Kessler, R.C., Chiu, W.T., Jin, R., Ruscio, A.M., Shear, K. and Walkers, E.E. (2006) "The epidemiology of panic attacks, panic disorder, and agoraphobia in the National Comorbidity Survey replication." *Archives of General Psychiatry*, 63, 4, 415–424. doi:10.1001/archpsyc.63.4.415.

Kessler, R.C., Angermeyer, M., Anthony, J.C., De Graaf, R. et al. (2007) "Lifetime prevalence and age-of-onset distributions of mental disorders in the World Health Organization's World Mental Health Survey Initiative." *World Psychiatry*, 6, 3, 168–176.

Linehan, M.M. (2015) *DBT Skills Training Manual* (second edition). London: Guildford Press.

Polanczyk, G.V., Salum, G.A., Sugaya, L.S., Caye, A. and Rohde, L.A. (2015) "Annual Research Review: A meta-analysis of the worldwide prevalence of mental disorders in children and adolescents." *Journal of Child Psychology and Psychiatry*, 56, 3, 1–21. doi: 10.1111/jcpp/12381.

Purdon, C. and Clark, D. (1993) "Obsessive intrusive thoughts in nonclinical subjects: Part 1 Content and relation with depressive, anxious and obsessional symptoms." *Behaviour, Research and Therapy*, 31, 713–720. doi:10.1016/0005-7967(93)90001-B.

REBT Network (2006) *Fear of Approaching Women*. Retrieved from www.rebtnetwork.org/ask/may06.html.

Rutter, M., Kim-Cohen, J. and Maughan, B. (2006) "Continuities and discontinuities in psychopathology between childhood and adult life." *The Journal of Child Psychology and Psychiatry, 47,* 3–4, 276–295. doi:10.1111/j.1469-7610.2006.01614.x.

Sood, E.D. and Kendall, P.C. (2007) "Assessing anxious self-talk in youth: The negative affectivity self-statement questionnaire – anxiety scale." *Cognitive Therapy and Research, 31,* 5, 603–618. doi:10.1007/s10608-006-9043-8.

Stewart, R.E. and Chambless, D.L. (2009) "Cognitive-behavioral therapy for adult anxiety disorders in clinical practice: A meta-analysis of effectiveness studies." *Journal of Consulting and Clinical Psychology, 77,* 4, 595–606. doi:10.1037/a0016032.

Veale, D. and Wilson, R. (2005) *Overcoming Obsessive Compulsive Disorder.* London: Constable and Robinson.

Wegner, D.M., Schneider, D.J., Carter, S.R. and White, T.L. (1987) "Paradoxical effects of thought suppression." *Attitudes and Social Cognition, 53,* 1, 5–13.

Williams, M. and Penman, D. (2011) *A Practical Guide to Finding Peace in a Frantic World.* London: Platkus.

World Health Organization (2018) *Global status report on alcohol and health.* Retrieved from www.who.int/substance_abuse/publications/global_alcohol_report/en.

Exercise 1

Living a life that fits with your values

This reflection exercise can help you to think about what is important to you in life, what kind of life you want to live, and then help you to live more the way that you want to. This can give you a greater sense of purpose and drive in what you do. This can then lead to increased personal resilience and less anxious thinking, and more clarity when making decisions.

There are two main ways to do this exercise, which complement each other (so maybe do both!).

ONE: Imagine that it's your 40th birthday party (way, way in the future). A friend decides to do a speech for you, which talks about you as a person, what is important to you, and what you have achieved in your life so far. What would you want them to say? Where would you want to be in your life by then?

TWO: Read the list of personal values below. Which ones stand out for you (some might jump out straight away)? Which do you feel that you relate to or are most important to you? Perhaps pick out four or five values, or add some more if you can think of them.

Friendship; Helping others; Making a contribution; Connections with others; Having fun; Achieving; Adventure; Challenging yourself; Being part of a group; Gaining knowledge/being knowledgeable; Pursuing a career; Passion for things; Money/good finances; Building/maintaining family relationships; Living in the moment; Health (physical/emotional); Faith/belief; Being loved; Creativity; Integrity; Responsibility; Security; Courage; Making a big difference; Leading others.

Now that you have your values, take each value at a time, and think about how much you are living your life by that value right now on a 0–5 scale (0 = not at all, 5 = completely). Then think about what you could do to bring yourself closer/stay close to each value.

For example, one of Sue's values is "having fun". She believes that life is too short to always be serious and wants to do more adventurous things. However, she recognises that at the moment, she is probably only doing this about a 2/5 as she is working a lot. So, she is now going to set herself a goal of "trying out a new activity" each month, such as paddleboarding (which she has wanted to do for ages).

Values Description Rating Goals
1
2
3
4
5

It can be useful to keep a note of your values and goals, and see if they change over time. This can prompt you to live your life closer to your goals, which will help you to have a more fulfilling life. Another way to do this is to ask someone close to you to "check-in" with you occasionally about these goals. So, if any of you do know Sue, feel free to prompt/ask her about the paddleboarding...

You can also use your values to help you to think about what's important to you when making decisions (see Chapter 2).

Exercise 2

Testing out your safety behaviours

What is my safety behaviour?
What am I going to do instead (describe in detail what you will/will not do)?

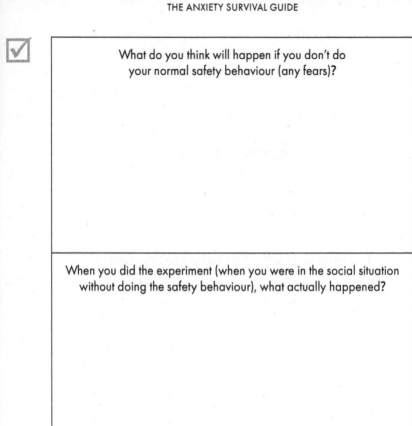

What do you think will happen if you don't do
your normal safety behaviour (any fears)?

When you did the experiment (when you were in the social situation
without doing the safety behaviour), what actually happened?

Any reflections? What did you learn from doing
this? What will you do next time?

Exercise 3

Thought-challenging sheet

What is the situation?	What is the thought?	How much do I believe it? %	What is the evidence (for and against)? Can I spot a thinking error?	How much do I believe it now? %	What would be a more accurate or helpful thought?

Exercise 4

Compassionate other exercise

This imagery exercise focuses on the creation of a soothing, compassionate and comforting "other" – this can be a person, an animal or an object. The important thing is that this "other" wants to support, comfort and be kind to you. Again, this "other" may change over time, and that is OK. This imagery can be useful when tackling difficult thoughts (see Chapter 4), where you can imagine what your soothing other would say to you to help you to find an alternative helpful thought.

Exercise: Soothing other

Gently close your eyes and relax your body. Allow your breathing to slow down to a comfortable pace, with any tension flowing out of your body on each out-breath. When you feel ready, imagine a soothing being moving towards you.

Imagine that they know about the pain that you are feeling and that they deeply understand. Feel that they want to help you to feel soothed and comforted. Allow them to take shape as they start to approach you.

What does your soothing other look like? Are they tall or small? Male or female? Old or young? A person, animal or object? Fluffy or smooth? How do they approach you?

How does your other try to soothe you? Do they look in your eyes? Give you a hug? Hold your hands?

Do they talk to you? What is their voice like? Is it gruff or smooth? Loud or soft? What do they say to help you to feel soothed and comforted? What would they tell you if they knew what you were thinking?

Allow these sights to come and go naturally in your mind, but stay with the feeling of safeness and calmness.

When you feel ready, allow yourself to come back into the room. You might want to wiggle your toes to slowly bring you back.

Exercise 5

List of positive activities

✧ Go for a walk in the woods

✧ Go to the seaside

✧ Take a bubble bath

✧ Go swimming

✧ Go for a run

✧ Invite a friend round for a cup of tea or coffee

✧ Telephone someone who makes you laugh

✧ Put on a song you love and dance around and sing super loud

✧ Go for a drive to somewhere beautiful

✧ Watch your favourite film

✧ Go for a massage

✧ Pick/buy yourself flowers

- ❖ Send a card to someone you love telling them what you love about them

- ❖ Watch YouTube videos of cats

- ❖ Take a little person to the park/to feed the ducks

- ❖ Play Scrabble with someone in your house

- ❖ Play Scrabble online with someone on the other side of the world

- ❖ Join a club (running/chess/knitting)

- ❖ Learn to crochet/knit/sew

- ❖ Go for a mindful walk

- ❖ Bake a cake

- ❖ Paint a picture

- ❖ Clean out your wardrobe

Exercise 6

Self-care plan

When I am stressed, I notice that:

- ◇
- ◇
- ◇
- ◇
- ◇
- ◇

I need to make sure that I am:

- ◇ getting enough sleep
- ◇ eating three meals a day with lots of fruit and vegetables
- ◇ getting active three times a week (at least a walk!)
- ◇ not drinking too much caffeine

◇ not relying on alcohol or other substances to cope with stress.

I can also take care of myself by:

◇ Doing positive activities such as:

    *

    *

    *

◇ Telling myself:

    *

    *

    *

I can ask other people to support me by:

◇

◇

◇

When/if things get really tough I will make sure I tell:

◇

◇

◇

Index

My Anxiety Handbook
Getting Back on Track
Sue Knowles, Bridie Gallagher and Phoebe McEwen

Paperback
ISBN: 978 1 78592 440 8
eISBN: 978 1 78450 813 5
192 pages

Helping young people with anxiety learn to recognise and manage their symptoms, this anxiety survival guide teaches young people aged 10+ how they can overcome their biggest worries.

Showing that anxiety is a normal human emotion that many people face, this book helps young people understand the ins and outs of their own anxiety and helps them to challenge the difficult patterns they may get into. Co-written with a college student who has experienced anxiety herself, it is a relatable and straightforward guide. As well as providing tried-and-tested advice and exercises that are proven to reduce feelings of anxiety, it includes recovery stories from young people who have managed their symptoms successfully.

With practical chapters on sleep, exam stress, transitions, and seeking extra help, this is a go-to guide for any tween, teen or young person living with anxiety.

Dr Sue Knowles is a senior clinical psychologist with longstanding experience of working with young people and their carers in a range of settings. She works for the psychological services organisation Changing Minds UK [www.changingmindsuk.com].

Dr Bridie Gallagher is a senior clinical psychologist working with adolescents in acute inpatient environments and secure welfare accommodation. She also teaches on the Leeds and Lancaster clinical psychology doctorate courses.

Phoebe McEwen is a college student with lived experience of anxiety.

You Can Change the World!

Everyday Teen Heroes Making a Difference Everywhere

Margaret Rooke

Forewords by Taylor Richardson and Katie Hodgetts @KTclimate

Paperback
ISBN: 978 1 78592 502 3
eISBN: 978 1 78450 897 5
320 pages

This inspirational book tells the stories of more than 50 of today's teenagers who've dared to change the world they live in. It's been written to show other teens they can do the same. Bestselling author Margaret Rooke asks teens about their experiences of being volunteers, social entrepreneurs and campaigners, online and beyond. They explain how they have survived in a world often obsessed by celebrity, social media and appearance, by refusing to conform to other's expectations.

If you want to achieve against the odds and create genuine impact, this book may be the encouragement you need. The interviews cover race, sexuality, violence, grief, neurodiversity, bullying and other issues central to life today.

Margaret Rooke has more than 25 years' experience writing for national newspapers, magazines and books. She has two teenage children. She is the author of the bestselling *Creative, Successful Dyslexic* and *Dyslexia is My Superpower*.

Anxiety is Really Strange

Steve Haines

Art by Sophie Standing

Hardback ISBN:
978 1 84819 407 6
Paperback ISBN:
978 1 848419 389 5
eISBN: 978 0 85701 345 3
40 pages

What is the difference between fear and excitement and how can you tell them apart? How do the mind and body make emotions? When can anxiety be good? This science-based graphic book addresses these questions and more, revealing just how strange anxiety is, but also how to unravel its mysteries and relieve its effects.

Understanding how anxiety is created by our nervous system trying to protect us, and how our fight-or-flight mechanisms can get stuck, can significantly lessen the fear experienced during anxiety attacks. In this guide, anxiety is explained in an easy-to-understand, engaging graphic format with tips and strategies to relieve its symptoms, and change the mind's habits for a more positive outlook.

Steve Haines has studied Yoga, Shiatsu, Biodynamic Craniosacral Therapy, and Trauma Releasing Exercises and works in healthcare and as a UK registered Chiropractor. Steve is the bestselling author of Pain is Really Strange and Trauma is Really Strange. He lives between London and Geneva (www.stevehaines.net).

Sophie Standing is a London-based illustrator and designer, specialising in human sciences. Her style combines digital and hand-made, with an emphasis on rich colour, textures and metaphorical concepts.

The CBT Art Activity Book
100 illustrated handouts for creative therapeutic work
Jennifer Guest

Paperback
ISBN: 978 1 84905 665 6
eISBN: 978 1 78450 168 6
136 pages

Explore complex emotions and enhance self-awareness with these 100 ready-to-use creative activities.

The intricate, attractive designs are illustrated in the popular zentangle style and are suitable for adults and young people, in individual or group work. The worksheets use cognitive behavioural therapy (CBT) and art as therapy to address outcomes including improved self-esteem, emotional wellbeing, anger management, coping with change and loss, problem solving and future planning. The colouring pages are designed for relaxing stress management and feature a complete illustrated alphabet and series of striking mandala designs.

Jennifer Guest has worked in clinical therapeutic practice as a counsellor for 14 years, working with adults, couples and young people in a variety of counselling centres and schools in the North of England. Jennifer is an Accredited Member of the British Association of Counsellors and Psychotherapists and has an honours degree in Art and Design. Currently she works for Relate, a charity that provides counselling services, and has her own private practice based in Yorkshire.